Margaret L. Lial • Raymond N. Greenwell • Nathan P. Ritchey

Finite Mathematics

Second Custom Edition for the University of South Alabama
MA 110

Taken from:
Finite Mathematics, Eleventh Edition
by Margaret L. Lial, Raymond N. Greenwell, and Nathan P. Ritchey

D1472949

Taken from:

Finite Mathematics, Eleventh Edition
by Margaret L. Lial, Raymond N. Greenwell, and Nathan P. Ritchey
Copyright © 2016, 2012, 2008 by Pearson Education, Inc.
New York, New York 10013

This special edition published in cooperation with Pearson Learning Solutions.

All trademarks, service marks, registered trademarks, and registered service marks are the property of their respective owners and are used herein for identification purposes only.

Pearson Learning Solutions, 330 Hudson Street, New York, New York 10013
A Pearson Education Company
www.pearsoned.com

Printed in the United States of America

000200010272037562

NP

ISBN 10: 1-323-42157-2
ISBN 13: 978-1-323-42157-4

Contents

Special Topics to Accompany Finite Mathematics

The following material is provided free to adopters at www.pearsonhighered.com/mathstatsresources:

Digraphs and Networks
- Graphs and Digraphs
- Dominance Graphs
- Communication Graphs
- Networks
- Review Exercises

Preface

Finite Mathematics is a thorough, applications-oriented text for students majoring in business, management, economics, or the life or social sciences. In addition to its clear exposition, this text consistently connects the mathematics to career and everyday-life situations. A prerequisite of two or three semesters of high school algebra is assumed. A greatly enhanced MyMathLab course, new applications and exercises, and other new learning tools make this 11th edition an even richer learning resource for students.

Our Approach

Our main goal is to present finite mathematics in a concise and meaningful way so that students can understand the full picture of the concepts they are learning and apply them to real-life situations. This is done through a variety of means.

Focus on Applications Making this course meaningful to students is critical to their success. Applications of the mathematics are integrated throughout the text in the exposition, the examples, the exercise sets, and the supplementary resources. We are constantly on the lookout for novel applications, and the text reflects our efforts to infuse it with relevance. Our research is showcased in the Index of Applications at the back of the book and the extended list of sources of real-world data on www.pearsonhighered.com/mathstatsresources. *Finite Mathematics* presents students with myriad opportunities to relate what they're learning to career situations through the *Apply It* question at the beginning of sections, the applied examples and exercises, and the *Extended Application* at the end of each chapter.

Pedagogy to Support Students Students need careful explanations of the mathematics along with examples presented in a clear and consistent manner. Additionally, students and instructors should a means to assess the basic prerequisite skills needed for the course content. This can be done with the *Prerequisite Skills Diagnostic Test*, located just prior to Chapter R. If the diagnostic test reveals gaps in basic skills, students can find help right within the text. Further, *Warm-Up Exercises* are now included at the beginning of many exercise sets. Within MyMathLab are additional diagnostic tests (one per chapter), and remediation is automatically personalized to meet student needs. Students will appreciate the many annotated examples within the text, the *Your Turn* exercises that follow examples, the *For Review* references, and the wealth of learning resources within MyMathLab.

Beyond the Textbook Students today want resources at their fingertips and, for them, that means digital. So Pearson has developed a robust MyMathLab course for *Finite Mathematics*. MyMathLab has a well-established and well-documented track record of helping students succeed in mathematics. The MyMathLab online course for this text contains over 3600 exercises to challenge students and provides help when they need it. Students who learn best through video can view (and review) section- and example-level videos within MyMathLab. These and other resources are available to students as a unified and reliable tool for their success.

New to the Eleventh Edition

Based on our experience in the classroom along with feedback from many instructors across the country, the focus of this revision is to improve the clarity of the presentation and provide students with more opportunities to learn, practice, and apply what they've learned on their own. This is achieved both in the presentation of the content and in the new features added to the text.

New Features

- *Warm-Up Exercises* were added to many exercise sets to provide an opportunity for students to refresh key prerequisite skills at "point of use."
- Graphing calculator screens have been updated to reflect the TI-84 Plus C, which features color and a much higher screen resolution. Additionally, the graphing calculator notes have been updated throughout.
- We added more "help text" annotations to examples. These notes, set in small blue type, appear next to the steps within worked-out examples and provide an additional aid for students with weaker algebra skills.
- For many years this text has featured enormous amounts of real data used in examples and exercises. The 11th edition will not disappoint in this area. We have added or updated 107 (12.5%) of the application exercises throughout the text.
- We updated exercises and examples based on user feedback and other factors. Of the 2646 exercises within the sections, 208 (7.8%) are new or updated. Of the 318 examples, 64 (20.1%) are new or updated.
- MyMathLab contains a wealth of new resources to help students learn and help you as you teach. Some resources were added or revised based on student usage of the *previous* edition of the MyMathLab course. For example, more exercises were added to those chapters and sections that are more widely assigned.
  - Hundreds of new exercises were added to the course to provide you with more options for assignments, including:
    - More application exercises throughout the text
    - *Setup & Solve* exercises that require students to specify how to set up a problem as well as solve it
    - Exercises that take advantage of the enhanced graphing tool
  - An Integrated Review version of the course contains preassigned diagnostic and remediation resources for key prerequisite skills. Skills Check Quizzes help diagnose gaps in skills prior to each chapter. MyMathLab then provides personalized help on only those skills that a student has not mastered.
  - The videos for the course have increased in number, type, and quality:
    - New videos feature more applications and more challenging examples.
    - In addition to full-length lecture videos, MyMathLab now includes assignable, shorter video clips that focus on a specific concept or example.
    - Tutorial videos involving graphing calculators are available to augment existing "by hand" methods, allowing you to tailor the help that students receive to how you incorporate graphing calculators into the course.
    - A Guide to Video-Based Instruction shows which exercises correspond to each video, making it easy to assess students after they watch an instructional video. This is perfect for flipped-classroom situations.
  - Learning Catalytics is a "bring your own device" student engagement, assessment, and classroom intelligence system. Students use any modern web-enabled device they already have—laptop, smartphone, or tablet. With Learning Catalytics, you assess students in real time, using open-ended tasks to probe student understanding. It allows you to engage students by creating open-ended questions that ask for numerical, algebraic, textual, or graphical responses—or just plain multiple-choice. Students who have access to MyMathLab have instant access to Learning Catalytics and can log in using their MyMathLab username and password. Learning Catalytics contains Pearson-created content for finite mathematics that allows you to take advantage of this exciting technology immediately.

New and Revised Content

The chapters and sections in the text are in the same order as the previous edition, making it easier for users to transition to the new edition. In addition to revising exercises and examples throughout, updating and adding real-world data, we made the following changes:

Chapter R
- Added new *Your Turn* exercises to ensure that there is a student assessment for each major concept.
- Added more detail to R.2 on factoring perfect squares.

Chapter 1
- Rewrote the part of 1.1 involving graphing lines, emphasizing different methods for graphing.
- Rewrote 1.2 on supply, demand, break-even analysis, and equilibrium; giving formal definitions that match what students would see in business and economics courses. All of the business applications were revised, according to recommendations from reviewers, to be more in line with business texts. Also added a new Example 6 on finding a cost function.
- Added color for pedagogical reasons to make content easier to follow.

Chapter 2
- In 2.1, added a new definition for consistent systems. Also added definitions of general solution, parameter, and particular solution and explanations of how to find each.
- In 2.5, added a shortcut for finding the inverse of a 2×2 matrix.

Chapter 3
- Revised two Technology Notes in 3.1, giving more details on how to graph an inequality and how to add color. Also added a new Example 6, which illustrates what happens when there is no feasible region.
- In 3.2, revised a Technology Note explaining how to find the points of intersection in the feasible region.

Chapter 4
- Added column headings to 4.1 to explain where basic variables are. Additionally, revised Example 4 to include more explanation and detail.
- Added a Caution note to 4.2 and revised the Technology Note for using Excel to solve linear programming problems.

Chapter 5
- In 5.1, revised Example 2 to add more detail regarding what each variable designates. Revised Examples 4–6 and 8–10 to better explain concepts and/or update real-world data. Revised Example 12 to include more explanation—important because we gave two methods to find compounding time (a graphing calculator method and an optional method that uses logarithms).
- Added new Technology Notes to 5.1, 5.2, and 5.3, explaining how to use the TVM Solver in the TI-84.
- Rewrote the 5.2 introduction and converted it into a new example on annuities. Also added a note on why particular variables were chosen and that these variables may look different in other places. Revised Examples 4 and 5 for content and added technology.
- In 5.3, revised Example 5 to better explain amortization schedules.

Chapter 6
- Updated and added numerous exercises.

Chapter 7
- Updated Examples in 7.1, 7.2, and 7.4 for content, data, and/or clarity.
- Added more explanation of independence to 7.5.
- Completely rewrote the Extended Application at the end of the chapter.

Chapter 8
- Updated and added numerous exercises as well as an example in 8.5.

Chapter 9
- Added Technology Notes explaining how to use the calculator to find probabilities, how to create a histogram, and so on.
- Reorganized 9.1 into two parts (frequency distributions and central tendency) and added new headings for mean, median, and mode. Also added a new Example 9, comparing mean and median when outliers exist.
- Switched the emphasis of 9.3 from using the table in the back of the book to using a calculator. (We still use the table but all of the answers are obtained using a calculator.) In that vein, we explained in great detail how to use the calculator to find the various probabilities, and changed Examples 1, 2, and 4.
- Rewrote the introduction to 9.4 as an example and converted other exposition into a second example to better illustrate the concepts being described. Added a Technology Note to the second new example.

Chapter 10
- Added more explanation of powers of the transition matrix in 10.1.

Chapter 11
- Revised the introductory material of 11.1 to create a new Example 1.
- Added more explanation to Example 3 in 11.2.

Features of *Finite Mathematics*
Chapter Opener

Each chapter opens with a quick introduction that relates to an application presented in the chapter.

Apply It

An Apply It question, typically at the start of a section, motivates the math content of the section by posing a real-world question that is then answered within the examples or exercises.

Teaching Tips

Teaching Tips are provided in the margins of the Annotated Instructor's Edition for those who are new to teaching this course.

For Review

For Review boxes are provided in the margin as appropriate, giving students just-in-time help with skills they should already know but may have forgotten. For Review comments sometimes include an explanation, while others refer students back to earlier parts of the book for a more thorough review.

> **FOR REVIEW**
>
> Recall that I is the identity matrix, a square matrix in which each element on the main diagonal is 1 and all other elements are 0.

Caution

Caution notes provide students with a quick "heads up" to common difficulties and errors.

> **CAUTION** If there is a 0 in the right-hand column, do not disregard that row, unless the corresponding number in the pivot column is negative or zero. In fact, such a row gives a quotient of 0, so it will automatically have the smallest ratio. It will not cause an increase in z, but it may lead to another tableau in which z can be further increased.

Your Turn Exercises

These exercises follow selected examples and provide students with an easy way to quickly stop and check their understanding. Answers are provided at the end of the section's exercises.

Technology Notes

Material on graphing calculators or Microsoft Excel is clearly labeled to make it easier for instructors to use this material (or not).

- **New** The figures depicting calculator screens now reflect the TI-84 Plus C, which features color and higher pixel counts.

TECHNOLOGY NOTE

Many graphing calculators have the capability of drawing a histogram. On a TI-84 Plus C calculator, enter the data by selecting STAT EDIT and then typing the entries in L_1. To create a histogram, select STATPLOT and 1:Plot1. Turn the plot ON and select the histogram icon in the Type row, as shown in Figure 2(a). Be sure that L_1 is entered for Xlist.

Select WINDOW to set up the intervals, as shown in Figure 2(b). The Xscl value gives the width of each interval. To draw the histogram, select GRAPH. Figure 2(c) shows the histogram for the data of Example 1. See the *Graphing Calculator and Excel Spreadsheet Manual* available with this text.

| (a) | (b) | (c) |

FIGURE 2

Exercise Sets

Basic exercises are followed by an Applications section, which is grouped by subheads such as "Business and Economics." Other types of exercises include the following:

- **New Warm-Up Exercises** at the beginning of most sections provide a chance for students to refresh the key prerequisite skills needed for the section's exercises.
- **Connections** exercises integrate topics presented in different sections or chapters and are indicated with ⬛.
- **Technology** exercises are labeled 📈 for graphing calculator and ▦ for spreadsheets.
- **Writing** exercises, labeled with ✎, provide students with an opportunity to explain important mathematical ideas.
- Exercises that are particularly challenging are denoted with a + in the Annotated Instructor's Edition only.
- The Annotated Instructor's Edition contains most answers right on the page. Overflow answers are at the back of the book.

Chapter Summary and Review

- The end-of-chapter **Summary** provides students with a quick summary of the key ideas of the chapter followed by a list of key definitions, terms, and examples.
- Chapter **Review Exercises** include Concept Check exercises and an ample set of Practice and Exploration exercises. This arrangement provides students with a comprehensive set of exercises to prepare for chapter exams.

Extended Applications

- Extended Applications are provided at the end of every chapter as in-depth applied exercises to help stimulate student interest. These activities can be completed individually or as group projects.

Flexible Syllabus

The flexibility of the text is indicated in the following chart of chapter prerequisites. As shown, the course could begin with either Chapter 1 or Chapter 7. Chapters 5 and 6 could be covered at any time, although Chapter 6 makes a nice introduction to Chapter 7.

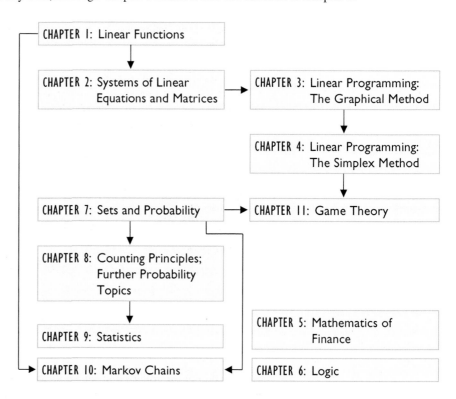

Supplements

FOR STUDENTS	FOR INSTRUCTORS

Student's Solutions Manual (in print and electronically within MyMathLab)

- Provides detailed solutions to all odd-numbered text exercises and sample chapter tests with answers.
- ISBN 0321997425 / 9780321997425

Supplementary Content (online only)

- Chapter on Digraphs and Networks
- Additional Extended Applications
- Comprehensive Source List
- Available at the Downloadable Student Resources site, www.pearsonhighered.com/mathstatsresources, and within MyMathLab

Annotated Instructor's Edition

- Includes all the answers, usually on the same page as the exercises, for quick reference
- Challenge problems labeled with +
- Numerous teaching tips
- ISBN 0321998782 / 9780321998781

Instructor's Solutions and Resource Manual (Download Only)

- Provides complete solutions to all exercises, two versions of a pre-test and final exam, and teaching tips.
- Available to qualified instructors within MyMathLab or through the Pearson Instructor Resource Center (www.pearsonhighered.com/irc).
- ISBN 0133864499 / 9780133864496

FOR STUDENTS

Graphing Calculator Manual for Applied Mathematics (downloadable)

- Contains detailed instruction for using the TI-83/TI-83+/T1-84+C
- Instructions are organized by topic.
- Downloadable from within MyMathLab

Excel Spreadheet Manual for Applied Mathematics (downloadable)

- Contains delailed instruction for using Excel 2013
- Instructions are organized by topic.
- Downloadable from within MyMathLab

FOR INSTRUCTORS

Powerpoint Presentations (Download only)

- Includes lecture content and key graphics from the book.
- Available to qualified instructors within MyMathLab or through the Pearson Instructor Resource Center (www.pearsonhighered.com/irc).
- ISBN 0321997476 / 9780321997470

TestGen Computerized Test Bank

- TestGen® (www.pearsoned.com/testgen) enables instructors to build, edit, print, and administer tests using a computerized bank of questions developed to cover all the objectives of the text.
- TestGen is algorithmically based, allowing instructors to create multiple but equivalent versions of the same question or test with the click of a button. Instructors can also modify test bank questions or add new questions.
- The software and testbank are available to qualified instructors within MyMathLab or through the Pearson Instructor Resource Center (www.pearsonhighered.com/irc).
- ISBN 0133864510 / 9780133864519

MyMathLab® Online Course (access code required)

MyMathLab delivers **proven results** in helping individual students succeed.

- MyMathLab has a consistently positive impact on the quality of learning in higher education math instruction. MyMathLab can be successfully implemented in any environment—lab-based, hybrid, fully online, traditional—and demonstrates the quantifiable difference that integrated usage has on student retention, subsequent success, and overall achievement.

- MyMathLab's comprehensive online gradebook automatically tracks your students' results on tests, quizzes, homework, and in the study plan. You can use the gradebook to quickly intervene if your students have trouble, or to provide positive feedback on a job well done. The data within MyMathLab's gradebook are easily exported to a variety of spreadsheet programs.

MyMathLab provides **engaging experiences** that personalize, stimulate, and measure learning for each student.

- **Personalized Learning:** MyMathLab offers two main features that support adaptive learning: personalized homework and the adaptive study plan. These features allow your students to work on just what they need to learn when it makes the most sense, maximizing their potential for understanding and success.

- **Exercises:** The homework and practice exercises in MyMathLab are correlated to the exercises in the textbook, and they regenerate algorithmically to give students unlimited opportunity for practice and mastery. The software provides helpful feedback when students enter incorrect answers and includes optional learning aids, including guided solutions, sample problems, animations, videos, and eText.

- **Learning and Teaching Tools** include:
  - **Learning Catalytics**—a "bring your own device" student engagement, assessment, and classroom intelligence system, included within MyMathLab. Includes questions written specifically for this course.
  - **Instructional videos**—full-length lecture videos as well as shorter example-based videos.
  - **Help for Gaps in Prerequisite Skills**—diagnostic quizzes tied to personalized assignments help address gaps in algebra skills that might otherwise impede success.
  - **Excel Spreadsheet Manual**—specifically written for this course.
  - **Graphing Calculator Manual**—specifically written for this course.
- **Complete eText** is available to students through MyMathLab courses for the lifetime of the edition, giving students unlimited access to the eBook within any course using that edition of the textbook.
- **MyMathLab Accessibility:** MyMathLab is compatible with the JAWS screen reader, which enables multiple-choice and free-response problem types to be read and interacted with via keyboard controls and math notation input. MyMathLab also works with screen enlargers, including ZoomText, MAGic, and SuperNova. And all MyMathLab videos have closed captioning. More information on this functionality is available at http://mymathlab.com/accessibility.

MyMathLab comes from an **experienced partner** with educational expertise and an eye on the future.

- Knowing that you are using a Pearson product means knowing that you are using quality content. This means that our eTexts are accurate and our assessment tools work. It means we are committed to making MyMathLab as accessible as possible.

- Whether you are just getting started with MyMathLab, or have a question along the way, we're here to help you learn about our technologies and how to incorporate them into your course.

- To learn more about how MyMathLab combines proven learning applications with powerful assessment and continuously adaptive capabilities, visit **www.mymathlab .com** or contact your Pearson representative.

Additional Online Courseware Options (access code required)

- **MathXL®** is the homework and assessment engine that runs MyMathLab. (MyMathLab is MathXL plus a learning management system.)
- **MyMathLab Integrated Review Course** contains preassigned diagnostic and remediation resources for key prerequisite skills. Skills Check Quizzes help diagnose gaps in skills prior to each chapter. MyMathLab then provides personalized help on just those skills that a student has not mastered.
- **MyMathLab® Plus** contains all the features of MyMathLab with convenient management tools and a dedicated services team. It includes batch enrollment so everyone can be ready to start class on the first day, login directly from your campus portal, advanced reporting features, and 24/7 support by email or online chat.

Acknowledgments

We wish to thank the following professors for their contributions in reviewing portions of this text:

Lowell Abrams, *The George Washington University*

Nathan Borchelt, *Clayton State University*

Jeffrey Breeding, *Fordham University*

Joanne Brunner, *Joliet Junior College*

James K. Bryan, Jr., *Merced College*

James Carolan, *Wharton County Junior College*

Michelle DeDeo, *University of North Florida*

Lauren Fern, *University of Montana*

Sharda K. Gudehithlu, *Wilbur Wright College*

Yvette Hester, *Texas A&M University*

Lynette J. King, *Gadsden State Community College*

Donna S. Krichiver, *Johnson County Community College*

Lia Liu, *University of Illinois at Chicago*

Donna M. Lynch, *Clinton Community College*

Phillip Miller, *Indiana University Southeast*

Marna Mozeff, *Drexel University*

Bishnu Naraine, *St. Cloud State University*

Leonard J. Nissim, *Fordham University*

Charles Odion, *Houston Community College*

Charles B. Pierre, *Clark Atlanta University*

Stela Pudar-Hozo, *Indiana University Northwest*

Nancy Ressler, *Oakton Community College*

Brian S. Rickard, *University of Arkansas*

Mary Alice Smeal, *Alabama State University*

Alexis Sternhell, *Delaware County Community College*

Charles Walsh, *College of Southern Maryland*

We also thank Elka Block and Frank Purcell for doing an excellent job updating the Student's Solutions Manual and Instructor's Solutions and Resource Manual. Further thanks go to our accuracy checkers Lisa Collette, Damon Demas, Paul Lorczak, and Rhea Meyerholtz. We are grateful to Karla Harby and Mary Ann Ritchey for their editorial assistance. We especially appreciate the staff at Pearson, whose contributions have been very important in bringing this project to a successful conclusion.

Raymond N. Greenwell
Nathan P. Ritchey

Prerequisite Skills Diagnostic Test

Below is a very brief test to help you recognize which, if any, prerequisite skills you may need to remediate in order to be successful in this course. After completing the test, check your answers in the back of the book. In addition to the answers, we have also provided the solutions to these problems in Appendix A. These solutions should help remind you how to solve the problems. For problems 5–10, the answers are followed by references to sections within Chapter R where you can find guidance on how to solve the problem and/or additional instruction. Addressing any weak prerequisite skills now will make a positive impact on your success as you progress through this course.

1. What percent of 50 is 10?

2. Simplify $\dfrac{13}{7} - \dfrac{2}{5}$.

3. Let x be the number of apples and y be the number of oranges. Write the following statement as an algebraic equation: "The total number of apples and oranges is 75."

4. Let s be the number of students and p be the number of professors. Write the following statement as an algebraic equation: "There are at least four times as many students as professors."

5. Solve for k: $7k + 8 = -4(3 - k)$.

6. Solve for x: $\dfrac{5}{8}x + \dfrac{1}{16}x = \dfrac{11}{16} + x$.

7. Write in interval notation: $-2 < x \le 5$.

8. Using the variable x, write the following interval as an inequality: $[-\infty, -3]$.

9. Solve for y: $5(y - 2) + 1 \le 7y + 8$.

10. Solve for p: $\dfrac{2}{3}(5p - 3) > \dfrac{3}{4}(2p + 1)$.

Finite Mathematics

6 Logic

The rules of a game often include complex conditional statements, such as "if you roll doubles, you can roll again, but if you roll doubles twice in a row, you lose a turn." As exercises in this chapter illustrate, logical analysis of complex statements helps us clarify not only the rules of games but any precise use of language, from legal codes to medical diagnoses.

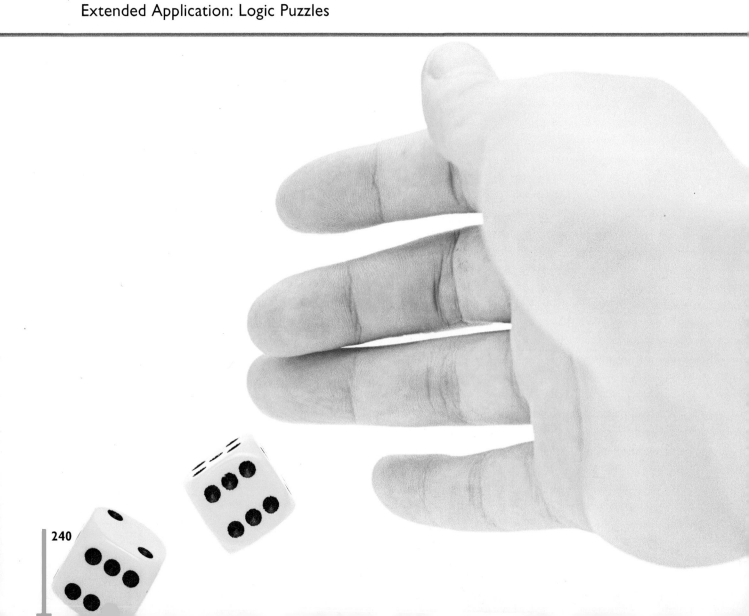

n 1943, Thomas Watson, head of IBM, made the now-infamous prediction, "I think there is a world market for maybe five computers." In 1977, Ken Olson, founder of Digital Equipment Corp., prophesied, "There is no reason anyone would want a computer in their home." ***Source: Microsoft Corp.*** Perhaps such predictions were so wrong because of the difficulty, in the early days of computing, of foreseeing later uses of the computer, such as for communication, shopping, entertainment, or information retrieval. It's rather amazing that such modern conveniences are made possible by a machine made of components based on mathematical logic. Even when you are using your computer for some seemingly nonmathematical activity, components, known as gates or switches, that have been developed from concepts that you will learn about in this chapter, are making it all possible.

6.1 Statements

APPLY IT How can a complex statement be analyzed to determine whether it is a truthful statement?
You will be asked to answer this question in Exercise 87.

Symbolic logic uses formal mathematics with symbols to represent statements and arguments in everyday language. Logic can help us determine whether a complex statement is true, as well as determine whether a conclusion necessarily follows from a set of assumptions.

Many kinds of sentences occur in ordinary language, including factual statements, opinions, commands, and questions. Symbolic logic discusses statements and opinions that may be true or false, but not commands or questions.

Statements

A **statement** is a declarative sentence that is either true or false, but not both simultaneously. For example, both of the following are statements:

Mount McKinley is the tallest mountain in North America.

$$15 - 9 = 10.$$

The first sentence is true, while the second is false. None of the following sentences are considered statements in logic, however, because they cannot be identified as being either true or false:

Tie your shoes.

Are we having fun yet?

This sentence is false.

The first sentence is a command or suggestion, while the second is a question. The third sentence is a paradox: If the sentence is true, then the sentence itself tells us that it must be false. But if what it says is false, then the sentence must be true. We avoid such paradoxes by disallowing statements that refer to themselves.

When one or more simple statements are combined with **logical connectives** such as *and*, *or*, *not*, and *if . . . then*, the result is called a **compound statement**, while the simple statements that make up the compound statement are called **component statements**.

EXAMPLE 1 Compound Statements

Decide whether each statement is compound.

(a) George Washington was the first U.S. president, and John Adams was his vice president.

SOLUTION This statement is compound using the connective *and*. The component statements are "George Washington was the first U.S. president" and "John Adams was his vice president."

(b) If what you've told me is true, then we are in great peril.

SOLUTION This statement is also compound. The component statements "what you've told me is true" and "we are in great peril" are linked with the connective *if . . . then*.

(c) We drove across New Mexico toward the town with the curious name Truth or Consequences.

SOLUTION This statement is not compound. Even though *or* is a connective, here it is part of the name of the city. It is not connecting two statements.

(d) The money is not there.

SOLUTION Most logicians consider this statement to be compound, even though it has just one component statement, and we will do so in this book. The connective *not* is applied to the component statement "The money is there." **TRY YOUR TURN 1**

YOUR TURN 1 Is the following statement compound? "I bought Ben and Jerry's ice cream."

We will study the *and*, *or*, and *not* connectives in detail in this section, and return to the *if . . . then* connective in the third section of this chapter.

Negation

The **negation** of the statement "I play the guitar" is "I do not play the guitar." There are equivalent ways to say the same thing, such as "It is not true that I play the guitar." The negation of a true statement is false, and the negation of a false statement is true.

EXAMPLE 2 Negation

Give the negation of each statement.

(a) California is the most populous state in the country.

SOLUTION Form the negation using the word *not*: "California is not the most populous state in the country."

(b) It is not raining today.

SOLUTION If a statement already has the word *not*, we can remove it to form the negation: "It is raining today." **TRY YOUR TURN 2**

YOUR TURN 2 Write the negation of the following statement. "Wal-Mart is not the largest corporation in the USA."

EXAMPLE 3 Negation

Write the negation of each inequality.

(a) $x > 11$

SOLUTION The negation of "x is greater than 11" is "x is *not* greater than 11," or $x \leq 11$.

(b) $4x + 9y \leq 36$

SOLUTION The negation is $4x + 9y > 36$. **TRY YOUR TURN 3**

YOUR TURN 3 Write the negation of the following inequality. $4x + 2y < 5$

Symbols

To simplify work with logic, symbols are used. Statements are represented with letters, such as p, q, or r, while several symbols for connectives are shown in the following table. The table also gives the type of compound statement having the given connective.

	Logic Symbols	
Connective	Symbol	Type of Statement
and	$\wedge$	Conjunction
or	$\vee$	Disjunction
not	$\sim$	Negation

The symbol $\sim$ represents the connective *not*. If p represents the statement "Barack Obama was president in 2014" then $\sim p$ represents "Barack Obama was not president in 2014." The statement $\sim p$ could also be translated as "It is not true that Barack Obama was president in 2014." There is usually more than one way to express a negation, and so your answer may not always agree exactly with ours. We recommend avoiding convoluted wording.

In applications, choosing meaningful letters will help you remember what the letter represents. While p may be perfectly good for representing a generic statement, a statement such as "Django is a good dog" might be better represented by the letter d.

EXAMPLE 4 Symbolic Statements

Let h represent "My backpack is heavy," and r represent "It's going to rain." Write each symbolic statement in words.

(a) $h \wedge r$

SOLUTION From the table, $\wedge$ represents *and*, so the statement represents

My backpack is heavy, and it's going to rain.

(b) $\sim h \vee r$

SOLUTION The *not* applies only to the first symbol, not the entire expression:

My backpack is not heavy, or it's going to rain.

(c) $\sim(h \vee r)$

SOLUTION Because of the parentheses, the *not* applies to the entire expression:

It is not the case that either my backpack is heavy or it's going to rain.

(d) $\sim(h \wedge r)$

SOLUTION Again, the *not* applies to the entire expression:

It is not the case that both my backpack is heavy and it's going to rain.

TRY YOUR TURN 4

YOUR TURN 4 Write the symbolic statement in words. $h \wedge \sim r$.

The statement in Example 4(c) is usually translated, "Neither h nor r," as in "Neither is my backpack heavy nor is it going to rain."

The negation of the negation of a statement is simply the statement itself. For example, the negation of the statement in Example 4(d) is $h \wedge r$, or "My backpack is heavy and it's going to rain." Symbolically, $\sim(\sim p)$ is equivalent to p.

We can represent the fact that the negation of a true statement is false and the negation of a false statement is true using a table known as a **truth table**, which shows all possible combinations of truth values for the component statements, as well as the corresponding truth value for the compound statement under consideration. Here is the truth table for negation.

Truth Table for the Negation *not p*

p	$\sim p$
T	F
F	T

Conjunction The word logicians use for "*p and q*," denoted $p \wedge q$, is **conjunction**. In everyday language, *and* conveys the idea that both component statements are true. For example, the statement

My birthday is in April and yours is in May

would be true only if my birthday is indeed in April and yours is in May. If either part were false, the statement would be considered false. We represent this definition of $p \wedge q$ symbolically using the following truth table for conjunction. Notice that there are four possible combinations of truth values for p and q.

Truth Table for the Conjunction *p and q*

p	q	$p \wedge q$
T	T	T
T	F	F
F	T	F
F	F	F

Although the order of the rows in a truth table is arbitrary, you should follow the order that we use, which is not only standard but also organized and easy to remember. A different method can make it hard to compare answers, and with a disorganized method one could easily miss a case or even have duplicate cases. Notice that in the columns labeled with a single variable (p or q), the rightmost column (the q column) alternates T, F, T, F. The next column to the left (the p column) has two T's followed by two F's. When we introduce truth tables with three variables, the leftmost column will have four T's followed by four F's.

YOUR TURN 5 Let p represent "$7 < 2$" and q represent "$4 > 3$." Find the truth value of $\sim p \wedge q$.

EXAMPLE 5 Truth Value

Let p represent "$5 > 3$" and let q represent "$6 < 0$." Find the truth value of $p \wedge q$.

SOLUTION Here p is true and q is false. Looking in the second row of the conjunction truth table shows that $p \wedge q$ is false.   **TRY YOUR TURN 5**

TECHNOLOGY NOTE

Some calculators have logic functions that allow the user to test the truth or falsity of statements involving $=$, $\neq$, $>$, $\geq$, $<$, and $\leq$. On the TI-84 Plus C calculator, functions from the TEST menu, illustrated in Figure 1, return a 1 when a statement is true and a 0 when a statement is false. Figure 2 shows the input of $4 > 9$ and the corresponding output of 0, indicating that the statement is false.

FIGURE 1   FIGURE 2

Example 5 can also be completed with the help of a TI-84 Plus C calculator. Using the LOGIC menu, illustrated in Figure 3, we input $5 > 3$ and $6 < 0$ into the calculator. The output is zero, shown in Figure 4, which means the statement is false.

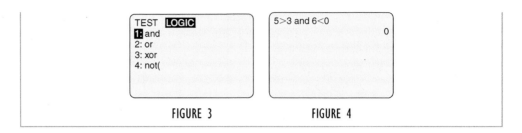

FIGURE 3   FIGURE 4

There's another word that has the same logical meaning as the word *and*, namely *but*. For example, the statement

I was not ready yesterday, but I am ready today

conveys the same logical meaning as "I was not ready yesterday, and I am ready today," with the additional idea of contrast between my status on the two days. Contrast may be relevant in normal conversation, but it makes no difference in logic.

Disjunction

In ordinary language, the word *or* can be ambiguous. For example, the statement

Those with a passport or driver's license will be admitted

means that anyone will be admitted who has a passport or a driver's license or both. On the other hand, the statement

You can have a piece of cake or a piece of fruit

probably means you cannot have both.

In logic, the word *or* has the first meaning, known as *inclusive disjunction* or just **disjunction**. It is written with the symbol $\vee$, so that $p \vee q$ means "p or q or both." It is only false when both component statements are false. The truth table for disjunction is given below.

Truth Table for the Disjunction p or q

p	q	$p \vee q$
T	T	T
T	F	T
F	T	T
F	F	F

NOTE
In English, the *or* is often interpreted as exclusive disjunction, not the way it is used in logic. For more on the exclusive disjunction, see Exercises 35–38 in the next section.

Compound Statements

The next two examples show how we can find the truth value of compound statements.

EXAMPLE 6   Truth Value of a Compound Statement

Suppose p is false, q is true, and r is false. What is the truth value of the compound statement $\sim p \wedge (q \vee \sim r)$?

SOLUTION   Here parentheses are used to group q and $\sim r$ together. Work first inside the parentheses. Since r is false, $\sim r$ will be true. Since $\sim r$ is true and q is true and an *or* statement is true when either component is true, $q \vee \sim r$ must be true. An *and* statement is only true when both components are true. Since $\sim p$ is true and $q \vee \sim r$ is true, the statement $\sim p \wedge (q \vee \sim r)$ is true.

The preceding paragraph may be interpreted using a short-cut symbolic method, letting T represent a true statement and F represent a false statement:

$$\sim p \wedge (q \vee \sim r)$$

$$\sim F \wedge (T \vee \sim F) \qquad p \text{ is false, } q \text{ is true, } r \text{ is false.}$$

$$T \wedge (T \vee T) \qquad \sim F \text{ gives T.}$$

$$T \wedge T \qquad T \vee T \text{ gives T.}$$

$$T. \qquad T \wedge T \text{ gives T.}$$

YOUR TURN 6 If p is false, q is true, and r is false, find the truth value of the statement: $(\sim p \wedge q) \vee r$.

The T in the final row indicates that the compound statement is true.

TRY YOUR TURN 6

EXAMPLE 7 Mathematical Statements

Let p represent the statement "$3 > 2$," q represent "$5 < 4$," and r represent "$3 < 8$." Decide whether the following statements are *true* or *false*.

(a) $\sim p \wedge \sim q$

SOLUTION Since p is true, $\sim p$ is false. By the *and* truth table, if one part of an "and" statement is false, the entire statement is false. This makes $\sim p \wedge \sim q$ false.

(b) $\sim (p \wedge q)$

SOLUTION First, work within the parentheses. Since p is true and q is false, $p \wedge q$ is false by the *and* truth table. Next, apply the negation. The negation of a false statement is true, making $\sim (p \wedge q)$ a true statement.

(c) $(\sim p \wedge r) \vee (\sim q \wedge \sim p)$

SOLUTION Here p is true, q is false, and r is true. This makes $\sim p$ false and $\sim q$ true. By the *and* truth table, the statement $\sim p \wedge r$ is false, and the statement $\sim q \wedge \sim p$ is also false. Finally,

$$(\sim p \wedge r) \vee (\sim q \wedge \sim p)$$
$$\downarrow \qquad\qquad \downarrow$$
$$F \quad \vee \quad F,$$

YOUR TURN 7 Let p represent "$7 < 2$," q represent "$4 > 3$," and r represent "$2 > 8$." Find the truth value of $p \vee (\sim q \wedge r)$.

which is false by the *or* truth table. (For an alternate solution, see Example 3(b) in the next section.)

TRY YOUR TURN 7

NOTE The expression $\sim p \wedge \sim q$ in part (a) is often expressed in English as "Neither p nor q." We saw at the end of Example 4 that the expression $\sim (p \vee q)$ can also be expressed as "Neither p nor q." As we shall see in the next section, the expressions $\sim p \wedge \sim q$ and $\sim (p \vee q)$ are equivalent.

TECHNOLOGY NOTE

Figure 5 shows the results of using a T1-84 Plus C calculator to solve parts (a) and (b) of Example 7.

not(3>2) and not (5<4)

0

not((3>2) and (5<4))

1

FIGURE 5

6.1 EXERCISES

Decide whether each of the following is a statement. If it is a statement, decide whether or not it is compound.

1. Montevideo is the capital of Uruguay.

2. John Jay was the first chief justice of the United States.

3. Don't feed the animals.

4. Do unto others as you would have them do unto you.

5. $2 + 2 = 5$ and $3 + 3 = 7$

6. $x < 7$ or $x > 14$

7. Got milk?

8. Is that all there is?

9. I am not a crook.

10. China does not have a population of more than 1 billion.

11. She enjoyed the comedy team of Penn and Teller.

12. The New Hampshire motto is "Live free or die."

13. If I get an A, I will celebrate.

14. If it's past 8:00, then we are late.

Give a negation of each inequality.

15. $y > 12$

16. $x < -6$

17. $q \geq 5$

18. $r \leq 19$

19. Try to negate the sentence "The exact number of words in this sentence is 10" and see what happens. Explain the problem that arises.

20. Explain why the negation of "$r > 4$" is not "$r < 4$."

Let b represent the statement "I'm getting better" and d represent the statement "My parrot is dead." Translate each symbolic statement into words.

21. $\sim b$

22. $\sim d$

23. $\sim b \vee d$

24. $b \wedge \sim d$

25. $\sim (b \wedge d)$

26. $\sim (b \vee d)$

Use the concepts introduced in this section to answer Exercises 27–32.

27. If q is false, what must be the truth value of $(p \wedge \sim q) \wedge q$?

28. If q is true, what must be the truth value of $q \vee (q \wedge \sim p)$?

29. If $p \wedge q$ is true, then q must be _____.

30. If $p \vee q$ is false, and p is false, then q must be _____.

31. If $\sim (p \vee q)$ is true, what must be the truth values of each of the component statements?

32. If $\sim (p \wedge q)$ is false, what must be the truth values of the component statements?

Let p represent a false statement and let q represent a true statement. Find the truth value of each compound statement.

33. $\sim p$

34. $\sim q$

35. $p \vee q$

36. $p \wedge q$

37. $p \vee \sim q$

38. $\sim p \wedge q$

39. $\sim p \vee \sim q$

40. $p \wedge \sim q$

41. $\sim (p \wedge \sim q)$

42. $\sim (\sim p \vee \sim q)$

43. $\sim [\sim p \wedge (\sim q \vee p)]$

44. $\sim [(\sim p \wedge \sim q) \vee \sim q]$

45. Is the statement $3 \geq 1$ a conjunction or a disjunction? Why?

46. Why is the statement $6 \geq 2$ true? Why is $6 \geq 6$ true?

Let p represent a true statement, and q and r represent false statements. Find the truth value of each compound statement.

47. $(p \wedge r) \vee \sim q$

48. $(q \vee \sim r) \wedge p$

49. $p \wedge (q \vee r)$

50. $(\sim p \wedge q) \vee \sim r$

51. $\sim (p \wedge q) \wedge (r \vee \sim q)$

52. $(\sim p \wedge \sim q) \vee (\sim r \wedge q)$

53. $\sim [(\sim p \wedge q) \vee r]$

54. $\sim [r \vee (\sim q \wedge \sim p)]$

Let p represent the statement "$2 > 7$," let q represent the statement "$8 \leq 6$," and let r represent the statement "$19 \leq 19$". Find the truth value of each compound statement.

55. $p \wedge r$

56. $p \vee \sim q$

57. $\sim q \vee \sim r$

58. $\sim p \wedge \sim r$

59. $(p \wedge q) \vee r$

60. $\sim p \vee (\sim r \vee \sim q)$

61. $(\sim r \wedge q) \vee \sim p$

62. $\sim (p \vee \sim q) \vee \sim r$

APPLICATIONS

Business and Economics

Income Tax The following excerpts appear in a guide for preparing income tax reports. *Source: Your Income Tax 2014.*

(a) Which filing status should you use?

(b) Scholarships and fellowships of a degree candidate are tax free to the extent that the grants pay for tuition and course-related fees, books, supplies, and equipment that are required for courses.

(c) You do not want to withhold too little from your pay and you do not want to withhold too much.

(d) Your spouse is not your dependent for tax purposes.

63. Which of these excerpts are statements?

64. Which of these excerpts are compound statements?

65. Write the negation of excerpt (d).

66. Determine p and q to symbolically represent excerpt (c).

Technology For Exercises 67–72, let *a* represent the statement "Apple Inc. developed the iPad," and *c* represent the statement, "Tim Cook is the CEO of Apple Inc." Convert each compound statement into symbols.

67. Apple Inc. developed the iPad, and Tim Cook is the CEO of Apple Inc.

68. Apple Inc. did not develop the iPad, and Tim Cook is not the CEO of Apple Inc.

69. Apple Inc. did not develop the iPad, or Tim Cook is the CEO of Apple Inc.

70. Apple Inc. developed the iPad, or Tim Cook is the CEO of Apple Inc.

71. Suppose the statements that Apple Inc. developed the iPad and that Tim Cook is CEO of Apple Inc. are both true. Which of Exercises 67–70 are true statements?

72. Suppose the statements that Apple Inc. developed the iPad and that Tim Cook is CEO of Apple Inc. are both false. Which of Exercises 67–70 are true statements?

Life Sciences

Medicine The following excerpts appear in a home medical reference book. *Source: American College of Physicians Complete Home Medical Guide.*

(a) Can you climb one or two flights of stairs without shortness of breath or heaviness or fatigue in your legs?

(b) Regularly doing exercises that concentrate on strengthening particular muscle groups and improving overall flexibility can help prevent back pain and keep you mobile.

(c) If you answered yes to all of the questions above, you are reasonably fit.

(d) These chemical compounds act as natural antidepressants, and they can help you feel more relaxed.

(e) You may find that exercise helps you cope with stress.

73. Which of these excerpts are statements?

74. Which of these excerpts are compound statements?

75. Write the negation of excerpt (e).

Social Sciences

Law The following excerpts appear in a guide to common laws. *Source: Law for Dummies.*

(a) If you're involved in an accident, regardless of who you think is at fault, stop your vehicle and inspect the damage.

(b) Don't be pressured into signing a contract.

(c) You can file a civil lawsuit yourself, or your attorney can do it for you.

(d) You can't marry unless you're at least 18 years old or unless you have the permission of your parents or guardian.

(e) The Bill of Rights defines the fundamental rights of all Americans.

76. Which of these excerpts are statements?

77. Which of these excepts are compound statements?

78. Write the negation of excerpt (e).

79. **Philosophy** Read each of the following quotes from ancient philosophers. Provide an argument why these quotes may or may not be called statements. *Source: Masterworks of Philosophy.*

(a) "A friend is a friend of someone."—Socrates

(b) "Every art, and every science reduced to a teachable form, and in like manner every action and moral choice, aims, it is thought, at some good: for which reason a common and by no means a bad description of what the Chief Good is, 'that which all things aim at.'"—Aristotle

(c) "Furthermore, Friendship helps the young to keep from error: the old, in respect of attention and such deficiencies in action as their weakness makes them liable to; and those who are in their prime, in respect of noble deeds, because they are thus more able to devise plans and carry them out."—Aristotle

80. **Bible** Read each of the following quotes from the biblical book Proverbs. Provide an argument why these quotes may or may not be called statements. *Source: NIV Bible.*

(a) "A gentle answer turns away wrath."—Proverbs 15:1

(b) "A hot-tempered person stirs up conflict, but the one who is patient calms a quarrel."—Proverbs 15:18

(c) "When justice is done, it brings joy to the righteous but terror to evildoers."—Proverbs 21:15

(d) "Do not exploit the poor because they are poor and do not crush the needy in court."—Proverbs 22:22

(e) "Apply your heart to instruction and your ears to words of knowledge."—Proverbs 23:12

General Interest

Football For Exercises 81–86, let *s* represent the statement "Seattle won the Super Bowl" and *m* represent the statement "Peyton Manning is the best quarterback." Convert each compound statement into symbols.

81. Seattle won the Super Bowl but Peyton Manning is not the best quarterback.

82. Seattle did not win the Super Bowl or Peyton Manning is not the best quarterback.

83. Seattle did not win the Super Bowl or Peyton Manning is the best quarterback.

84. Seattle did not win the Super Bowl but Peyton Manning is the best quarterback.

85. Neither did Seattle win the Super Bowl nor is Peyton Manning the best quarterback.

86. Either Seattle won the Super Bowl or Peyton Manning is the best quarterback, and it is not the case that both Seattle won the Super Bowl and Peyton Manning is the best quarterback.

87. **APPLY IT** Suppose the statements that Seattle won the Super Bowl and that Peyton Manning is the best quarterback are both true. Which of Exercises 81–86 are true statements?

88. Suppose the statements that Seattle won the Super Bowl and that Peyton Manning is the best quarterback are both false. Which of Exercises 81–86 are true statements?

YOUR TURN ANSWERS ▬▬

1. No **2.** Wal-Mart is the largest corporation in the USA.

3. $4x + 2y \geq 5$

4. My backpack is heavy, and it's not going to rain.

5. True

6. True

7. False

6.2 Truth Tables and Equivalent Statements

APPLY IT Under what conditions would a buyer protection guarantee be false?
In Exercise 44 of this section, we will see how a truth table can help to answer this question.

In the previous section, we created truth tables for some simple logical expressions. We will now create truth tables for more complex statements, and determine for what values of the individual component statements the complex statement is true. We will continue to use the following standard format for listing the possible truth values in compound statements involving two statements.

p	q	Compound Statement
T	T	
T	F	
F	T	
F	F	

EXAMPLE 1 **Truth Tables**

(a) Construct a truth table for $(\sim p \wedge q) \vee \sim q$.

SOLUTION Begin by listing all possible combinations of truth values for p and q. Then find the truth values of $\sim p \wedge q$. Start by listing the truth values of $\sim p$, which are the opposite of those of p.

p	q	$\sim p$
T	T	F
T	F	F
F	T	T
F	F	T

Use only the "$\sim p$" column and the "q" column, along with the *and* truth table, to find the truth values of $\sim p \wedge q$. List them in a separate column.

p	q	$\sim p$	$\sim p \wedge q$
T	T	F	F
T	F	F	F
F	T	T	T
F	F	T	F

Next include a column for $\sim q$.

p	q	$\sim p$	$\sim p \wedge q$	$\sim q$
T	T	F	F	F
T	F	F	F	T
F	T	T	T	F
F	F	T	F	T

Finally, make a column for the entire compound statement. To find the truth values, use *or* to combine $\sim p \wedge q$ with $\sim q$.

p	q	$\sim p$	$\sim p \wedge q$	$\sim q$	$(\sim p \wedge q) \vee \sim q$
T	T	F	F	F	F
T	F	F	F	T	T
F	T	T	T	F	T
F	F	T	F	T	T

YOUR TURN 1 Construct a truth table for $p \wedge (\sim p \vee q)$. If p and q are both true, find the truth value of $p \wedge (\sim p \vee q)$.

(b) Suppose both p and q are true. Find the truth value of $(\sim p \wedge q) \vee \sim q$.

SOLUTION Look in the first row of the final truth table above, where both p and q have truth value T. Read across the row to find that the compound statement is false.

TRY YOUR TURN 1

EXAMPLE 2 Truth Table

Construct a truth table for the following statement:

I'm bringing the food, or Heather League's bringing the food and I'm not.

SOLUTION If we let i represent "I'm bringing the food" and h represent "Heather League is bringing the food," the statement can be represented symbolically as $i \vee (h \wedge \sim i)$. Proceed as shown in the following truth table.

i	h	$\sim i$	$h \wedge \sim i$	$i \vee (h \wedge \sim i)$
T	T	F	F	T
T	F	F	F	T
F	T	T	T	T
F	F	T	F	F

YOUR TURN 2 Construct a truth table for the following statement: "I do not order pizza, or you do not make dinner and I order pizza."

Notice from the truth table above that the only circumstances under which the original statement is false is when both statements "I'm bringing the food" and "Heather League is bringing the food" are false.

TRY YOUR TURN 2

If a compound statement involves three component statements p, q, and r, we will use the following format in setting up the truth table.

p	q	r	Compound Statement
T	T	T	
T	T	F	
T	F	T	
T	F	F	
F	T	T	
F	T	F	
F	F	T	
F	F	F	

As we mentioned in the previous section, the rightmost column (the r column) alternates T, F, T, F. The next column to the left (the q column) has two T's followed by two F's, and then repeats this pattern. The leftmost column has four T's followed by four F's.

EXAMPLE 3 Truth Tables

(a) Construct a truth table for $(\sim p \wedge r) \vee (\sim q \wedge \sim p)$.

SOLUTION This statement has three component statements, p, q, and r. The truth table thus requires eight rows to list all possible combinations of truth values of p, q, and r. The final truth table is formed in much the same way as in the previous examples.

p	q	r	$\sim p$	$\sim p \wedge r$	$\sim q$	$\sim q \wedge \sim p$	$(\sim p \wedge r) \vee (\sim q \wedge \sim p)$
T	T	T	F	F	F	F	F
T	T	F	F	F	F	F	F
T	F	T	F	F	T	F	F
T	F	F	F	F	T	F	F
F	T	T	T	T	F	F	T
F	T	F	T	F	F	F	F
F	F	T	T	T	T	T	T
F	F	F	T	F	T	T	T

(b) Suppose p is true, q is false, and r is true. Find the truth value of $(\sim p \wedge r) \vee (\sim q \wedge \sim p)$.

SOLUTION By the third row of the truth table in part (a), the compound statement is false. (This is an alternate method for working part (c) of Example 7 of the previous section.)

Notice that the truth table in Example 3(a) has three component statements and eight rows. The truth tables for the conjunction and disjunction have two component statements, and each table has four rows. The truth table for the negation has one component and two rows. These are summarized in the next table. Can we use this information to determine the number of rows in a truth table with n components?

Number of Rows in a Truth Table	
Number of Statements	**Number of Rows**
1	$2 = 2^1$
2	$4 = 2^2$
3	$8 = 2^3$

One strategy for solving this type of problem is noticing a pattern and using *inductive reasoning*, or reasoning that uses particular facts to find a general rule. If n is a counting number, and a logical statement is composed of n component statements, we can use inductive reasoning to conjecture that its truth table will have 2^n rows. This can be proved using ideas in Chapter 8.

Intuitively, it's not hard to see why adding a statement doubles the number of rows. For example, if we wanted to construct a truth table with the four statements p, q, r, and s, we could start with the truth table for p, q, and r, which has eight rows. We must let s have the value of T for each of these rows, and we must also let s have the value of F for each of these rows, giving a total of 16 rows.

> ### Number of Rows in a Truth Table
> A logical statement having n component statements will have 2^n rows in its truth table.

Alternative Method for Constructing Truth Tables

After making a reasonable number of truth tables, some people prefer the shortcut method shown in Example 4, which repeats Examples 1 and 3.

EXAMPLE 4   Truth Tables

Construct the truth table for each statement.

(a) $(\sim p \wedge q) \vee \sim q$

    SOLUTION   Start by inserting truth values for $\sim p$ and for q.

p	q	$(\sim p \wedge q) \vee \sim q$	
T	T	F	T
T	F	F	F
F	T	T	T
F	F	T	F

Next, use the *and* truth table to obtain the truth values of $\sim p \wedge q$.

p	q	$(\sim p \wedge q) \vee \sim q$		
T	T	F	F	T
T	F	F	F	F
F	T	T	T	T
F	F	T	F	F

Now disregard the two preliminary columns of truth values for $\sim p$ and for q, and insert truth values for $\sim q$.

p	q	$(\sim p \wedge q) \vee \sim q$	
T	T	F	F
T	F	F	T
F	T	T	F
F	F	F	T

Finally, use the *or* truth table.

p	q	$(\sim p \wedge q) \vee \sim q$		
T	T	F	F	F
T	F	F	T	T
F	T	T	T	F
F	F	F	T	T

These steps can be summarized as follows.

p	*q*	(~*p* ∧ *q*) ∨ ~*q*
T	T	F F T F F
T	F	F F F T T
F	T	T T T T F
F	F	T F F T T
		① ② ① ④ ③

The circled numbers indicate the order in which the various columns of the truth table were found.

(b) $(\sim p \wedge r) \vee (\sim q \wedge \sim p)$

SOLUTION Work as follows.

p	*q*	*r*	(~*p* ∧ *r*) ∨ (~*q* ∧ ~*p*)
T	T	T	F F T F F F F
T	T	F	F F F F F F F
T	F	T	F F T F T F F
T	F	F	F F F F T F F
F	T	T	T T T T F F T
F	T	F	T F F F F F T
F	F	T	T T T T T T T
F	F	F	T F F T T T T
			① ② ① ⑤ ③ ④ ③

Equivalent Statements One application of truth tables is illustrated by showing that two statements are equivalent; by definition, two statements are **equivalent** if they have the same truth value in *every* possible situation. The columns of each truth table that were the last to be completed will be exactly the same for equivalent statements.

EXAMPLE 5 **Equivalent Statements**

Are the statements

$$\sim p \wedge \sim q \quad \text{and} \quad \sim (p \vee q)$$

equivalent?

SOLUTION To find out, make a truth table for each statement, with the following results.

p	*q*	~*p* ∧ ~*q*
T	T	F
T	F	F
F	T	F
F	F	T

p	*q*	~(*p* ∨ *q*)
T	T	F
T	F	F
F	T	F
F	F	T

Since the truth values are the same in all cases, as shown in the columns in color, the statements $\sim p \wedge \sim q$ and $\sim (p \vee q)$ are equivalent. Equivalence is written with a three-bar symbol, ≡. Using this symbol, $\sim p \wedge \sim q \equiv \sim (p \vee q)$.

In the same way, the statements $\sim p \vee \sim q$ and $\sim(p \wedge q)$ are equivalent. We call these equivalences **De Morgan's Laws.***

> ### De Morgan's Laws
> For any statements p and q,
>
> $$\sim(p \vee q) \equiv \sim p \wedge \sim q$$
> $$\sim(p \wedge q) \equiv \sim p \vee \sim q.$$

DeMorgan's Laws can be used to find the negations of certain compound statements.

EXAMPLE 6   Negation

Find the negation of each statement, applying De Morgan's Laws to simplify.

(a) It was a dark and stormy night.

SOLUTION   If we first rephrase the statement as "The night was dark and the night was stormy," we can let d represent "the night was dark" and s represent "the night was stormy." The original compound statement can then be written $d \wedge s$. The negation of $d \wedge s$ is $\sim(d \wedge s)$. Using the second of De Morgan's Laws, $\sim(d \wedge s) \equiv \sim d \vee \sim s$. In words this reads:

> The night was not dark or the night was not stormy.

In retrospect, this should be obvious. If it's not true that the night was dark and stormy, then either the night wasn't dark or it wasn't stormy.

(b) Either John will play the guitar or George will not sing.

SOLUTION   In this book, we interpret "either . . . or" as disjunction; the word "either" just highlights that a disjunction is about to occur. Using the first of De Morgan's Laws, $\sim(j \vee \sim g) \equiv \sim j \wedge \sim(\sim g)$. Using the observation from the last section that the negation of a negation of a statement is simply the statement, we can simplify the last statement to $\sim j \wedge g$. In words this reads:

> John will not play the guitar and George will sing.

(c) $(\sim p \wedge q) \vee \sim r$

SOLUTION   After negating, we apply the first of De Morgan's Laws, changing $\vee$ to $\wedge$:

$$\sim[(\sim p \wedge q) \vee \sim r] \equiv \sim(\sim p \wedge q) \wedge \sim(\sim r).$$

The last term simplifies to r. Applying the second of De Morgan's Laws to the first term yields

$$\sim(\sim p \wedge q) \wedge r \equiv (p \vee \sim q) \wedge r,$$

where we have replaced $\sim(\sim p)$ with p. (From now on, we will make this simplification without mentioning it.)   TRY YOUR TURN 3 ▆▆▆

YOUR TURN 3 Find the negation of the following statement: "You do not make dinner or I order pizza."

▆▆▆

---

*Augustus De Morgan (1806–1871) was born in India, where his father was serving as an English army officer. After studying mathematics at Cambridge, he prepared for a career in law because his performance on the challenging Tripos Exam in mathematics was not very good. Nevertheless, De Morgan was offered a position as chair of the department of mathematics at London University. He wrote and taught mathematics with great clarity and dedication, and he was also an excellent flutist.

┌─ 6.2 WARM-UP EXERCISES ─

Let p and q represent true statements, and r represent a false statement. Find the truth value of each compound statement.

W1. $(p \wedge q) \vee (\sim p \wedge r)$ *(Sec. 6.1)*

W2. $\sim[p \vee (q \wedge \sim r)]$ *(Sec. 6.1)*

6.2   EXERCISES

Give the number of rows in the truth table for each compound statement.

1. $p \vee \sim r$

2. $p \wedge (r \wedge \sim s)$

3. $(\sim p \wedge q) \vee (\sim r \vee \sim s) \wedge r$

4. $[(p \vee q) \wedge (r \wedge s)] \wedge (t \vee \sim p)$

5. $[(\sim p \wedge \sim q) \wedge (\sim r \wedge s \wedge \sim t)] \wedge (\sim u \vee \sim v)$

6. $[(\sim p \wedge \sim q) \vee (\sim r \vee \sim s)] \vee [(\sim m \wedge \sim n) \wedge (u \wedge \sim v)]$

7. If the truth table for a certain compound statement has 64 rows, how many distinct component statements does it have?

8. Is it possible for the truth table of a compound statement to have exactly 48 rows? Why or why not?

Construct a truth table for each compound statement.

9. $\sim p \wedge q$

10. $\sim p \vee \sim q$

11. $\sim(p \wedge q)$

12. $p \vee \sim q$

13. $(q \vee \sim p) \vee \sim q$

14. $(p \wedge \sim q) \wedge p$

15. $\sim q \wedge (\sim p \vee q)$

16. $\sim p \vee (\sim q \wedge \sim p)$

17. $(p \vee \sim q) \wedge (p \wedge q)$

18. $(\sim p \wedge \sim q) \vee (\sim p \vee q)$

19. $(\sim p \wedge q) \wedge r$

20. $r \vee (p \wedge \sim q)$

21. $(\sim p \wedge \sim q) \vee (\sim r \vee \sim p)$

22. $(\sim r \vee \sim p) \wedge (\sim p \vee \sim q)$

23. $\sim(\sim p \wedge \sim q) \vee (\sim r \vee \sim s)$

24. $(\sim r \vee s) \wedge (\sim p \wedge q)$

Write the negation of each statement, applying De Morgan's Laws to simplify.

25. It's vacation, and I am having fun.

26. Rachel Schindler was elected president and Lauren Rayappu was elected treasurer.

27. Either the door was unlocked or the thief broke a window.

28. Sue brings the wrong book or she forgets the notes.

29. I'm ready to go, but Jackie Senich isn't.

30. You can lead a horse to water, but you cannot make him drink.

31. $12 > 4$ or $8 = 9$

32. $2 + 3 = 5$ and $12 + 13 = 15$

33. Larry or Moe is out sick today.

34. You and I have gone through a lot.

35. Complete the truth table for *exclusive disjunction*. The symbol $\underline{\vee}$ represents "one or the other is true, but not both."

p	q	$p \underline{\vee} q$
T	T	
T	F	
F	T	
F	F	

Exclusive disjunction

Decide whether the following compound statements are true or false. Remember from Exercise 35 that $\underline{\vee}$ is the exclusive disjunction; that is, assume "either p or q is true, but not both."

36. $(3 + 1 = 4) \underline{\vee} (2 + 5 = 7)$

37. $(3 + 1 = 4) \underline{\vee} (2 + 5 = 9)$

38. $(3 + 1 = 7) \underline{\vee} (2 + 5 = 7)$

39. Let p represent $2\sqrt{6} - 4\sqrt{5} > -1$, q represent

$$\frac{14 - 7\sqrt{8}}{2.5 - \sqrt{5}} > -22, \text{ and } s \text{ represent } \frac{7 - \dfrac{5}{\sqrt{3}}}{\sqrt{8} - 2} < \frac{\sqrt{3}}{\sqrt{2}}.$$

Use the LOGIC menu on a graphing calculator to find the truth value of each statement.

(a) $p \wedge q$

(b) $\sim p \wedge q$

(c) $\sim(p \vee q)$

(d) $(s \wedge \sim p) \vee (\sim s \wedge q)$

Find a logic statement involving p and q that generates each of the following truth tables.

40.

p	q	?
T	T	F
T	F	T
F	T	F
F	F	F

41.

p	q	?
T	T	T
T	F	F
F	T	T
F	F	T

APPLICATIONS

Business and Economics

42. **Income Tax**   The following statement appears in a guide for preparing income tax reports. Use one of De Morgan's Laws to write the negation of this statement. *Source: Your Income Tax 2014.*

Tips of less than $20 per month are taxable but are not subject to withholding.

43. Warranty The following statement appears in an iPhone warranty guide. Use one of De Morgan's Laws to negate this statement. *Source: AppleCare Protection Plan.*

> Service will be performed at the location, or the store may send the Covered Equipment to an Apple repair service location to be repaired.

44. eBay APPLY IT The eBay Buyer Protection plan guarantees that a buyer will receive an item and that it will be as described, or eBay will cover the purchase price plus shipping. Let *r* represent "A buyer will receive an item," *d* represent "It will be as described," and *e* represent "eBay will cover the purchase price plus shipping." Write the guarantee symbolically, and then construct a truth table for the statement, putting the variables in the order *r*, *d*, and *e*. Under what conditions would the guarantee be false? *Source: eBay®.*

45. Guarantees The guarantee on a brand of vacuum cleaner reads: "You will be completely satisfied or we will refund your money without asking any questions." Let *s* represent "You will be completely satisfied," *r* represent "We will refund your money," and *q* represent "We will ask you questions." Write the guarantee symbolically and then construct a truth table for the statement, putting the variables in the order *s*, *r*, *q*. Under what conditions would the guarantee be false?

Life Sciences

46. Medicine The following statements appear in a home medical reference book. Define *p* and *q* so that the statements can be written symbolically. Then negate each statement. *Source: American College of Physicians Complete Home Medical Guide.*

(a) Tissue samples may be taken from almost anywhere in the body, and the procedure used depends on the site.

(b) The procedure can be carried out quickly in the doctor's office and is not painful.

(c) Fluid samples may be examined for infection, or the cells in the fluid may be separated and examined to detect other abnormalities.

Social Sciences

47. Law Attorneys sometimes use the phrase "and/or." This phrase corresponds to which usage of the word *or*: inclusive or exclusive?

48. Law The following statement appears in a guide to common laws. Define *p* and *q* so that the statement can be written symbolically. Then negate the statement. *Source: Law for Dummies.*

> You can file a complaint yourself as you would if you were using small claims court, or your attorney can file one for you.

49. Presidential Quote Use one of De Morgan's Laws to rewrite the negation of the following quote made by President John F. Kennedy at Vanderbilt University on March 18, 1963:

> Liberty without learning is always in peril, and learning without liberty is always in vain. *Source: Masters of Chiasmus.*

50. Politician Senator Pompous B. Blowhard made the following campaign promise: "I will cut taxes and eliminate the deficit, or I will not run for reelection." Let *c* represent "I will cut taxes," let *e* represent "I will eliminate the deficit," and let *r* represent "I will run for reelection." Write the promise symbolically and then construct a truth table for the statement, putting the variables in the order *c*, *e*, *r*. Under what conditions would the promise be false?

General Interest

51. Yahtzee® The following statement appears in the instructions for the Milton Bradley game Yahtzee®. Negate the statement. *Source: Milton Bradley Company.*

> You could reroll the die again for your Large Straight or set aside the 2 Twos and roll for your Twos or for 3 of a Kind.

52. Logic Puzzles Raymond Smullyan is one of today's foremost writers of logic puzzles. Smullyan proposed a question, based on the classic Frank Stockton short story, in which a prisoner must make a choice between two doors: Behind one is a beautiful lady, and behind the other is a hungry tiger. What if each door has a sign, and the prisoner knows that only one sign is true? The sign on Door 1 reads: In this room there is a lady and in the other room there is a tiger. The sign on Door 2 reads: In one of these rooms there is a lady and in one of these rooms there is a tiger. With this information, determine what is behind each door. *Source: The Lady or the Tiger? And Other Logic Puzzles.*

53. Describe how a search engine on the Internet uses key words and logical connectives to locate information.

YOUR TURN ANSWERS

1.

p	q	$\sim p$	$\sim p \lor q$	$p \land (\sim p \lor q)$
T	T	F	T	T
T	F	F	F	F
F	T	T	T	F
F	F	T	T	F

true

2. Let *p* represent "I order pizza" and *d* represent "you make dinner."

p	d	$\sim d$	$\sim d \land p$	$\sim p$	$\sim p \lor (\sim d \land p)$
T	T	F	F	F	F
T	F	T	T	F	T
F	T	F	F	T	T
F	F	T	F	T	T

3. You make dinner and I do not order pizza.

6.3 The Conditional and Circuits

How can logic be used in the design of electrical circuits?
This question will be answered in this section.

Conditionals

A **conditional** statement is a compound statement that uses the connective *if . . . then*, or anything equivalent. For example:

> *If* it rains, *then* I carry my umbrella.
>
> *If* the president comes, *then* security will be tight.
>
> *If* the check doesn't arrive today, I will call to find out why.

In the last statement, the word *then* was implied but not explicitly stated; the sentence is equivalent to the statement "If the check doesn't arrive today, *then* I will call to find out why." In each of these statements, the component after the word *if* gives a condition under which the last component is true. The last component is the statement coming after the word *then* (or, in the third statement, the implied *then*). There may be other conditions under which the last component is true. In the second statement, for example, it might be true that even if the president doesn't come, security will be tight because the vice president is coming.

The conditional is written with an arrow, so that "if *p*, then *q*" is symbolized as

$$p \rightarrow q.$$

We read $p \rightarrow q$ as "*p* implies *q*" or "if *p*, then *q*." In the conditional $p \rightarrow q$, the statement *p* is the **antecedent**, while *q* is the **consequent**.

There are many equivalent forms of the conditional. For example, the statement

> Winners never quit

can be rephrased as

> If you are a winner, then you never quit.

There are other forms of the conditional that we will study in the next section.

Just as we defined conjunction and disjunction using a truth table, we will now do the same for the conditional. To see how such a table should be set up, we will analyze the following statement that might be made by a cereal company:

> If you eat Wheat Crunchies, then you'll be full of energy.

Let *e* represent "You eat Wheat Crunchies" and *f* represent "You'll be full of energy." As before, there are four possible combinations of truth values for the two component statements.

	Wheat Crunchies Analysis		
Possibility	Eat Wheat Crunchies?	Full of Energy?	
1	Yes	Yes	*e* is T, *f* is T
2	Yes	No	*e* is T, *f* is F
3	No	Yes	*e* is F, *f* is T
4	No	No	*e* is F, *f* is F

Let's consider each of these possibilities.

1. If you eat Wheat Crunchies and indeed find that you are full of energy, then you must conclude that the company's claim is true, so place T in the first row of the truth table. This does not necessarily mean that eating Wheat Crunchies caused you to be full of energy; perhaps you are full of energy for some other reason unrelated to what you ate for breakfast.

2. If you eat Wheat Crunchies and are not full of energy, then the company's claim is false, so place F in the second row of the truth table.

3. If you don't eat Wheat Crunchies and yet find that you are full of energy, this doesn't invalidate the company's claim. They only promised results if you ate Wheat Crunchies; they made no claims about what would happen if you don't eat Wheat Crunchies. We will, therefore, place T in the third row of the truth table.

4. If you don't eat Wheat Crunchies and are not full of energy, you can't very well blame the company. Because they can still claim that their promise is true, we will place T in the fourth row.

The discussion above leads to the following truth table.

Truth Table for the Conditional *if p, then q*

p	q	$p \rightarrow q$
T	T	T
T	F	F
F	T	T
F	F	T

The truth table for the conditional leads to some counterintuitive conclusions, because *if . . . then* sometimes has other connotations in English, as the following examples illustrate.

EXAMPLE 1 **Truth Value**

Suppose you get a 61 on the test and you pass the course. Find the truth value of the following statement:

> If you get a 70 or higher on the test, then you pass the course.

SOLUTION The first component of this conditional is false, while the second is true. According to the third line of the truth table for the conditional, this statement is true.

This result may surprise you. Even though the statement only says what happens if you get a 70 or higher on the test, perhaps you also infer from the statement that if you don't get 70 or higher, you won't pass the course. This is a common interpretation of *if . . . then*, but it is not consistent with our truth table above. This interpretation is called the *biconditional* and will be discussed in the next section. ▪

EXAMPLE 2 **Truth Value**

Find the truth value of each of the following statements.

(a) If the earth is shaped like a cube, then elephants are smaller than mice.

    SOLUTION Both components of this conditional are false. According to the fourth line of the truth table for the conditional, this statement is true.

YOUR TURN 1 Find the truth value of the following statement. "If Little Rock is the capital of Arkansas, then New York City is the capital of New York."

(b) If the earth is shaped like a cube, then George Washington was the first president of the United States.

SOLUTION The first component of this conditional is false, while the second is true. According to the third line of the truth table for the conditional, this statement is true, even though it may seem like an odd statement. **TRY YOUR TURN 1**

The following observations come from the truth table for $p \rightarrow q$.

Special Characteristics of Conditional Statements

1. $p \rightarrow q$ is false only when the antecedent (p) is *true* and the consequent (q) is *false*.
2. If the antecedent (p) is *false*, then $p \rightarrow q$ is automatically *true*.
3. If the consequent (q) is *true*, then $p \rightarrow q$ is automatically *true*.

EXAMPLE 3 Conditional Statement

Write *true* or *false* for each statement. Here T represents a true statement, and F represents a false statement.

(a) $T \rightarrow (6 = 3)$

SOLUTION Since the antecedent is true, while the consequent, $6 = 3$, is false, the given statement is false by the first point mentioned above.

(b) $(5 < 2) \rightarrow F$

SOLUTION The antecedent is false, so the given statement is true by the second observation.

YOUR TURN 2 Determine if the following statement is *true* or *false:* $(4 > 5) \rightarrow F$.

(c) $(3 \neq 2 + 1) \rightarrow T$

SOLUTION The consequent is true, making the statement true by the third characteristic of conditional statements. **TRY YOUR TURN 2**

EXAMPLE 4 Truth Value

Given that p, q, and r are all false, find the truth value of the statement

$$(p \rightarrow \sim q) \rightarrow (\sim r \rightarrow q).$$

SOLUTION Using the shortcut method explained in Example 6 of Section 6.1, we can replace p, q, and r with F (since each is false) and proceed as before, using the negation and conditional truth tables as necessary.

$$(p \rightarrow \sim q) \rightarrow (\sim r \rightarrow q)$$
$$(F \rightarrow \sim F) \rightarrow (\sim F \rightarrow F) \quad \text{\textit{p, q, r} are false.}$$
$$(F \rightarrow T) \rightarrow (T \rightarrow F) \quad \text{Use the negation truth table.}$$
$$T \rightarrow F \quad \text{Use the conditional truth table.}$$
$$F$$

YOUR TURN 3 If p, q, and r are all false, find the truth value of the statement $\sim q \rightarrow (p \rightarrow r)$.

The statement $(p \rightarrow \sim q) \rightarrow (\sim r \rightarrow q)$ is false when p, q, and r are all false. **TRY YOUR TURN 3**

Truth tables for compound statements involving conditionals are found using the techniques described in the previous section. The next example shows how this is done.

EXAMPLE 5 Truth Table

Construct a truth table for each statement.

(a) $(\sim p \rightarrow \sim q) \wedge \sim(p \vee \sim q)$

> **SOLUTION** First insert the truth values of $\sim p$ and of $\sim q$. Then find the truth values of $\sim p \rightarrow \sim q$.

p	q	$\sim p$	$\sim q$	$\sim p \rightarrow \sim q$
T	T	F	F	T
T	F	F	T	T
F	T	T	F	F
F	F	T	T	T

> Next use p and $\sim q$ to find the truth values of $p \vee \sim q$ and then $\sim(p \vee \sim q)$.

p	q	$\sim p$	$\sim q$	$\sim p \rightarrow \sim q$	$p \vee \sim q$	$\sim(p \vee \sim q)$
T	T	F	F	T	T	F
T	F	F	T	T	T	F
F	T	T	F	F	F	T
F	F	T	T	T	T	F

> Finally, add the column for the statement $(\sim p \rightarrow \sim q) \wedge \sim(p \vee \sim q)$.

p	q	$\sim p$	$\sim q$	$\sim p \rightarrow \sim q$	$p \vee \sim q$	$\sim(p \vee \sim q)$	$(\sim p \rightarrow \sim q) \wedge \sim(p \vee \sim q)$
T	T	F	F	T	T	F	F
T	F	F	T	T	T	F	F
F	T	T	F	F	F	T	F
F	F	T	T	T	T	F	F

(b) $(p \rightarrow q) \rightarrow (\sim p \vee q)$

> **SOLUTION** Go through steps similar to the ones above.

p	q	$p \rightarrow q$	$\sim p$	$\sim p \vee q$	$(p \rightarrow q) \rightarrow (\sim p \vee q)$
T	T	T	F	T	T
T	F	F	F	F	T
F	T	T	T	T	T
F	F	T	T	T	T

As the truth table in Example 5(a) shows, the statement $(\sim p \rightarrow \sim q) \wedge \sim(p \vee \sim q)$ is always false, regardless of the truth values of the components. Such a statement is called a **contradiction**. Most contradictions consist of two statements that cannot simultaneously be true that are united with a conjunction. The simplest such statement is $p \wedge \sim p$.

Notice from the truth table in Example 5(b) that the statement $(p \rightarrow q) \rightarrow (\sim p \vee q)$ is always true, regardless of the truth values of the components. Such a statement is called a **tautology**. Other examples of tautologies (as can be checked by forming truth tables) include $p \vee \sim p$, $p \rightarrow p$, $(\sim p \vee \sim q) \rightarrow \sim(q \wedge p)$, and so on. An important point here is that there are compound statements (such as $p \vee \sim p$) that are true (or false) independent of the truth values of the component parts; the truth depends on the logical structure alone. By the way, the truth tables in Example 5 also could have been found by the alternative method shown in the previous section.

Notice from the third and fifth columns of the truth table in Example 5(b) that $p \rightarrow q$ and $\sim p \vee q$ are equivalent.

Writing a Conditional as an *or* Statement

$$p \rightarrow q \text{ is equivalent to } \sim p \vee q.$$

YOUR TURN 4 Write the following statement without using *if . . . then*: "If you do the homework, then you will pass the quiz."

EXAMPLE 6 **Equivalent Statements**

Write the following statement without using *if . . . then*.

> If this is your first time, we're glad you're here.

SOLUTION Letting f represent "This is your first time" and g represent "We're glad you're here," the conditional may be restated as $\sim f \vee g$, or in words:

> This is not your first time or we're glad you're here.

TRY YOUR TURN 4

Since

$$p \rightarrow q \equiv \sim p \vee q,$$

we can take the negation of both sides of this equivalence to get

$$\sim(p \rightarrow q) \equiv \sim(\sim p \vee q).$$

By applying De Morgan's Law to the right side, we have

$$\sim(p \rightarrow q) \equiv \sim(\sim p) \wedge \sim q$$
$$\equiv p \wedge \sim q.$$

This gives us an equivalent form for the negation of the conditional.

Negation of $p \rightarrow q$

The negation of $p \rightarrow q$ is $p \wedge \sim q$.

EXAMPLE 7 **Negation**

Write the negation of each statement.

(a) If you go to the left, I'll go to the right.

SOLUTION Let y represent "You go to the left" and i represent "I'll go to the right." Then the original statement is represented $y \rightarrow i$. As we showed earlier, the negation of this is $y \wedge \sim i$, which can be translated into words as

> You go to the left and I won't go to the right.

(b) It must be alive if it is breathing.

SOLUTION First, we must restate the given statement in *if . . . then* form:

> If it is breathing, then it must be alive.

Based on our earlier discussion, the negation is

YOUR TURN 5 Write the negation of the following statement: "If you are on time, then we will be on time."

> It is breathing and it is not alive. **TRY YOUR TURN 5**

A common error occurs when students try to write the negation of a conditional statement as another conditional statement. As seen in Example 7, the negation of a conditional statement is written as a conjunction.

APPLY IT **Circuits** One of the first nonmathematical applications of symbolic logic was seen in the master's thesis of Claude Shannon in 1937. Shannon showed how the logic developed almost a century earlier by British mathematician George Boole could be used as an aid in designing electrical **circuits**. His work was immediately taken up by the designers of computers. These computers, then in the developmental stage, could be simplified and built for less money using the ideas of Shannon.

To see how Shannon's ideas work, look at the electrical switch shown in Figure 6. We assume that current will flow through this switch when it is closed and not when it is open.

Figure 7 shows two switches connected in **series**; in such a circuit, current will flow only when both switches are closed. Note how closely a series circuit corresponds to the conjunction $p \wedge q$. We know that $p \wedge q$ is true only when both p and q are true.

A circuit corresponding to the disjunction $p \vee q$ can be found by drawing a **parallel** circuit, as in Figure 8. Here, current flows if either p *or* q is closed or if both p *and* q are closed.

The circuit in Figure 9 corresponds to the statement $(p \vee q) \wedge \sim q$, which is a compound statement involving both a conjunction and a disjunction.

The way that logic is used to simplify an electrical circuit depends on the idea of equivalent statements, from Section 6.2. Recall that two statements are equivalent if they have exactly the same truth table final column. The symbol $\equiv$ is used to indicate that the two statements are equivalent. Some of the equivalent statements that we shall need are shown in the following box.

Open circuit

FIGURE 6

Series circuit

FIGURE 7

Parallel circuit

FIGURE 8

FIGURE 9

Equivalent Statements

1. (a) $p \vee q \equiv q \vee p$		Commutative Laws
(b) $p \wedge q \equiv q \wedge p$		
2. (a) $p \vee (q \vee r) \equiv (p \vee q) \vee r$		Associative Laws
(b) $p \wedge (q \wedge r) \equiv (p \wedge q) \wedge r$		
3. (a) $p \vee (q \wedge r) \equiv (p \vee q) \wedge (p \vee r)$		Distributive Laws
(b) $p \wedge (q \vee r) \equiv (p \wedge q) \vee (p \wedge r)$		
4. (a) $\sim(p \wedge q) \equiv \sim p \vee \sim q$		De Morgan's Laws
(b) $\sim(p \vee q) \equiv \sim p \wedge \sim q$		
5. (a) $p \vee p \equiv p$		Idempotent Laws
(b) $p \wedge p \equiv p$		
6. (a) $(p \wedge q) \vee p \equiv p$		Absorption Laws
(a) $(p \vee q) \wedge p \equiv p$		
7. $\sim(\sim p) \equiv p$		Double Negative
8. $p \rightarrow q \equiv \sim p \vee q$		Conditional as an "or"
9. $p \rightarrow q \equiv \sim q \rightarrow \sim p$		Contrapositive

If T represents any true statement and F represents any false statement, then

10. (a) $p \vee T \equiv T$		Identity Laws
(b) $p \wedge T \equiv p$		
(c) $p \vee F \equiv p$		
(d) $p \wedge F \equiv F$		
11. (a) $p \vee \sim p \equiv T$		Negation Laws
(b) $p \wedge \sim p \equiv F$		

This list may seem formidable, but if we break it down, it turns out to be not so bad.

First, notice that the first six equivalences come in pairs, in which ∨ is replaced with ∧ and vice versa. This illustrates the **Principle of Duality**, which states that if a logical equivalence contains no logical operators other than ∨, ∧, and ~ (that is, it does not contain →), then we may replace ∨ with ∧ and vice versa, and replace T with F and vice versa, and the new equivalence is still true. This means that we need to keep track of just one from each pair of equivalences, although we have put both in the table for completeness.

Next, notice that equivalences 1 and 2 are just the familiar **Commutative** and **Associative Laws** for addition or multiplication, which means you can rearrange the order and rearrange the parentheses in an expression involving only ∧ or only ∨. You are asked to prove these using a truth table in Exercises 61–68.

Equivalence 3 is just the familiar **Distributive Law** of multiplication over addition. In normal multiplication, however, you *cannot* distribute $2 + (3 \times 5)$ to get $(2 + 3) \times (2 + 5)$. In other words, you cannot distribute addition over multiplication. But you can distribute ∧ over ∨ and vice versa. You are asked to prove these using a truth table in Exercises 65 and 66.

De Morgan's Laws, given as equivalence 4, were discussed in the previous section.

Equivalence 5, the **Idempotent Laws**, may seem trivially true, so you may wonder why we bother stating them. The reason is that they are useful in simplifying circuits, as we shall see in Example 8. Equivalence 7, the **Double Negative**, is similar in this regard.

Equivalence 6, the **Absorption Laws**, may be less obvious, but they, too, are useful in simplifying circuits, as we shall see in Example 9. Their proofs are in Exercises 67 and 68.

Equivalence 8, the **Conditional as an "or"** statement, was discussed earlier in this section. Equivalence 9, the Contrapositive, is very important and will be discussed in the next section.

Equivalences 10 and 11, the **Identity** and **Negation Laws**, should be fairly obvious. We only list them here because, just like equivalences 5 and 7, they can help us simplify circuits. Notice that the Principle of Duality applies to these equivalences.

Circuits can be used as models of compound statements, with a closed switch corresponding to T, while an open switch corresponds to F. The method for simplifying circuits is explained in the following example.

EXAMPLE 8 **Circuit**

Simplify the circuit in Figure 10.

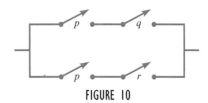

FIGURE 10

SOLUTION At the top of Figure 10, p and q are connected in series, and at the bottom, p and r are connected in series. These are interpreted as the compound statements $p \wedge q$ and $p \wedge r$, respectively. These two conjunctions are connected in parallel, as indicated by the figure treated as a whole. Therefore, we write the disjunction of the two conjunctions:

$$(p \wedge q) \vee (p \wedge r).$$

(Think of the two switches labeled "p" as being controlled by the same handle.) By the Distributive Law (equivalence statement 3),

$$(p \wedge q) \vee (p \wedge r) \equiv p \wedge (q \vee r),$$

which has the circuit of Figure 11. This new circuit is logically equivalent to the one in Figure 10 and yet contains only three switches instead of four—which might well lead to a large savings in manufacturing costs. ■

FIGURE 11

EXAMPLE 9 Circuit

Simplify the circuit in Figure 12.

FIGURE 12

SOLUTION The diagram shows q in series with a circuit containing two parallel components, one containing q and $\sim p$, and the other containing p. Thus the circuit can be represented by the logical statement

$$q \wedge [(q \wedge \sim p) \vee p].$$

Notice that for the expression in brackets, we can use the Commutative Law to put the p first, and then we can use the Distributive Law, which leads to a series of simplifications.

$q \wedge [(q \wedge \sim p) \vee p] \equiv q \wedge [p \vee (q \wedge \sim p)]$	Commutative Law
$\equiv q \wedge [(p \vee q) \wedge (p \vee \sim p)]$	Distributive Law
$\equiv q \wedge [(p \vee q) \wedge \text{T}]$	Negation Law
$\equiv q \wedge (p \vee q)$	Identity Law
$\equiv (p \vee q) \wedge q$	Commutative Law
$\equiv (q \vee p) \wedge q$	Commutative Law
$\equiv q$	Absorption Law

The circuit simplified to a single switch! We hope this convinces you of the power of logic. Notice that we used the Commutative Law three times simply to get terms into a form in which another equivalence applies. This could be avoided if we just added more equivalences to our previous list, such as the Distributive Laws in the reverse order. This would, however, make our list even longer, so we will not do that, even though it means that we need an occasional extra step in our proofs. ▬

EXAMPLE 10 Circuit

Draw a circuit for $p \rightarrow (q \wedge \sim r)$.

SOLUTION By the equivalent statement Conditional as an "or," $p \rightarrow q$ is equivalent to $\sim p \vee q$. This equivalence gives $p \rightarrow (q \wedge \sim r) \equiv \sim p \vee (q \wedge \sim r)$, which has the circuit diagram in Figure 13. ▬

FIGURE 13

6.3 WARM-UP EXERCISES

Construct a truth table for each statement.

W1. $(p \wedge \sim q) \vee \sim p$ *(Sec. 6.2)*

W2. $(p \vee \sim q) \wedge q$ *(Sec. 6.2)*

6.3 EXERCISES

In Exercises 1–6, decide whether each statement is true or false, and explain why.

1. If the antecedent of a conditional statement is false, the conditional statement is true.

2. If the consequent of a conditional statement is true, the conditional statement is true.

3. If q is true, then $(p \wedge q) \rightarrow q$ is true.

4. If p is true, then $\sim p \rightarrow (q \vee r)$ is true.

5. Given that $\sim p$ is true and q is false, the conditional $p \rightarrow q$ is true.

6. Given that $\sim p$ is false and q is false, the conditional $p \rightarrow q$ is true.

7. In a few sentences, explain how we determine the truth value of a conditional statement.

8. Explain why the statement "If $3 = 5$, then $4 = 6$" is true.

Tell whether each conditional is true or false. Here T represents a true statement and F represents a false statement.

9. $F \rightarrow (4 \neq 7)$

10. $(6 \geq 6) \rightarrow F$

11. $(4 = 11 - 7) \rightarrow (8 > 0)$

12. $(4^2 \neq 16) \rightarrow (4 - 4 = 8)$

Let d represent "She dances tonight," let s represent "He sings loudly," and let e represent "I'm leaving early." Express each compound statement in words.

13. $d \rightarrow (e \wedge s)$

14. $(d \wedge s) \rightarrow e$

15. $\sim s \rightarrow (d \vee \sim e)$

16. $(\sim d \vee \sim e) \rightarrow \sim s$

Let d represent "My dog ate my homework," let f represent "I receive a failing grade," and let g represent "I'll run for governor." Express each compound statement in symbols.

17. My dog ate my homework, or if I receive a failing grade, then I'll run for governor.

18. I'll run for governor, and if I receive a failing grade, then my dog did not eat my homework.

19. I'll run for governor if I don't receive a failing grade.

20. I won't receive a failing grade if my dog didn't eat my homework.

Find the truth value of each statement. Assume that p and r are false, and q is true.

21. $\sim r \rightarrow p$

22. $\sim q \rightarrow r$

23. $\sim p \rightarrow (q \wedge r)$

24. $(\sim r \vee p) \rightarrow p$

25. $\sim q \rightarrow (p \wedge r)$

26. $(\sim p \wedge \sim q) \rightarrow (p \wedge \sim r)$

27. $(p \rightarrow \sim q) \rightarrow (\sim p \wedge \sim r)$

28. $(p \rightarrow \sim q) \wedge (p \rightarrow r)$

29. Explain why, if we know that p is true, we also know that

$$[r \vee (p \vee s)] \rightarrow (p \vee q)$$

is true, even if we are not given the truth values of q, r, and s.

30. Construct a true statement involving a conditional, a conjunction, a disjunction, and a negation (not necessarily in that order), that consists of component statements p, q, and r, with all of these component statements false.

31. Using the table of equivalent statements rather than a truth table, explain why the statement $(\sim p \rightarrow \sim q) \wedge \sim (p \vee \sim q)$ in Example 5(a) must be a contradiction.

32. What is the minimum number of times that F must appear in the final column of a truth table for us to be assured that the statement is not a tautology?

Construct a truth table for each statement. Identify any tautologies or contradictions.

33. $\sim q \rightarrow p$

34. $p \rightarrow \sim q$

35. $(p \vee \sim p) \rightarrow (p \wedge \sim p)$

36. $(p \wedge \sim q) \wedge (p \rightarrow q)$

37. $(p \vee q) \rightarrow (q \vee p)$

38. $(\sim p \rightarrow \sim q) \rightarrow (p \wedge q)$

39. $r \rightarrow (p \wedge \sim q)$

40. $[(r \vee p) \wedge \sim q] \rightarrow p$

41. $(\sim r \rightarrow s) \vee (p \rightarrow \sim q)$

42. $(\sim p \wedge \sim q) \rightarrow (\sim r \rightarrow \sim s)$

Write each statement as an equivalent statement that does not use the *if . . . then* connective. Remember that $p \rightarrow q$ is equivalent to $\sim p \vee q$.

43. If your eyes are bad, your whole body will be full of darkness.

44. If you meet me halfway, this will work.

45. I'd buy that car if I had the money.

46. I would watch out if I were you.

Write the negation of each statement. Remember that the negation of $p \rightarrow q$ is $p \wedge \sim q$.

47. If you ask me, I will do it.

48. If you are not part of the solution, you are part of the problem.

49. If you don't love me, I won't be happy.

50. If he's my brother, then he's not heavy.

Use truth tables to decide which of the pairs of statements are equivalent.

51. $p \rightarrow q$; $\sim p \vee q$

52. $\sim (p \rightarrow q)$; $p \wedge \sim q$

53. $p \rightarrow q$; $q \rightarrow p$

54. $q \rightarrow p$; $\sim p \rightarrow \sim q$

55. $p \rightarrow \sim q$; $\sim p \vee \sim q$

56. $p \rightarrow q$; $\sim q \rightarrow \sim p$

57. $p \wedge \sim q$; $\sim q \rightarrow \sim p$

58. $\sim p \wedge q$; $\sim p \rightarrow q$

In some approaches to logic, the only connectives are $\sim$ and $\rightarrow$, and the other logical connectives are defined in terms of these.* Verify this by using a truth table to demonstrate the following equivalences.

59. $p \wedge q \equiv \sim (p \rightarrow \sim q)$

60. $p \vee q \equiv \sim p \rightarrow q$

In Exercises 61–68, construct a truth table to prove each law.

61. $p \vee q \equiv q \vee p$, the Commutative Law for $\vee$

62. $p \wedge q \equiv q \wedge p$, the Commutative Law for $\wedge$

63. $p \vee (q \vee r) \equiv (p \vee q) \vee r$, the Associative Law for $\vee$

64. $p \wedge (q \wedge r) \equiv (p \wedge q) \wedge r$, the Associative Law for $\wedge$

65. $p \vee (q \wedge r) \equiv (p \vee q) \wedge (p \vee r)$, the Distributive Law for $\vee$ over $\wedge$

66. $p \wedge (q \vee r) \equiv (p \wedge q) \vee (p \wedge r)$, the Distributive Law for $\wedge$ over $\vee$

67. $(p \wedge q) \vee p \equiv p$, the first Absorption Law

68. $(p \vee q) \wedge p \equiv p$, the second Absorption Law

*For example, see Stefan Bilaniuk, *A Problem Course in Mathematical Logic*, euclid.trentu.ca/math/sb/pcml.

Write a logical statement representing each circuit. Simplify each circuit when possible.

69.

70.

71.

72.

73.

74.

75.

76.

Draw circuits representing the following statements as they are given. Simplify if possible.

77. $p \wedge (q \vee \sim p)$

78. $(\sim p \wedge \sim q) \wedge \sim r$

79. $(p \vee q) \wedge (\sim p \wedge \sim q)$

80. $(\sim q \wedge \sim p) \vee (\sim p \vee q)$

81. $[(p \vee q) \wedge r] \wedge \sim p$

82. $[(\sim p \wedge \sim r) \vee \sim q] \wedge (\sim p \wedge r)$

83. $\sim q \rightarrow (\sim p \rightarrow q)$

84. $\sim p \rightarrow (\sim p \vee \sim q)$

85. $[(p \wedge q) \vee p] \wedge [(p \vee q) \wedge q]$

86. $[(p \wedge q) \vee (p \wedge q)] \vee (p \wedge r)$

87. Explain why the circuit

will always have exactly one open switch. What does this circuit simplify to?

88. Refer to Figures 10 and 11 in Example 8. Suppose the cost of the use of one switch for an hour is 3¢. By using the circuit in Figure 11 rather than the circuit in Figure 10, what is the savings for a year of 365 days, assuming that the circuit is in continuous use?

APPLICATIONS

Business and Economics

89. Income Tax The following statements appear in a guide for preparing income tax reports. Rewrite each statement with an equivalent statement using *or*. *Source: Your Income Tax 2014.*

(a) If you are married at the end of the year, you may file a joint return with your spouse.

(b) A bequest received by an executor from an estate is tax free if it is not compensation for services.

(c) If a course improves your current job skills but leads to qualification for a new profession, the course is not deductable.

90. Warranty A protection plan for the iPhone states: "Service will be performed at the location, or the store may send the Covered Equipment to an Apple repair service location to be repaired." *Source: AppleCare Protection Plan.*

(a) Rewrite the statement with an equivalent statement using the *if . . . then* connective.

(b) Write the negation of the statement.

91. Stocks An investor announces, "If the value of my portfolio exceeds $100,000 or the price of my stock in Ford Motor Company falls below $50 per share, then I will sell all my shares of Ford stock and I will give the proceeds to the United Way." Let *v* represent "The value of my portfolio exceeds $100,000," *p* represent "The price of my stock in Ford Motor Company falls below $50 per share," *s* represent "I will sell all my shares of Ford stock," and *g* represent "I will give the proceeds to the United Way."

(a) Convert the statement into symbols.

(b) Find the truth value of the statement if my portfolio is worth $80,000, Ford Motor stock is at $56 per share, I sell my Ford Motor stock, and I keep the proceeds.

(c) Explain under what circumstances the statement will be true or false.

(d) Find the negation of the statement.

Life Sciences

92. Medicine The following statement appears in a home medical reference book. Rewrite this statement replacing the *if . . . then* with an *or* statement. Then negate that statement. *Source: American College of Physicians Complete Home Medical Guide.*

If you are exercising outside, it is important to protect your skin and eyes from the sun.

Social Sciences

93. The following statements appear in a guide to common law. Write an equivalent statement using the *if . . . then* connective. *Source: Law for Dummies*.

(a) You can file a civil lawsuit yourself, or your attorney can do it for you.

(b) Your driver's license may come with restrictions, or restrictions may sometimes be added on later.

(c) You can't marry unless you're at least 18 years old, or unless you have the permission of your parents or guardian.

YOUR TURN ANSWERS

1. False   **2.** True   **3.** True

4. You do not do the homework, or you will pass the quiz.

5. You are on time and we will not be on time.

6.4 More on the Conditional

APPLY IT   Is it possible to rewrite statements in a medical guide in one or more ways? *This question will be answered in Exercise 44.*

The conditional can be written in several ways. For example, the word *then* might not be explicitly stated, so the statement "If I'm here, then you're safe" might become "If I'm here, you're safe." Also, the consequent (the *then* component) might come before the antecedent (the *if* component), as in "You're safe if I'm here." In this section we will examine other translations of the conditional.

Alternative Forms of the Conditional   Another way to express the conditional is with the word *sufficient*. For example, the statement

If it rains in the valley, then snow is falling on the mountain

can be written

Rain in the valley is sufficient for snow to fall on the mountain.

This statement claims that one condition guaranteeing snow to fall on top of the mountain is rain in the valley. The statement doesn't claim that this is the only condition under which snow falls on the mountain; perhaps snow falls on the mountain on days when it's perfectly clear in the valley. On the other hand, assuming the statement to be true, you won't see rain in the valley unless snow is falling on the mountain. In other words,

Snow falling on the mountain is necessary for rain in the valley.

To summarize this discussion, the statement "if p, then q" is sometimes stated in the form "p is sufficient for q" and sometimes in the form "q is necessary for p." To keep track of these two forms, notice that the antecedent is the sufficient part, while the consequent is the necessary part.

There are other common translations of $p \rightarrow q$. We have collected the most common ones in the box below.

Common Translations of $p \rightarrow q$

The conditional $p \rightarrow q$ can be translated in any of the following ways.

If p, then q.	p is sufficient for q.
If p, q.	q is necessary for p.
p implies q.	All p's are q's.
p only if q.	q if p.
q when p.	

The translation of $p \rightarrow q$ into these various word forms does not in any way depend on the truth or falsity of $p \rightarrow q$.

EXAMPLE 1 Equivalent Statements

Write the following statement in eight different equivalent ways, using the common translations of $p \rightarrow q$ in the box above:

If you answer this survey, then you will be entered in the drawing.

SOLUTION

If you answer this survey, you will be entered in the drawing.

Answering this survey implies that you will be entered in the drawing.

You answer this survey only if you will be entered in the drawing.

You will be entered in the drawing when you answer this survey.

Answering this survey is sufficient for you to be entered in the drawing.

Being entered in the drawing is necessary for you to answer this survey.

All who answer this survey will be entered in the drawing.

You will be entered in the drawing if you answer this survey.

EXAMPLE 2 Equivalent Statements

Write each statement in the form "if p, then q."

(a) Possession of a valid identification card is necessary for admission.

SOLUTION If you are admitted, then you possess a valid identification card.

(b) You should use this door only if there is an emergency.

SOLUTION If you should use this door, then there is an emergency.

(c) All who are weary can come and rest.

SOLUTION If you are weary, then you can come and rest. TRY YOUR TURN 1

YOUR TURN 1 Write each statement in the form "if p, then q."
(a) Being happy is sufficient for you to clap your hands.
(b) All who seek shall find.

> CAUTION | Notice that "p only if q" is not the same as "p if q." The first means $p \rightarrow q$, while the second means $q \rightarrow p$.

EXAMPLE 3 Symbolic Statements

Let r represent "A triangle is a right triangle" and s represent "The sum of the squares of the two sides equals the square of the hypotenuse." Write each statement in symbols.

(a) A triangle is a right triangle if the sum of the squares of the two sides equals the square of the hypotenuse.

SOLUTION

$$s \rightarrow r$$

(b) A triangle is a right triangle only if the sum of the squares of the two sides equals the square of the hypotenuse.

SOLUTION

$$r \rightarrow s$$

Converse, Inverse, and Contrapositive

Example 3(b) gives a statement of the Pythagorean theorem. Example 3(a) gives what is called the **converse** of the Pythagorean theorem. The converse of a statement $p \rightarrow q$ is the statement $q \rightarrow p$. For example, the converse of the statement

If today is Monday, then we have to put out the garbage

is the statement

If we have to put out the garbage, then today is Monday.

Although both the Pythagorean theorem and its converse are true, the converse of a true statement is not necessarily true, as we shall see in Example 4.

A second statement related to the conditional is the **inverse**, in which both the antecedent and consequent are negated. The inverse of the first statement above is

If today is not Monday, then we do not have to put out the garbage.

The inverse of a statement $p \rightarrow q$ is the statement $\sim p \rightarrow \sim q$. The inverse, like the converse, is not necessarily true, even if the original statement is true.

The third and final statement related to the conditional is the **contrapositive**, in which the antecedent and consequent are negated and interchanged. The contrapositive of the first statement above is

If we do not have to put out the garbage, then today is not Monday.

The contrapositive of a statement $p \rightarrow q$ is the statement $\sim q \rightarrow \sim p$. We will show in a moment that the contrapositive is logically equivalent to the original statement, so that if one is true, the other is also true. First, we summarize the three statements related to the original conditional statement below.

Related Conditional Statements

Original Statement	$p \rightarrow q$	(If p, then q.)
Converse	$q \rightarrow p$	(If q, then p.)
Inverse	$\sim p \rightarrow \sim q$	(If not p, then not q.)
Contrapositive	$\sim q \rightarrow \sim p$	(If not q, then not p.)

In the following truth table, we include the conditional $p \rightarrow q$ as well as the three related forms. Notice that the original conditional and the contrapositive are equivalent; that is, whenever one is true, so is the other. Notice also that the converse and the inverse are equivalent to each other. Finally, notice that the original conditional is not equivalent to the converse or the inverse; for example, in line 2 of the table, where p is true and q is false, the original conditional and the contrapositive are both false, but the inverse and converse are true.

		Original	Converse	Inverse	Contrapositive
			Equivalent		
				Equivalent	
p	q	$p \rightarrow q$	$q \rightarrow p$	$\sim p \rightarrow \sim q$	$\sim q \rightarrow \sim p$
T	T	T	T	T	T
T	F	F	T	T	F
F	T	T	F	F	T
F	F	T	T	T	T

This discussion is summarized in the box on the next page.

Equivalences

The original statement and the contrapositive are equivalent, and the converse and the inverse are equivalent.

EXAMPLE 4 **Related Conditional Statements**

Consider the following statement:

If Cauchy is a cat, then Cauchy is a mammal.

Write each of the following.

(a) The converse

SOLUTION Let c represent "Cauchy is a cat" and m represent "Cauchy is a mammal." Then the original statement is $c \rightarrow m$, and the converse is $m \rightarrow c$, or

If Cauchy is a mammal, then Cauchy is a cat.

Notice that in this case the original statement is true, while the converse is false, because Cauchy might be a mammal that is not a cat, such as a horse.

(b) The inverse

SOLUTION The inverse of $c \rightarrow m$ is $\sim c \rightarrow \sim m$, or

If Cauchy is not a cat, then Cauchy is not a mammal.

The inverse, like the converse, is false in this case.

(c) The contrapositive

SOLUTION The contrapositive of $c \rightarrow m$ is $\sim m \rightarrow \sim c$, or

If Cauchy is not a mammal, then Cauchy is not a cat.

In this case the contrapositive is true, as it must be if the original statement is true.

YOUR TURN 2 Write the converse, inverse, and contrapositive of the following statement: "If I get another ticket, then I lose my license." Which is equivalent to the original statement?

Biconditionals

As we saw earlier, both the Pythagorean theorem and its converse are true. That is, letting r represent "A triangle is a right triangle" and s represent "The sum of the squares of the two sides equals the square of the hypotenuse," both $s \rightarrow r$ and $r \rightarrow s$ are true. In words, we say s *if and only if* r (often abbreviated s iff r). (Recall that *only if* is the opposite of *if . . . then*.) This is called the **biconditional** and is written $s \leftrightarrow r$. You can think of the biconditional as being defined by the equivalence

$$p \leftrightarrow q \equiv (p \rightarrow q) \wedge (q \rightarrow p)$$

or by the following truth table.

Truth Table for the Biconditional p *if and only if* q

p	q	$p \leftrightarrow q$
T	T	T
T	F	F
F	T	F
F	F	T

EXAMPLE 5 **Biconditional Statements**

Tell whether each statement is true or false.

(a) George Washington is the first president of the United States if and only if John Adams is the second president of the United States.

SOLUTION Since both component statements are true, the first row of the truth table tells us that this biconditional is true.

(b) Alaska is one of the original 13 states if and only if kangaroos can fly.

SOLUTION Since both component statements are false, the last row of the truth table tells us that this biconditional is true.

(c) $2 + 2 = 4$ if and only if $7 > 10$.

SOLUTION The first component statement is true, but the second is false. The second row of the truth table tells us that this biconditional is false.   TRY YOUR TURN 3

> **YOUR TURN 3** Determine if the following statement is *true* or *false*. "New York City is the capital of the United States if and only if Paris is the capital of France."

Notice in the truth table and the previous example that when p and q have the same truth value, $p \leftrightarrow q$ is true; when p and q have different truth values, $p \leftrightarrow q$ is false.

In this and the previous two sections, truth tables have been derived for several important types of compound statements. The summary that follows describes how these truth tables may be remembered.

Summary of Basic Truth Tables

1. $\sim p$, the **negation** of p, has truth value opposite of p.
2. $p \wedge q$, the **conjunction**, is true only when both p and q are true.
3. $p \vee q$, the **disjunction**, is false only when both p and q are false.
4. $p \rightarrow q$, the **conditional**, is false only when p is true and q is false.
5. $p \leftrightarrow q$, the **biconditional**, is true only when p and q have the same truth value.

6.4 WARM-UP EXERCISES

Construct a truth table for each statement.

W1. $(p \vee q) \rightarrow \sim p$ *(Sec. 6.3)*

W2. $\sim q \rightarrow (p \wedge q)$ *(Sec. 6.3)*

6.4 EXERCISES

For each given statement, write (a) the converse, (b) the inverse, and (c) the contrapositive in *if . . . then* form. In some of the exercises, it may be helpful to restate the statement in *if . . . then* form.

1. If the exit is ahead, then I don't see it.

2. If I finish reading this novel, then I'll write a review.

3. If I knew you were coming, I'd have cleaned the house.

4. If I'm the bottom, you're the top.

5. Mathematicians wear pocket protectors.

6. Beggars can't be choosers.

7. $p \rightarrow \sim q$

8. $\sim q \rightarrow \sim p$

9. $p \rightarrow (q \vee r)$ (*Hint:* Use one of De Morgan's Laws as necessary.)

10. $(r \vee \sim q) \rightarrow p$ (*Hint:* Use one of De Morgan's Laws as necessary.)

11. Discuss the equivalences that exist among the direct conditional statement, the converse, the inverse, and the contrapositive.

12. State the contrapositive of "If the square of a natural number is even, then the natural number is even." The two statements must have the same truth value. Use several examples and inductive reasoning to decide whether both are true or both are false.

Write each statement in the form "if *p* . . . then *q*."

13. Your signature implies that you accept the conditions.

14. His tardiness implies that he doesn't care.

15. You can take this course pass/fail only if you have prior permission.

16. You can purchase this stock only if you have $1000.

17. You can skate on the pond when the temperature is below 10°.

18. The party will be stopped when more than 200 people attend.

19. Eating 10 hot dogs is sufficient to make someone sick.

20. Two hours in the desert sun is sufficient to give the typical person a sunburn.

21. A valid passport is necessary for travel to France.

22. Support from the party bosses is necessary to get the nomination.

23. For a number to have a real square root, it is necessary that it be nonnegative.

24. For a number to have a real square root, it is sufficient that it be nonnegative.

25. All brides are beautiful.

26. All passengers for Hempstead must change trains at Jamaica station.

27. A number is divisible by 3 if the sum of its digits is divisible by 3.

28. A number is even if its last digit is even.

29. One of the following statements is not equivalent to all the others. Which one is it?

   (a) *r* only if *s*.

   (b) *r* implies *s*.

   (c) If *r*, then *s*.

   (d) *r* is necessary for *s*.

30. Use the statement "Being 65 years old is sufficient for being eligible for Medicare" to explain why "*p* is sufficient for *q*" is equivalent to "if *p*, then *q*."

31. Use the statement "Being over 21 is necessary for entering this club" to explain why "*p* is necessary for *q*" is equivalent to "if *q*, then *p*."

32. Explain why the statement "Elephants can fly if and only if Africa is the smallest continent" is true.

Identify each statement as *true* or *false*.

33. $5 = 9 - 4$ if and only if $8 + 2 = 10$.

34. $3 + 1 \neq 6$ if and only if $8 \neq 8$.

35. $8 + 7 \neq 15$ if and only if $3 \times 5 \neq 9$.

36. $6 \times 2 = 14$ if and only if $9 + 7 \neq 16$.

37. China is in Asia if and only if Mexico is in Europe.

38. The moon is made of green cheese if and only if Hawaii is one of the United States.

Construct a truth table for each statement.

39. $(\sim p \wedge q) \leftrightarrow (p \rightarrow q)$

40. $(p \leftrightarrow \sim q) \leftrightarrow (\sim p \vee q)$

APPLICATIONS

Business and Economics

41. Income Tax The following excerpts appear in a guide for preparing income tax reports. Write each of the statements in *if . . . then* form. *Source: Your Income Tax 2014.*

   (a) Determining which mutual-funds shares are being sold is necessary to figure your gain or loss.

   (b) Expenses are excludable from income only if they would qualify for the dependent care credit.

   (c) A child is not a qualifying child if he or she provides over half of his or her own support.

42. Income Tax The following excerpt appears in a guide for preparing income tax reports. Write the statement in *if . . . then* form. Find the contrapositive of this statement. *Source: Your Income Tax 2014.*

   Some benefits are allowed on separate returns only if you live apart from your spouse for all or part of the year.

43. Credit Cards The following statement appeared in a card member agreement for a Chase Visa Card. Write the converse, inverse, and contrapositive. Which statements are equivalent? *Source: JP Morgan Chase & Co.*

   If your account is in default, we may close your account without notice.

Life Sciences

44. APPLY IT The following statement is from a home medical guide. Write the statement in four different ways, using the common translations of $p \rightarrow q$. (See Example 1.) *Source: American College of Physicians Complete Home Medical Guide.*

   When you sleep well, you wake up feeling refreshed and alert.

45. Polar Bears The following statement is with regard to polar bear cubs. *Source: National Geographic.*

   If there are triplets, the most persistent stands to gain an extra meal and it may eat at the expense of another.

   (a) Use symbols to write this statement.

   (b) Write the contrapositive of this statement.

Social Sciences

46. Law The following statements appear in a guide to common laws. Write the statement in *if . . . then* form. *Source: Law for Dummies.*

   (a) When you buy a car, you must register it right away.

   (b) All states have financial responsibility laws.

   (c) Your insurer pays the legitimate claims of the injured party and defends you in court if you're sued.

47. Law The following statements appear in a guide to common laws. Write the converse, inverse, and contrapositive of the statements. Which statements are equivalent? *Source: Law for Dummies*.

(a) If you are married, then you can't get married again.

(b) If you pay for your purchase with a credit card, you are protected by the Fair Credit Billing Act.

(c) If you hit a parked car, you're expected to make a reasonable effort to locate the owner.

48. Philosophy Aristotle once said, "If liberty and equality, as is thought by some, are chiefly to be found in democracy, they will be best attained when all persons alike share in the government to the utmost." Write the contrapositive of this statement. *Source: Bartlett's Familiar Quotations*.

49. Political Development It has been argued that political development in Western Europe will increase if and only if social assimilation is increasing. *Source: International Organizational*.

(a) Express this statement symbolically, and construct a truth table for it.

(b) The author of the article quoted above says that it is true that political development in Western Europe is increasing, but it is false that social assimilation is increasing. What can then be said about the original statement?

50. Libya Referring to Libya's offer to pay $2.7 billion in compensation for the families of those killed in the 1988 crash of Pan Am flight 103, a White House official said, "This is a necessary step, but it is not sufficient [for the United States to drop sanctions against Libya]." Letting d represent "the United States drops sanctions against Libya" and l represent "Libya offers to pay compensation," write the White House official's statement as a statement in symbolic logic. *Source: The New York Times*.

51. Education It has been argued that "a high level of education . . . comes close to being a necessary [condition for democracy]." For the purpose of this exercise, consider "comes close to being" as meaning "is," and assume the statement refers to a country. Write the statement in *if . . . then* form, and then write the converse, inverse, and contrapositive of the statement. Which one of these is equivalent to the original statement? *Source: The American Political Science Review*.

52. Political Alliances According to political scientist Howard Rosenthal, "the presence of [a Modéré] incumbent can be regarded as a necessary condition for a R.P.F. alliance." Write the statement in *if . . . then* form, and then write the converse, inverse, and contrapositive of the statement. Which one of these is equivalent to the original statement? *Source: The American Political Science Review.**

53. Test of Reasoning A test devised by psychologist Peter Wason is designed to test how people reason. As an example of this test, volunteers are given the rule, "If a card has a D on

*The R.P.F. and Modéré are the names of political parties in France.

one side, then it must have a 3 on the other side." Volunteers view four cards displaying D, F, 3, and 7, respectively. They are told that each card has a letter on one side and a number on the other. Which cards do they need to turn over to determine if the rule has been violated? In Wason's experiments, fewer than one-fourth of the participants gave the correct answer. *Source: Science News*.

54. Test of Reasoning In another example of a Wason test (see previous exercise), volunteers are given the rule, "If an employee works on the weekend, then that person gets a day off during the week." Volunteers are given four cards displaying "worked on the weekend," "did not work on the weekend," "did get a day off," and "did not get a day off." Volunteers were told that one side of the card tells whether an employee worked on the weekend, and the other side tells whether an employee got a day off. Which cards must be turned over to determine if the rule has been violated? In a set of experiments, volunteers told to take the perspective of the employees tended to give the correct answer, while volunteers told to take the perspective of employers tended to turn over the second and third card.

General Interest

55. Sayings Rewrite each of the following statements as a conditional in *if . . . then* form. Then write two statements that are equivalent to the *if . . . then* statements. (*Hint:* Write the contrapositive of the statement and rewrite the conditional statement using *or.*)

(a) Nothing ventured, nothing gained.

(b) The best things in life are free.

(c) Every cloud has a silver lining.

56. Sayings Think of some wise sayings that have been around for a long time, and state them in *if . . . then* form.

57. Games Statements similar to the ones below appear in the instructions for various Milton Bradley games. Rewrite each statement in *if . . . then* form and then write an equivalent statement using *or. Source: Milton Bradley Company*.

(a) You can score in this box only if the dice show any sequence of four numbers.

(b) When two or more words are formed in the same play, each is scored.

(c) All words labeled as a part of speech are permitted.

YOUR TURN ANSWERS

1. (a) If you are happy, then you clap your hands.

(b) If you seek, then you shall find.

2. *Converse:* If I lose my license, then I get another ticket. *Inverse:* If I didn't get another ticket, then I didn't lose my license. *Contrapositive:* If I didn't lose my license, then I didn't get another ticket. The contrapositive is equivalent.

3. False.

6.5 Analyzing Arguments and Proofs

If I could be in two places at the same time, then I'd come to your game. I did not come to your game, so can I conclude that I can't be in two places at the same time?
This question will be analyzed using truth tables in Example 2 of this section.

In this section, we will analyze and construct logical arguments, or proofs, that can be used to determine whether a given set of statements produces a sensible conclusion. A logical argument is made up of **premises** and **conclusions**. The premises are statements that we accept for the sake of the argument. It is not the purpose of logic to determine whether or not the premises are actually true. In logic, we suppose the premises to be true and then ask what statements follow using the laws of logic. The statements that follow are the conclusions. The argument is considered *valid* if the conclusions must be true when the premises are true.

Valid and Invalid Arguments

An argument is **valid** if the fact that all the premises are true forces the conclusion to be true. An argument that is not valid is **invalid**, or a **fallacy**.

In other words, in an invalid argument, it is possible for the premises to be true and the conclusion to be false.

It is very important to note that *valid* and *true* are not the same—an argument can be valid even though the conclusion is false. (See the discussion after Example 3.)

We will begin by using truth tables to determine whether certain types of arguments are valid or invalid. We will then use the results from these examples to demonstrate a more powerful method of proving that an argument is valid or invalid. As our first example, consider the following argument.

> If it's after midnight, then I must go to sleep.
>
> It's after midnight.
> _____
>
> I must go to sleep.

Here we use the common method of placing one premise over another, with the conclusion below a line. Alternatively, we could indicate that the last line is a conclusion using "therefore," as in "Therefore, I must go to sleep."

To test the validity of this argument, we begin by identifying the component statements found in the argument. We will use the generic variables p and q here, rather than meaningful variable names, so the argument will have a generic form.

> p represents "It's after midnight";
>
> q represents "I must go to sleep."

Now we write the two premises and the conclusion in symbols:

> Premise 1: $p \rightarrow q$
> Premise 2: p
> _____
> Conclusion: q　.

To decide if this argument is valid, we must determine whether the conjunction of both premises implies the conclusion for all possible cases of truth values for p and q.

Therefore, write the conjunction of the premises as the antecedent of a conditional statement, and the conclusion as the consequent.

$$[(p \rightarrow q) \quad \wedge \quad p] \quad \rightarrow \quad q$$

$\uparrow$ Premise $\quad$ $\uparrow$ and $\quad$ $\uparrow$ premise $\quad$ $\uparrow$ implies $\quad$ $\uparrow$ conclusion.

Finally, construct the truth table for the conditional statement, as shown below.

p	q	$p \rightarrow q$	$(p \rightarrow q) \wedge p$	$[(p \rightarrow q) \wedge p] \rightarrow q$
T	T	T	T	T
T	F	F	F	T
F	T	T	F	T
F	F	T	F	T

Since the final column, shown in color, indicates that the conditional statement that represents the argument is true for all possible truth values of p and q, the statement is a tautology. Thus, the argument is valid.

The pattern of the argument in the preceding example,

$$p \rightarrow q$$
$$\underline{p}$$
$$q \quad ,$$

is a common one and is called **Modus Ponens**, or the *law of detachment.*

In summary, to test the validity of an argument using a truth table, go through the steps in the box that follows.

Testing the Validity of an Argument with a Truth Table

1. Assign a letter to represent each component statement in the argument.
2. Express each premise and the conclusion symbolically.
3. Form the symbolic statement of the entire argument by writing the *conjunction* of *all* the premises as the antecedent of a conditional statement and the conclusion of the argument as the consequent.
4. Complete the truth table for the conditional statement formed in step 3. If it is a tautology, then the argument is valid; otherwise, it is invalid.

EXAMPLE 1   Determining Validity

Determine whether the argument is *valid* or *invalid.*

> If I win the lottery, then I'll buy a new house.
>
> I bought a new house.
> _____
>
> I won the lottery.

SOLUTION   Let p represent "I win the lottery" and let q represent "I'll buy a new house." Using these symbols, the argument can be written in the form

$$p \rightarrow q$$
$$\underline{q}$$
$$p \quad .$$

To test for validity, construct a truth table for the statement

$$[(p \rightarrow q) \wedge q] \rightarrow p.$$

p	q	$p \rightarrow q$	$(p \rightarrow q) \wedge q$	$[(p \rightarrow q) \wedge q] \rightarrow p$
T	T	T	T	T
T	F	F	F	T
F	T	T	T	F
F	F	T	F	T

The third row of the final column of the truth table shows F, and this is enough to conclude that the argument is invalid. Even if the premises are true, the conclusion that I won the lottery is not necessarily true. Perhaps I bought a new house with money I inherited. ■

If a conditional and its converse were logically equivalent, then an argument of the type found in Example 1 would be valid. Since a conditional and its converse are *not* equivalent, the argument is an example of what is sometimes called the **Fallacy of the Converse**.

EXAMPLE 2 **Determining Validity**

Determine whether the argument is *valid* or *invalid*.

> If I could be in two places at the same time, I'd come to your game.
>
> I did not come to your game.
> _____
> I cannot be in two places at the same time.

APPLY IT **SOLUTION** If p represents "I could be in two places at the same time" and q represents "I'd come to your game," the argument becomes

$$p \rightarrow q$$
$$\frac{\sim q}{\sim p} \quad .$$

The symbolic statement of the entire argument is

$$[(p \rightarrow q) \wedge \sim q] \rightarrow \sim p.$$

The truth table for this argument, shown below, indicates a tautology, and the argument is valid.

p	q	$p \rightarrow q$	$\sim q$	$(p \rightarrow q) \wedge \sim q$	$\sim p$.	$[(p \rightarrow q) \wedge \sim q] \rightarrow \sim p$
T	T	T	F	F	F	T
T	F	F	T	F	F	T
F	T	T	F	F	T	T
F	F	T	T	T	T	T

The pattern of reasoning of this example is called **Modus Tollens**, or the *law of contraposition*. ■

With reasoning similar to that used to name the fallacy of the converse, the fallacy

$$p \rightarrow q$$
$$\frac{\sim p}{\sim q}$$

is often called the **Fallacy of the Inverse**. An example of such a fallacy is "If it rains, I get wet. It doesn't rain. Therefore, I don't get wet."

EXAMPLE 3 **Determining Validity**

Determine whether the argument is *valid* or *invalid*.

> I'll win this race or I'll eat my hat.
> I didn't win this race.
> _____
> I'll eat my hat.

SOLUTION Let p represent "I'll win this race" and let q represent "I'll eat my hat." Using these symbols, the argument can be written in the form

$$p \vee q$$
$$\underline{\sim p}$$
$$q \quad .$$

Set up a truth table for

$$[(p \vee q) \wedge \sim p] \rightarrow q.$$

p	q	$p \vee q$	$\sim p$	$(p \vee q) \wedge \sim p$	$[(p \vee q) \wedge \sim p] \rightarrow q$
T	T	T	F	F	T
T	F	T	F	F	T
F	T	T	T	T	T
F	F	F	T	F	T

The statement is a tautology and the argument is valid. Any argument of this form is valid by the law of **Disjunctive Syllogism**. ▬

Suppose you notice a few months later that I didn't win the race or eat my hat. You object that the conclusion of the argument in Example 3 is false. Did that make the argument invalid? No. The problem is that I lied about the first premise, namely, that I would win the race or eat my hat. A valid argument only guarantees that *if* all the premises are true, then the conclusion must also be true. Whether the premises of an argument are actually true is a separate issue. I might have a perfectly valid argument, yet you disagree with my conclusion because you disagree with one or more of my premises.

EXAMPLE 4 **Determining Validity**

Determine whether the following argument is *valid* or *invalid*.

> If you make your debt payments late, you will damage your credit record.
> If you damage your credit record, you will have difficulty getting a loan.
> _____
> If you make your debt payments late, you will have difficulty getting a loan.

SOLUTION Let p represent "you make your debt payments late," let q represent "you will damage your credit record," and let r represent "you will have difficulty getting a loan." The argument takes on the general form

$$p \rightarrow q$$
$$\underline{q \rightarrow r}$$
$$p \rightarrow r.$$

Make a truth table for the following statement:

$$[(p \rightarrow q) \wedge (q \rightarrow r)] \rightarrow (p \rightarrow r).$$

It will require eight rows.

p	q	r	$p \rightarrow q$	$q \rightarrow r$	$p \rightarrow r$	$(p \rightarrow q) \wedge (q \rightarrow r)$	$[(p \rightarrow q) \wedge (q \rightarrow r)] \rightarrow (p \rightarrow r)$
T	T	T	T	T	T	T	T
T	T	F	T	F	F	F	T
T	F	T	F	T	T	F	T
T	F	F	F	T	F	F	T
F	T	T	T	T	T	T	T
F	T	F	T	F	T	F	T
F	F	T	T	T	T	T	T
F	F	F	T	T	T	T	T

This argument is valid since the final statement is a tautology. The pattern of argument shown in this example is called **Reasoning by Transitivity**, or the *law of hypothetical syllogism.*

A summary of the valid and invalid forms of argument presented so far is given below.

Valid Argument Forms

Modus Ponens	Modus Tollens	Disjunctive Syllogism	Reasoning by Transitivity
$p \rightarrow q$	$p \rightarrow q$	$p \vee q$	$p \rightarrow q$
p	$\sim q$	$\sim p$	$q \rightarrow r$
q	$\sim p$	q	$p \rightarrow r$

Invalid Argument Forms (Fallacies)

Fallacy of the Converse	Fallacy of the Inverse
$p \rightarrow q$	$p \rightarrow q$
q	$\sim p$
p	$\sim q$

When an argument contains three or more premises, creating a truth table becomes too tedious. Instead, we show that an argument is invalid by trying to find a way to make the premises true and the conclusion false. We show that an argument is valid by creating a chain of the valid argument forms to construct a proof. We will illustrate these ideas in the next several examples.

EXAMPLE 5 Determining Validity

Determine whether the following argument is *valid* or *invalid.*

> If Ed reaches the semifinals, then Liz will be happy.
>
> If Liz is not happy, then Roxanne will bake her a cake.
>
> Roxanne did not bake Liz a cake.
>
> Therefore, Ed reaches the semifinals.

SOLUTION Let e represent "Ed reaches the semifinals," l represent "Liz is happy," and r represent "Roxanne bakes Liz a cake." The symbolic form of the argument is as follows.

1. $e \rightarrow l$		Premise
2. $\sim l \rightarrow r$		Premise
3. $\underline{\sim r}$		Premise
e		Conclusion

Our strategy will be to apply the valid argument forms either to the premises or to conclusions that have already been reached. Notice, for example, that we can apply Modus Tollens to lines 2 and 3 to reach $\sim(\sim l) \equiv l$. We write this as follows, giving the statements and the argument form used.

4. l \qquad\qquad 2, 3, Modus Tollens

From statements 1 and 4, can we conclude e? Only if we use the Fallacy of the Converse! Thus this argument appears to be invalid. To see if this is the case, we investigate whether it is possible to make the premises true and the conclusion false. Write the premises and the conclusion with the desired truth value next to each.

1. $e \rightarrow l$	T
2. $\sim l \rightarrow r$	T
3. $\underline{\sim r}$	T
e	F

In statement 3, to make $\sim r$ true, we know that r must be false. From the conclusion, e must be false. Statement 1 is then automatically true. To make statement 2 true, simply make l true, so $\sim l$ is false. In summary, the following assignment of truth values make all the premises true, yet the conclusion is false.

$$e = \text{"Ed reaches the semifinals"} = F$$
$$l = \text{"Liz is happy"} = T$$
$$r = \text{"Roxanne bakes Liz a cake"} = F \qquad \text{TRY YOUR TURN 1} \blacksquare$$

YOUR TURN 1 Determine whether the following argument is *valid* or *invalid*. You watch television tonight or you write your paper tonight. If you write your paper tonight, then you will get a good grade. You get a good grade. Therefore, you did not watch television tonight.

Let's summarize what we have seen.

- To show that an argument is valid, prove it using the four valid argument forms discussed in this section. We can also use any of the laws given in the Equivalent Statement box in Section 6.3.

- To show that an argument is invalid, give an assignment of truth values that makes the premises true and the conclusion false.

It's not always clear which of these two strategies you should try first, but if one doesn't work, try the other. An argument may be valid, but it may not be provable using only the rules learned so far. In the next section we will study additional rules for proving arguments. When all else fails, you can always create a truth table, but if the argument has many variables, this could be very tedious.

EXAMPLE 6 Determining Validity

Lewis Carroll* gave humorous logic puzzles in his book *Symbolic Logic*. In each puzzle, he presented several premises, and the reader was to find valid conclusions. Here is one of his puzzles. What is the valid conclusion? *Source: The Complete Works of Lewis Carroll.*

> Babies are illogical.
>
> Nobody is despised who can manage a crocodile.
>
> Illogical persons are despised.

---

*Lewis Carroll is the pseudonym for Charles Dodgson (1832–1898), mathematician and author of *Alice in Wonderland*.

SOLUTION First, write each premise in *if . . . then* form.

> If you are a baby, then you are illogical.
>
> If you can manage a crocodile, then you are not despised.
>
> If you are illogical, then you are despised.

Let *b* represent "you are a baby," *i* represent "you are illogical," *m* represent "you can manage a crocodile," and *d* represent "you are despised." The statements can then be written symbolically as

1. $b \rightarrow i$ Premise

2. $m \rightarrow {\sim}d$ Premise

3. $i \rightarrow d$ Premise

Notice that we can combine the first and third statements using reasoning by transitivity.

4. $b \rightarrow d$ 1, 3, Transitivity

How can we combine this with statement 2, which has not yet been used? Both statements 2 and 4 have *d* at the end, but in statement 2 the *d* is negated. Use the contrapositive to get statement 2 in a more useful form.

5. $d \rightarrow {\sim}m$ 2, Contrapositive

Now we can use transitivity.

6. $b \rightarrow {\sim}m$ 4, 5, Transitivity

In words, the conclusion is "If you are a baby, then you cannot manage a crocodile," or, as Lewis Carroll put it, "Babies cannot manage crocodiles." ▬

Often there are different ways to do a proof. In the previous example, you might first apply contrapositive to statement 2, and then combine the result with statement 3 using transitivity, and finally combine that result with statement 1 using transitivity. In the exercises in this textbook, your proofs might look different from those in the back of the book but still be correct.

EXAMPLE 7   Determining Validity

Determine whether the following argument is *valid* or *invalid*.

> If tomorrow is Saturday and sunny, then it is a beach day.
>
> Tomorrow is Saturday.
>
> Tomorrow is not a beach day.
>
> Therefore, tomorrow must not be sunny.

SOLUTION Let *t* represent "tomorrow is Saturday," *s* represent "tomorrow is sunny," and *b* represent "tomorrow is a beach day." We give a proof that this argument is valid.

1. $(t \wedge s) \rightarrow b$ Premise

2. t Premise

3. ${\sim}b$ Premise

4. ${\sim}(t \wedge s)$ 1, 3, Modus Tollens

5. ${\sim}t \vee {\sim}s$ 4, De Morgan's Law

6. ${\sim}s$ 2, 5, Disjunctive Syllogism

How did we figure out this proof? We started by looking for a rule of logic that combines two of the three premises. Notice that statement 3 has the negation of the right side of

YOUR TURN 2 Determine whether the following argument is *valid* or *invalid*. You will not put money in the parking meter or you will not buy a cup of coffee. If you do not put money in the parking meter, you will get a ticket. You did not get a ticket. Therefore, you did not buy a cup of coffee.

statement 1; this is a clue that Modus Tollens might be helpful. Once we get statement 4, using one of De Morgan's Laws is an obvious choice, as it should be whenever we see a negation over ∧ or ∨. Statement 2 still hasn't been used at this point, but notice that it is the negation of one part of the ∨ in statement 5, leading us to try Disjunctive Syllogism.

TRY YOUR TURN 2

EXAMPLE 8 **Determining Validity**

Determine whether the following argument is *valid* or *invalid*.

If your teeth are white, you use Extreme Bright toothpaste.

If your teeth are white, you will be more attractive.

Therefore, if you use Extreme Bright toothpaste, you will be more attractive.

SOLUTION Let w represent "your teeth are white," t represent "you use Extreme Bright toothpaste," and a represent "you will be more attractive."

In symbolic form, this argument can be written as follows.

$$\begin{array}{c} w \rightarrow t \\ \underline{w \rightarrow a} \\ t \rightarrow a \end{array}$$

This looks like a misguided attempt at using reasoning by transitivity and so appears invalid. To show this, we need to find a way to make the premises true and the conclusion false. The only way the conclusion, $t \rightarrow a$, can be false is if t is true and a is false. Both premises will automatically be true if we make w false. Thus the argument is invalid. The following assignment of truth values make all the premises true and the conclusion false.

$$w = \text{"your teeth are white"} = \text{F}$$
$$t = \text{"you use Extreme Bright toothpaste"} = \text{T}$$
$$a = \text{"you will be more attractive"} = \text{F}$$

6.5 WARM-UP EXERCISES

Write the contrapositive of each statement, and simplify using one of De Morgan's Laws.

W1. $p \rightarrow (q \vee \sim r)$ *(Sec. 6.4)*

W2. $(p \wedge \sim q) \rightarrow \sim r$ *(Sec. 6.4)*

6.5 EXERCISES

Each of the following arguments is either valid by one of the forms of valid arguments discussed in this section or is a fallacy by one of the forms of invalid arguments discussed. (See the summary boxes.) Decide whether the argument is *valid* or *invalid*, and give the form that applies.

1. If she weighs the same as a duck, she's made of wood.

If she's made of wood, she's a witch.

If she weighs the same as a duck, she's a witch.

2. If passing is out of the question, there's no point in going to class.

If there's no point in going to class, then attending college makes no sense.

If passing is out of the question, then attending college makes no sense.

3. If I had the money, I'd go on vacation.

I have the money.

I go on vacation.

4. If I were a rabbit, I'd hop away.

I am a rabbit.

I hop away.

5. If you want to make trouble, the door is that way.

The door is that way.

You want to make trouble.

6. If you finish the test, you can leave early.

You can leave early.

You finish the test.

7. If Andrew Crowley plays, the opponent gets shut out.

The opponent does not get shut out.

Andrew Crowley does not play.

8. If you want to follow along, we're on p. 315.

We're not on p. 315.

You don't want to follow along.

9. "If we evolved a race of Isaac Newtons, that would not be progress." (quote from Aldous Huxley)

We have not evolved a race of Isaac Newtons.

That is progress.

10. "If I have seen farther than others, it is because I stood on the shoulders of giants." (quote from Sir Isaac Newton)

I have not seen farther than others.

I have not stood on the shoulders of giants.

11. Something is rotten in the state of Denmark, or my name isn't Hamlet.

My name is Hamlet.

Something is rotten in the state of Denmark.

12. "We shall conquer together or we shall die together." (quote from Winston Churchill)

We shall not die together.

We shall conquer together.

Determine whether each argument is valid or invalid. If it is valid, give a proof. If it is invalid, give an assignment of truth values to the variables that makes the premises true and the conclusion false.

13. $p \vee q$

p

$\sim q$

14. $p \vee \sim q$

p

$\sim q$

15. $p \rightarrow q$

$q \rightarrow p$

$p \wedge q$

16. $\sim p \rightarrow q$

p

$\sim q$

17. $\sim p \rightarrow \sim q$

q

p

18. $p \rightarrow \sim q$

q

$\sim p$

19. $p \rightarrow q$

$\sim q$

$\sim p \rightarrow r$

r

20. $p \vee q$

$\sim p$

$r \rightarrow \sim q$

$\sim r$

21. $p \rightarrow q$

$q \rightarrow r$

$\sim r$

$\sim p$

22. $p \rightarrow q$

$r \rightarrow \sim q$

$p \rightarrow \sim r$

23. $p \rightarrow q$

$q \rightarrow \sim r$

p

$r \vee s$

s

24. $p \rightarrow q$

$\sim p \rightarrow r$

$s \rightarrow \sim q$

$\sim r \rightarrow \sim s$

Use a truth table, similar to those in Examples 1–4, to prove each rule of logic. The rules in Exercises 25–27 are known as *simplification*, *amplification*, and *conjunction*, respectively.

25. $p \wedge q$

p

26. p

$p \vee q$

27. p

q

$p \wedge q$

28. Lori Hales made the following observation: "If I want to determine whether an argument leading to the statement

$$[(p \rightarrow q) \wedge \sim q] \rightarrow \sim p$$

is valid, I only need to consider the lines of the truth table that lead to T for the column headed $(p \rightarrow q) \wedge \sim q$." Lori was very perceptive. Can you explain why her observation was correct?

APPLICATIONS

For Exercises 29–37, determine whether each of the following arguments is *valid* or *invalid*. If it is valid, give a proof. If it is invalid, give an assignment of truth values to the variables that makes the premises true and the conclusion false.

Business and Economics

29. **Investment** If Alex invests in AT&T, Sophia will invest in Sprint Nextel. Victor will invest in Verizon or Alex invests in AT&T. Victor will not invest in Verizon. Therefore, Sophia will invest in Sprint Nextel.

30. **Credit** If you make your debt payments late, you will damage your credit record. If you damage your credit record, you will have trouble getting a loan. You do not have trouble getting a loan. Therefore, you do not make your debt payments late.

31. **Stock Market** It is a bearish market. If prices are rising, then it is not a bearish market. If prices are not rising, then the investor will sell stocks. Therefore, the investor will not sell stocks.

Life Sciences

32. **Classification** If the animal is a reptile, then it belongs to the chordate phylum. The animal either belongs to the echinoderm phylum or the chordate phylum. It does not belong to the echinoderm phylum. Therefore, it is not a reptile.

33. **Classification** The animal is a spider or it is an insect. If it is a spider, then it has eight legs and it has two main body parts. It does not have eight legs or it does not have two main body parts. Therefore, it is an insect.

Social Sciences

34. **Politics** If Boehme runs for senator, then Hoffman will run for governor. If Tobin runs for congressman, then Hoffman will not run for governor. Therefore, if Tobin runs for congressman, then Boehme will not run for senator.

General Interest

35. Appliances If the air conditioner is on, the microwave doesn't work. If the microwave doesn't work, the radio stops getting static. The microwave doesn't work or the radio is getting static. Therefore, if the air conditioner is on, the radio is getting static.

36. Electricity If the electricity is on and the circuits are intact, then the television should work. The television isn't working. Therefore, the electricity is not on or the circuits are not intact.

37. Baseball The Yankees will be in the World Series or the Phillies won't be there. If the Phillies are not in the World Series, the National League cannot win. In fact, the National League wins. Therefore, the Yankees are in the World Series.

38. Time Suppose that you ask someone for the time and you get the following response:

"If I tell you the time, then we'll start chatting. If we start chatting, then you'll want to meet me at a truck stop. If we meet at a truck stop, then we'll discuss my family. If we discuss my family, then you'll find out that my daughter is available for marriage. If you find out that she is available for marriage, then you'll want to marry her. If you want to marry her, then my life will be miserable since I don't want my daughter married to some fool who can't afford a $20 watch."

Use Reasoning by Transitivity to draw a valid conclusion.

Lewis Carroll Exercises 39–44 are from problems in Lewis Carroll's book *Symbolic Logic*. Write each premise in symbols, and then give a conclusion that uses all the premises and yields a valid argument. *Source: The Complete Works of Lewis Carroll.*

39. Let d be "it is a duck," p be "it is my poultry," o be "one is an officer," and w be "one waltzes."

(a) No ducks waltz.

(b) No officers ever decline to waltz.

(c) All my poultry are ducks.

(d) Give a conclusion that yields a valid argument.

40. Let l be "one is able to do logic," j be "one is fit to serve on a jury," s be "one is sane," and y be "he is your son."

(a) Everyone who is sane can do logic.

(b) No lunatics are fit to serve on a jury.

(c) None of your sons can do logic.

(d) Give a conclusion that yields a valid argument.

41. Let h be "one is honest," p be "one is a pawnbroker," b be "one is a promise breaker," t be "one is trustworthy," c be "one is very communicative," and w be "one is a wine drinker."

(a) Promise breakers are untrustworthy.

(b) Wine drinkers are very communicative.

(c) A man who keeps his promise is honest.

(d) No teetotalers are pawnbrokers. (*Hint:* Assume "teetotaler" is the opposite of "wine drinker.")

(e) One can always trust a very communicative person.

(f) Give a conclusion that yields a valid argument.

42. Let g be "it is a guinea pig," i be "it is hopelessly ignorant of music," s be "it keeps silent while the *Moonlight Sonata* is being played," and a be "it appreciates Beethoven."

(a) Nobody who really appreciates Beethoven fails to keep silent while the *Moonlight Sonata* is being played.

(b) Guinea pigs are hopelessly ignorant of music.

(c) No one who is hopelessly ignorant of music ever keeps silent while the *Moonlight Sonata* is being played.

(d) Give a conclusion that yields a valid argument.

43. Let s be "it begins with 'Dear Sir'," c be "it is crossed," d be "it is dated," f be "it is filed," i be "it is in black ink," t be "it is in the third person," r be "I can read it," p be "it is on blue paper," o be "it is on one sheet," and b be "it is written by Brown."

(a) All the dated letters in this room are written on blue paper.

(b) None of them are in black ink, except those that are written in the third person.

(c) I have not filed any of them that I can read.

(d) None of them that are written on one sheet are undated.

(e) All of them that are not crossed are in black ink.

(f) All of them written by Brown begin with "Dear Sir."

(g) All of them written on blue paper are filed.

(h) None of them written on more than one sheet are crossed.

(i) None of them that begin with "Dear Sir" are written in the third person.

(j) Give a conclusion that yields a valid argument.

44. Let p be "he is going to a party," b be "he brushes his hair," s be "he has self-command," l be "he looks fascinating," o be "he is an opium eater," t be "he is tidy," and w be "he wears white kid gloves."

(a) No one who is going to a party ever fails to brush his hair.

(b) No one looks fascinating if he is untidy.

(c) Opium eaters have no self-command.

(d) Everyone who has brushed his hair looks fascinating.

(e) No one wears white kid gloves unless he is going to a party. (*Hint:* "not a unless b" $\equiv a \rightarrow b$.)

(f) A man is always untidy if he has no self-command.

(g) Give a conclusion that yields a valid argument.

YOUR TURN ANSWERS ▬▬

1. Invalid;

t = "you watch television tonight" = T,

p = "you write your paper tonight" = F,

g = "you get a good grade" = T.

2. Valid

1. $\sim m \vee \sim c$	Premise	
2. $\sim m \rightarrow t$	Premise	
3. $\sim t$	Premise	
4. m	2,3, Modus Tollens	
5. $\sim c$	1,4 Disjunctive Syllogism	

6.6 Analyzing Arguments with Quantifiers

APPLY IT **If some U.S. presidents won the popular vote and George W. Bush is the U.S. president, did he win the popular vote?**
This question will be analyzed in Example 6 of this section.

There is a subtle but important point that we have ignored in some of the logic puzzles of the previous section. Consider the statement "Babies are illogical" in Example 6 in that section. We reinterpreted this statement as "If you are a baby, then you are illogical." Letting b represent "you are a baby" and i represent "you are illogical," we wrote this statement as $b \to i$. This was perfectly adequate for solving that puzzle. But now suppose we want to add two more premises: "Madeleine is a baby" and "Noa is a baby." It would seem that two valid conclusions are: "Madeleine is illogical" and "Noa is illogical." But how do we write these statements symbolically? We can't very well have b represent both "Madeleine is a baby" and "Noa is a baby." We might try letting these two statements be represented by m and n, but then it's not clear how we can combine m or n with $b \to i$.

Logicians solve this problem with the use of **quantifiers**. The words *all*, *each*, *every*, and *no(ne)* are called **universal quantifiers**, while words and phrases such as *some, there exists*, and *(for) at least one* are called **existential quantifiers**. Quantifiers are used extensively in mathematics to indicate *how many* cases of a particular situation exist.

In the previous example, we could let $b(x)$ represent "x is a baby," where x could represent any baby. Then $b(m)$ could represent "Madeleine is a baby" and $b(n)$ could represent "Noa is a baby." We want to say that $b(x) \to i(x)$ *for all x*. Logicians use the symbol $\forall$ to represent "for all." We could then represent the statement "Babies are illogical" as

$$\forall x \, [b(x) \to i(x)].$$

Suppose, instead, that we don't want to claim that all babies are illogical, but that some babies are illogical, or, equivalently, that there exists someone who is a baby and who is illogical. Logicians use the symbol $\exists$ to represent "there exists." We could then write the statement "Some babies are illogical" as

$$\exists x \, [b(x) \wedge i(x)].$$

NOTE
The important point to note here is that when a statement contains the word "all," a universal quantifier ($\forall$) is usually called for, and when it contains the word "some," an existential quantifier ($\exists$) is usually called for.

Negation of Quantifiers
We must be careful in forming the negation of a statement involving quantifiers. Suppose we wish to say that the statement "Babies are illogical" is false. This is *not* the same as saying "Babies are logical." Maybe some babies are illogical and some are logical. Let $b(x)$ represent "x is a baby" and $i(x)$ represent "x is illogical." To deny the claim that for all x, the statement $b(x) \to i(x)$ is true, is equivalent to saying that for some x, the statement $b(x) \to i(x)$ is false. Thus,

$$\sim \{\forall x \, [b(x) \to i(x)]\} \equiv \exists x \, \{\sim[b(x) \to i(x)]\}.$$

Recall from Section 6.3 that the right side of this last statement is equivalent to $\exists x \, \{[b(x) \wedge \sim i(x)]\}$. Therefore,

$$\sim \{\forall x \, [b(x) \to i(x)]\} \equiv \exists x \, \{[b(x) \wedge \sim i(x)]\}.$$

This last statement makes intuitive sense; it says that if it's false that all babies are illogical, then there exists someone who is a baby and who is not illogical. In other words, some babies are logical.

In a similar way, suppose we wish to say that the statement "Some babies are illogical" is false. To deny the existence of an x such that $b(x) \wedge i(x)$ is the same as saying that for all x, the statement $b(x) \wedge i(x)$ is false. Thus,

$$\sim \{\exists x \, [b(x) \wedge i(x)]\} \equiv \forall x \, \{\sim[b(x) \wedge i(x)]\}.$$

Recall from Section 6.3 that $\sim(p \rightarrow q) \equiv p \wedge \sim q$, so negating both sides of this equivalence and replacing q with $\sim q$ implies $\sim(p \wedge q) \equiv p \rightarrow \sim q$. We can use this fact to rewrite the previous equivalence as

$$\sim\{\exists x \, [b(x) \wedge i(x)]\} \equiv \forall x \, \{[b(x) \rightarrow \sim i(x)]\}.$$

This equivalence makes intuitive sense. It says that if it's false that some babies are illogical, then all babies are not illogical, which can be phrased more clearly as "All babies are logical."

Let's summarize the above discussion.

Negations of Quantified Statements

Statement	Symbolic	Negation	Symbolic for Negation
$s(x)$ is true for all x.	$\forall x \, [s(x)]$	$s(x)$ is false for some x.	$\exists x \, [\sim s(x)]$
$s(x)$ is true for some x.	$\exists x \, [s(x)]$	$s(x)$ is false for all x.	$\forall x \, [\sim s(x)]$

Essentially, negation changes a $\forall$ into a $\exists$ and vice versa.

EXAMPLE 1   Negation

Write each statement symbolically. Then write the negation symbolically, and translate the negation back into words.

(a) Some Texans eat quiche.

SOLUTION Let $t(x)$ represent "x is a Texan" and $q(x)$ represent "x eats quiche." The statement can be written as

$$\exists x \, [t(x) \wedge q(x)].$$

Its negation is

$$\forall x \, \{\sim[t(x) \wedge q(x)]\},$$

which is equivalent to

$$\forall x \, [t(x) \rightarrow \sim q(x)].$$

In words, "All Texans don't eat quiche," which can be expressed more clearly as "No Texan eats quiche."

(b) Some Texans do not eat quiche.

SOLUTION Using the notation from part (a), the statement can be written as

$$\exists x \, [t(x) \wedge \sim q(x)].$$

Its negation is

$$\forall x \, \{\sim[t(x) \wedge \sim q(x)]\},$$

which is equivalent to

$$\forall x \, [t(x) \rightarrow q(x)].$$

In words, "All Texans eat quiche."

(c) No Texans eat quiche.

SOLUTION This is the same as saying "All Texans do not eat quiche," which can be written as

$$\forall x \, [t(x) \rightarrow \sim q(x)].$$

Its negation is

$$\exists x \, \{\sim[t(x) \rightarrow \sim q(x)]\},$$

which is equivalent to

$$\exists x \, [t(x) \wedge q(x)].$$

In words, "Some Texans eat quiche." Notice that the statements in parts (a) and (c) are negations of each other. **TRY YOUR TURN 1**

YOUR TURN 1 Write each statement symbolically. Then write the negation symbolically, and translate the negation back into words.

(a) All college students study.
(b) Some professors are not organized.

Just as we had rules for analyzing arguments without quantifiers in the last section, there are also rules for analyzing arguments with quantifiers. Instead of presenting such rules, we will instead demonstrate a visual technique based on **Euler diagrams**, illustrated in the following examples. Euler (pronounced "oiler") diagrams are named after the great Swiss mathematician Leonhard Euler (1707–1783).

EXAMPLE 2 Determining Validity

Represent the following argument symbolically. Is the argument valid?

> All elephants have wrinkles.
>
> Babar is an elephant.
> _____
>
> Babar has wrinkles.

SOLUTION If we let $e(x)$ represent "x is an elephant," $w(x)$ represent "x has wrinkles," and b represent "Babar," we could represent the argument symbolically as follows.

$$\forall x \, [e(x) \rightarrow w(x)]$$
$$\underline{e(b)}$$
$$w(b)$$

Notice that this argument resembles Modus Ponens from the previous section, but with a quantifier, so we suspect that the argument is valid. To verify our suspicion, we draw regions to represent the first premise. One is the region for "elephants." Since all elephants have wrinkles, the region for "elephants" goes inside the region for "have wrinkles," as in Figure 14(a).

The second premise, "Babar is an elephant," suggests that "Babar" should go inside the region representing "elephants." Let b represent "Babar." Figure 14(b) shows that "Babar" is also inside the region for "have wrinkles." Therefore, if both premises are true, the conclusion that "Babar has wrinkles" must also be true. Euler diagrams illustrate that this argument is valid. **TRY YOUR TURN 2**

YOUR TURN 2 Represent the following argument symbolically. Is the argument valid?

All insects are arthropods.
A bee is an insect.
_____
A bee is an arthropod.

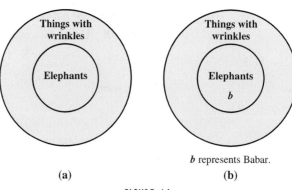

b represents Babar.

(a)   (b)

FIGURE 14

EXAMPLE 3   Determining Validity

Represent the following argument symbolically. Is the argument valid?

> All frogs are slimy.
>
> Kermit is not slimy.
> _____
> Kermit is not a frog.

SOLUTION   If we let $f(x)$ represent "x is a frog," $s(x)$ represent "x is slimy," and k represent "Kermit," we could represent the argument symbolically as follows.

$$\forall x\,[f(x) \rightarrow s(x)]$$
$$\underline{\sim s(k)\qquad\qquad}$$
$$\sim f(k)$$

This argument resembles Modus Tollens with a quantifier, so it is probably valid. We will use an Euler diagram to verify this.

YOUR TURN 3   Represent the following argument symbolically. Is the argument valid?
All birds have wings.
Rover does not have wings.
_____
Rover is not a bird.

In Figure 15(a) below, the region for "frogs" is drawn entirely inside the region for "slimy." Since "Kermit is *not* slimy," place a k for "Kermit" *outside* the region for "slimy." (See Figure 15(b).) Placing the k outside the region for "slimy" automatically places it outside the region for "frogs." Thus, if the first two premises are true, the conclusion that Kermit is not a frog must also be true, so the argument is valid.

TRY YOUR TURN 3

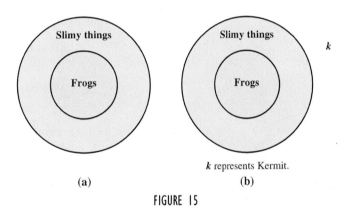

(a)   (b)

k represents Kermit.

FIGURE 15

EXAMPLE 4   Determining Validity

Represent the following argument symbolically. Is the argument valid?

> All well-run businesses generate profits.
>
> Monsters, Inc., generates profits.
> _____
> Monsters, Inc., is a well-run business.

SOLUTION   If we let $w(x)$ represent "x is a well-run business," $p(x)$ represent "x generates profits," and m represent "Monsters, Inc.," we could represent the argument symbolically as follows.

$$\forall x\,[w(x) \rightarrow p(x)]$$
$$\underline{p(m)\qquad\qquad}$$
$$w(m)$$

This argument resembles the Fallacy of the Converse with a quantifier. We will use an Euler diagram to verify that the argument is invalid.

YOUR TURN 4 Represent the following argument symbolically. Is the argument valid?

Every man has his price.

Sam has his price.

Sam is a man.

The region for "well-run business" goes entirely inside the region for "generates a profit." (See Figure 16.) It is not clear where to put the *m* for "Monsters, Inc." It must go inside the region for "generates profits," but it could go inside or outside the region "well-run business." Even if the premises are true, the conclusion may or may not be true, so the argument is invalid. **TRY YOUR TURN 4**

FIGURE 16

As we mentioned in the previous section, the validity of an argument is not the same as the truth of its conclusion. The argument in Example 4 was invalid, but the conclusion "Monsters, Inc." may or may not be true. We cannot make a valid conclusion.

EXAMPLE 5 Determining Validity

Represent the following argument symbolically. Is the argument valid?

> All squirrels eat nuts.
>
> All those who eat nuts are healthy.
>
> All who are healthy avoid cigarettes.
>
> All squirrels avoid cigarettes.

SOLUTION If we let $s(x)$ represent "x is a squirrel," $e(x)$ represent "x eats nuts," $h(x)$ represent "x is healthy," and $a(x)$ represent "x avoids cigarettes," we could represent the argument symbolically as follows.

$$\forall x \, [s(x) \rightarrow e(x)]$$
$$\forall x \, [e(x) \rightarrow h(x)]$$
$$\frac{\forall x \, [h(x) \rightarrow a(x)]}{\forall x \, [s(x) \rightarrow a(x)]}$$

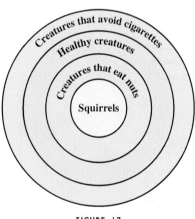

FIGURE 17

This argument should remind you of Reasoning by Transitivity. We will use the Euler diagram in Figure 17 to verify that the argument is valid. If each premise is true, then the conclusion must be true because the region for "squirrels" lies completely within the region for "avoid cigarettes." Thus, the argument is valid.

Our last example in this section illustrates an argument with the word "some," which means that an existential quantifier is needed.

EXAMPLE 6 Determining Validity

Represent the following argument symbolically. Is the argument valid?

> Some U.S. presidents have won the popular vote.
>
> George W. Bush is president of the United States.
>
> George W. Bush won the popular vote.

APPLY IT   **SOLUTION**   If we let $p(x)$ represent "x is a U.S. president," $v(x)$ represent "x won the popular vote," and w represent "George W. Bush," we could represent the argument symbolically as follows.

$$\exists x \left[p(x) \wedge v(x) \right]$$
$$\underline{p(w)}$$
$$v(w)$$

This argument doesn't resemble any of those in the previous section. An Euler diagram might help us see whether this argument is valid or not. The first premise is sketched in Figure 18(a). We have indicated that some U.S. presidents have won the popular vote by putting an x in the region that belongs to both the set of presidential candidates who have won the popular vote and the set of U.S. presidents. There are two possibilities for w, as shown in Figure 18(b).

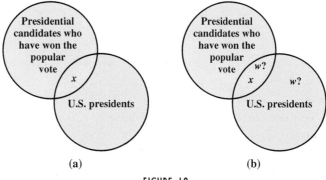

(a)   (b)

FIGURE 18

YOUR TURN 5   Represent the following argument symbolically. Is the argument valid?
Some vegetarians eat eggs.
Sarah is a vegetarian.
Sarah eats eggs.

One possibility is that Bush won the popular vote; the other is that Bush did not win the popular vote. Since the truth of the premises does not force the conclusion to be true, the argument is invalid.

This argument is not valid regardless of whether George W. Bush won the popular vote. In fact, in 2000 George W. Bush was elected president even though he received 50,456,002 votes, compared with 50,999,897 for Al Gore. Bush did win the popular vote in 2004. **Source: Federal Election Commission.**   TRY YOUR TURN 5

6.6 WARM-UP EXERCISES

Give an assignment of truth values to the variables that makes the premises true and the conclusion false.

W1. $r \rightarrow q$ *(Sec. 6.5)*

$\underline{p \vee r}$

$q \rightarrow p$

W2. $p \rightarrow r$ *(Sec. 6.5)*

$\underline{\sim r \wedge \sim p}$

$p \vee q$

6.6   EXERCISES

For Exercises 1–6, (a) write the statement symbolically, (b) write the negative of the statement in part (a), and (c) translate your answer from part (b) into words.

1. Some books are bestsellers.

2. Every dog has his day.

3. No CEO sleeps well at night.

4. There's no place like Alaska.

5. All the leaves are brown.

6. Some days are better than other days.

In Exercises 7–20, (a) represent the argument symbolically, and (b) use an Euler diagram to determine if the argument is valid.

7. Graduates want to find good jobs.

   Theresa Cortesini is a graduate.

   Theresa Cortesini wants to find a good job.

8. All sophomores have earned at least 60 credits.

   Laura Johnson is a sophomore.

   Laura Johnson has earned at least 60 credits.

9. All professors are covered with chalk dust.

   John Tezber is covered with chalk dust.

   John Tezber is a professor.

10. All dinosaurs are extinct.

    The dodo is extinct.

    The dodo is a dinosaur.

11. All accountants use spreadsheets.

    Nancy Hart does not use spreadsheets.

    Nancy Hart is not an accountant.

12. All fish have gills.

    Whales do not have gills.

    Whales are not fish.

13. Some people who are turned down for a mortgage have a second income.

    All people who are turned down for a loan need a mortgage broker.

    Some people with a second income need a mortgage broker.

14. Some residents of Minnesota don't like snow.

    All skiers like snow.

    Some residents of Minnesota are not skiers.

15. Some who wander are lost.

    Paul Burke wanders.

    Paul Burke is lost.

16. Some old houses have root cellars.

    My house has a root cellar.

    My house is old.

17. Some psychologists are university professors.

    Some psychologists have a private practice.

    Some university professors have a private practice.

18. Someone who is responsible must pay for this.

    Jim Pringle is responsible.

    Jim Pringle must pay for this.

19. Everybody is either a saint or a sinner.

    Some people are not saints.

    Some people are sinners.

20. If you're here for the first time, we want to make you feel welcome.

    If you're here after being gone for a while, we want to make you feel welcome.

    Some people are here for the first time or are here after being gone for a while.

    There are some people here whom we want to make feel welcome.

21. Refer to Example 4. If the second premise and the conclusion were interchanged, would the argument then be valid?

22. Refer to Example 5. Give a different conclusion than the one given there, so that the argument is still valid.

Construct a valid argument based on the Euler diagram shown.

23.

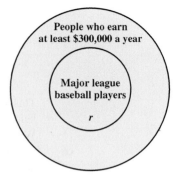

r represents Ryan Howard.

24.

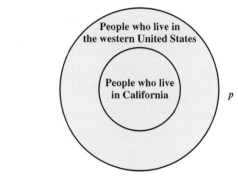

r represents Paulette Stamey.

As mentioned in the text, an argument can have a true conclusion yet be invalid. In these exercises, each argument has a true conclusion. Identify each argument as valid or invalid.

25. All houses have roofs.

    All roofs have nails.

    All houses have nails.

26. All platypuses have bills.

    All ducks have bills.

    A platypus is not a duck.

27. All mammals have fur.

    All tigers have fur.

    All tigers are mammals.

28. All mammals have fur.

    All tigers are mammals.

    All tigers have fur.

29. California is adjacent to Arizona.

    Arizona is adjacent to Nevada.

    California is adjacent to Nevada.

30. Seattle is northwest of Boise.

    Seattle is northwest of Salt Lake City.

    Boise is northwest of Salt Lake City.

31. A rectangle has four sides.

    A square has four sides.

    A square is a rectangle.

32. No integer is irrational.

The number π is irrational.

The number π is not an integer.

33. Explain the difference between the following statements:

All students did not pass the test.
Not all students passed the test.

34. Write the following statement using *every:* There is no one here who has not done that at one time or another.

APPLICATIONS

Business and Economics

35. Advertising Incorrect use of quantifiers often is heard in everyday language. Suppose you hear that a local electronics chain is having a 30% off sale, and the radio advertisement states, "All items are not available in all stores." Do you think that, literally translated, the ad really means what it says? What do you think really is meant? Explain your answer.

36. Portfolios Repeat Exercise 35 for the following: "All people don't have the time to devote to maintaining their financial portfolios properly."

Life Sciences

37. Schizophrenia The following diagram shows the relationship between people with schizophrenia, people with a mental disorder, and people who live in California.

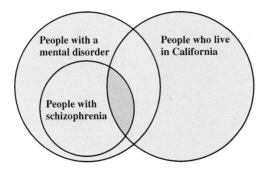

Which of the following conclusions are valid?

(a) All those with schizophrenia have a mental disorder.

(b) All those with schizophrenia live in California.

(c) Some of those with a mental disorder live in California.

(d) Some of those who live in California do not have schizophrenia.

(e) All those with a mental disorder have schizophrenia.

Social Sciences

Constitution Each of the following exercises gives a passage from the U.S. Constitution, followed by another statement. (a) Translate the passage from the Constitution into a statement in symbolic logic. (b) Find a valid conclusion using as premises the passage from the Constitution and the statement that follows it. (c) Illustrate the argument with an Euler diagram.

38. All legislative powers herein granted shall be vested in a Congress of the United States . . . (Article 1, Section 1)

The power to collect taxes is a legislative power herein granted.

39. No person shall be a Representative who shall not have attained to the age of twenty-five years, and been seven years a citizen of the United States, and who shall not, when elected, be an inhabitant of that State in which he shall be chosen. (Article 1, Section 2)

John Boehner is a Representative.

40. No bill of attainder or ex post facto law shall be passed. (Article 1, Section 9)

The law forbidding members of the Communist Party to serve as an officer or as an employee of a labor union was a bill of attainder. *Source: United States V. Brown.*

41. No State shall enter into any treaty, alliance, or confederation. (Article 1, Section 10)

Texas is a state.

General Interest

42. Bible Write the negation of each of the following quotes from the Bible. *Source: NIV Bible.*

(a) "Everyone who hears about this will laugh with me."—Genesis 21:6

(b) "Someone came to destroy your lord the king."—1 Samuel 26:15

(c) "There is no one who does good."—Psalm 53:3

(d) "Everyone is the friend of one who gives gifts."—Proverbs 19:6

(e) "Everyone who quotes proverbs will quote this proverb about you: 'Like mother, like daughter.'"—Ezekiel 16:44

Animals In Exercises 43–48, the premises marked *A*, *B*, and *C* are followed by several possible conclusions. Take each conclusion in turn, and check whether the resulting argument is *valid* or *invalid.*

(A) All kittens are cute animals.

(B) All cute animals are admired by animal lovers.

(C) Some dangerous animals are admired by animal lovers.

43. Some kittens are dangerous animals.

44. Some cute animals are dangerous.

45. Some dangerous animals are cute.

46. Kittens are not dangerous animals.

47. All kittens are admired by animal lovers.

48. Some things admired by animal lovers are dangerous animals.

YOUR TURN ANSWERS

1. (a) $\forall x\, [c(x) \rightarrow s(x)]$; negation: $\exists x\, [c(x) \wedge \sim s(x)]$, "Some college students do not study."

(b) $\exists x\, [p(x) \wedge \sim o(x)]$; negation: $\forall x\, [p(x) \rightarrow o(x)]$, "All professors are organized."

2. $\forall x\, [i(x) \rightarrow a(x)]$

$\dfrac{i(b)}{a(b)}$

3. $\forall x\, [b(x) \rightarrow w(x)]$

$\dfrac{\sim w(r)}{\sim b(r)}$

4. $\forall x\, [m(x) \rightarrow p(x)]$

$\dfrac{p(s)}{m(s)}$

5. $\exists x\, [v(x) \wedge e(x)]$

$\dfrac{v(s)}{e(s)}$

CHAPTER REVIEW

SUMMARY

In this chapter we introduced symbolic logic, which uses letters to represent statements, and symbols for words such as

- *and* (conjunction, denoted by $\wedge$),
- *or* (disjunction, denoted by $\vee$),
- *not* (negation, denoted by $\sim$),
- *if . . . then* (conditional, denoted by $\rightarrow$), and
- *if and only if* (biconditional, denoted by $\leftrightarrow$).

Statements are declarative sentences that are either true or false, but not both simultaneously. Using logical connectives, we can combine two or more statements to form a compound statement. Truth values of various compound statements were explored using truth tables. We saw that two logical statements are equivalent (denoted as $\equiv$) if they have the same truth value. We used symbolic logic to design circuits, and then used logical equivalences to simplify the circuits. We saw that the contrapositive, a statement related to the conditional, is equivalent to the original conditional statement, but that two other related statements, the inverse and the converse, are not equivalent to the original conditional statement. We next explored how to prove valid arguments and give counterexamples to invalid arguments. Finally, we discussed the quantifiers *for all* (denoted by $\forall$) and *there exists* (denoted by $\exists$), and we used Euler diagrams to determine the validity of an argument involving quantifiers.

Truth Tables for Logical Operators	p	q	$p \wedge q$	$p \vee q$	$p \rightarrow q$	$p \leftrightarrow q$
	T	T	T	T	T	T
	T	F	F	T	F	F
	F	T	F	T	T	F
	F	F	F	F	T	T

Writing a Conditional as an *or* Statement	$p \rightarrow q \equiv \sim p \vee q$

Negation of a Conditional Statement	$\sim(p \rightarrow q) \equiv p \wedge \sim q$

Equivalent Statements

1. (a) $p \vee q \equiv q \vee p$ Commutative Laws
   (b) $p \wedge q \equiv q \wedge p$
2. (a) $p \vee (q \vee r) \equiv (p \vee q) \vee r$ Associative Laws
   (b) $p \wedge (q \wedge r) \equiv (p \wedge q) \wedge r$
3. (a) $p \vee (q \wedge r) \equiv (p \vee q) \wedge (p \vee r)$ Distributive Laws
   (b) $p \wedge (q \vee r) \equiv (p \wedge q) \vee (p \wedge r)$
4. (a) $\sim(p \wedge q) \equiv \sim p \vee \sim q$ De Morgan's Laws
   (b) $\sim(p \vee q) \equiv \sim p \wedge \sim q$
5. (a) $p \vee p \equiv p$ Idempotent Laws
   (b) $p \wedge p \equiv p$
6. (a) $(p \wedge q) \vee p \equiv p$ Absorption Laws
   (b) $(p \vee q) \wedge p \equiv p$
7. $\sim(\sim p) \equiv p$ Double Negative
8. $p \rightarrow q \equiv \sim p \vee q$ Conditional as an "or"
9. $p \rightarrow q \equiv \sim q \rightarrow \sim p$ Contrapositive

If T represents any true statement and F represents any false statement, then

10. (a) $p \vee T \equiv T$ Identity Laws
    (b) $p \wedge T \equiv p$
    (c) $p \vee F \equiv p$
    (d) $p \wedge F \equiv F$
11. (a) $p \vee \sim p \equiv T$ Negation Laws
    (b) $p \wedge \sim p \equiv F$

Common Translations of $p \to q$	If p, then q.	p is sufficient for q.
	If p, q.	q is necessary for p.
	p implies q.	All p's are q's.
	p only if q.	q if p.
	q when p.	

Related Conditional Statements

The contrapositive is equivalent to the original statement. However, the converse and inverse are not equivalent to the original statement, although they are equivalent to each other.

Original Statement	$p \to q$
Converse	$q \to p$
Inverse	$\sim p \to \sim q$
Contrapositive	$\sim q \to \sim p$

Valid Argument Forms

Modus Ponens	Modus Tollens	Disjunctive Syllogism	Reasoning by Transitivity
$p \to q$	$p \to q$	$p \vee q$	$p \to q$
p	$\sim q$	$\sim p$	$q \to r$
q	$\sim p$	q	$p \to r$

Invalid Argument Forms (Fallacies)

Fallacy of the Converse	Fallacy of the Inverse
$p \to q$	$p \to q$
q	$\sim p$
p	$\sim q$

KEY TERMS

6.1
statement
logical connective
compound statement
component statement
negation
truth table
conjunction
disjunction

6.2
equivalent
De Morgan's Laws

6.3
conditional

antecedent
consequent
contradiction
tautology
circuit
series
parallel
Principle of Duality
Commutative Law
Associative Law
Distributive Law
Idempotent Laws
Double Negative
Absorption Laws

Conditional as an "or"
Identity Laws
Negation Laws

6.4
converse
inverse
contrapositive
biconditional

6.5
premise
conclusion
valid
invalid

fallacy
Modus Ponens
Fallacy of the Converse
Modus Tollens
Fallacy of the Inverse
Disjunctive Syllogism
Reasoning by Transitivity

6.6
quantifier
universal quantifier
existential quantifier
Euler diagram

REVIEW EXERCISES

CONCEPT CHECK

Determine whether each of the following statements is true or false, and explain why.

1. A compound statement is a negation, a conjunction, a disjunction, a conditional, or a biconditional.

2. A truth table with 5 variables has 10 rows.

3. A truth table can have an odd number of rows.

4. Using one of De Morgan's Laws, the negation of a disjunction may be written as a conditional.

5. The negation of a conditional statement is a disjunction.

6. Elements in a circuit that are in parallel are connected in a logic statement with an *or*.

7. A tautology might be false.

8. A statement might be true even though its inverse is false.

9. The conclusion of a valid argument must be true.

10. The conclusion of a fallacy must be false.

11. Euler diagrams can be used to determine whether an argument with quantifiers is valid or invalid.

12. The negation of a statement with the universal quantifier involves the existential quantifier.

PRACTICE AND EXPLORATIONS

Write the negation of each statement.

13. If she doesn't pay me, I won't have enough cash.

14. We played the Titans and the Titans won.

Let *l* represent "He loses the election" and let *w* represent "He wins the hearts of the voters." Write each statement in symbols.

15. He loses the election, but he wins the hearts of the voters.

16. If he wins the hearts of the voters, then he doesn't lose the election.

17. He loses the election only if he doesn't win the hearts of the voters.

18. He loses the election if and only if he doesn't win the hearts of the voters.

Using the same statements as for Exercises 15–18, write each mathematical statement in words.

19. $\sim l \wedge w$ **20.** $\sim (l \vee \sim w)$

Assume that *p* is true and that *q* and *r* are false. Find the truth value of each statement.

21. $\sim q \wedge \sim r$ **22.** $r \vee (p \wedge \sim q)$

23. $r \rightarrow (s \vee r)$ (The truth value of the statement *s* is unknown.)

24. $p \leftrightarrow (p \rightarrow q)$

25. Explain in your own words why, if *p* is a statement, the biconditional $p \leftrightarrow \sim p$ must be false.

26. State the necessary conditions for

(a) a conditional statement to be false;

(b) a conjunction to be true;

(c) a disjunction to be false.

Construct a truth table for each statement. Is the statement a tautology?

27. $p \wedge (\sim p \vee q)$ **28.** $\sim (p \wedge q) \rightarrow (\sim p \vee \sim q)$

Write each conditional statement in *if . . . then* form.

29. All mathematicians are loveable.

30. You can have dessert only if you eat your vegetables.

31. Having at least as many equations as unknowns is necessary for a system to have a unique solution.

32. Having a feasible region is sufficient for a linear programming problem to have a minimum.

For each statement, write (a) the converse, (b) the inverse, and (c) the contrapositive.

33. If the proposed regulations have been approved, then we need to change the way we do business.

34. $(p \vee q) \rightarrow \sim r$ (Use one of De Morgan's Laws to simplify.)

Write a logical statement representing each circuit. Simplify each circuit when possible.

35.

36.

Draw the circuit representing each statement as it is given. Simplify if possible.

37. $(p \wedge q) \vee (p \wedge p)$ **38.** $p \wedge (p \vee q)$

For Exercises 39 and 40, consider the exclusive disjunction introduced in Exercises 35–38 of Section 6.2. In exclusive disjunction, denoted by $p \veebar q$, either *p* or *q* is true, but not both.

39. Use a truth table to show that
$p \veebar q \equiv (p \vee q) \wedge \sim (p \wedge q)$.

40. Use a truth table to show that
$p \veebar q \equiv \sim [(p \vee q) \rightarrow (p \wedge q)]$.

41. Consider the statement "If this year is 2010, then $1 + 1 = 3$."

(a) Is the above statement true?

(b) Was the above statement true in 2010?

(c) Discuss how a statement such as the one above changes its truth value over time and how this agrees or disagrees with your intuitive notion of whether a conditional statement is true or false.

42. (a) Consider the statement "If Shakespeare didn't write *Hamlet*, then someone else did." Explain why this statement is true.

(b) Consider the statement "If Shakespeare hadn't written *Hamlet*, then someone else would have." Explain why this statement should be false in any reasonable logic.

(c) If we let *s* represent "Shakespeare wrote *Hamlet*" and *e* represent "someone else wrote *Hamlet*," then the logic of this chapter leads us to represent either the statement of part (a) or part (b) as $\sim s \rightarrow e$. Discuss the issue of how this statement could be true in part (a) but false in part (b). *Source: Formal Logic: Its Scope and Limit.*

Each of the following arguments is either valid by one of the forms of valid arguments discussed in this chapter or is a fallacy by one of the forms of invalid arguments discussed. Decide whether the argument is valid or invalid, and give the form that applies.

43. If you're late one more time, you'll be docked.

    You're late one more time.
    _____
    You'll be docked.

44. If the company makes a profit, its stock goes up.

    The company doesn't make a profit.
    _____
    Its stock doesn't go up.

45. The instructor is late or my watch is wrong.

    My watch is not wrong.
    _____
    The instructor is late.

46. If the parent is loving, then the child will be happy.

    If the child is happy, then the teacher can teach.
    _____
    If the parent is loving, then the teacher can teach.

47. If you play that song one more time, I'm going nuts.

    I'm going nuts.
    _____
    You play that song one more time.

48. If it's after five, the store is closed.

    The store is not closed.
    _____
    It's not after five.

Determine whether each argument is *valid* or *invalid*. If it is valid, give a proof. If it is invalid, give an assignment of truth values to the variables that makes the premises true and the conclusion false.

49. If we hire a new person, then we'll spend more on training. If we rewrite the manual, then we won't spend more on training. We rewrite the manual. Therefore, we don't hire a new person.

50. It is not true that Smith or Jones received enough votes to qualify. But if Smith got enough votes to qualify, then the election was rigged. Therefore, the election was not rigged.

51. $\sim p \rightarrow \sim q$
    $\underline{q \rightarrow p}$
    $p \vee q$

52. $p \rightarrow q$
    $\underline{r \rightarrow \sim q}$
    $p \rightarrow \sim r$

In Exercises 53 and 54, (a) write the statement symbolically, (b) write the negation of the statement in part (a), and (c) translate your answer from part (b) into words.

53. All dogs have a license.

54. Some cars have manual transmissions.

In Exercises 55 and 56, (a) represent the argument symbolically, and (b) use an Euler diagram to determine whether the argument is valid.

55. All members of that fraternity do well academically.

    Jordan Enzor is a member of that fraternity.
    _____
    Jordan Enzor does well academically.

56. Some members of that fraternity don't do well academically.

    Bart Stewart does well academically.
    _____
    Bart Stewart is not a member of that fraternity.

57. Construct a truth table for $p \rightarrow (q \rightarrow r)$ and $(p \rightarrow q) \rightarrow r$. Are these two statements equivalent?

58. (a) Convert the statement $p \rightarrow (q \rightarrow r)$ into an equivalent statement with an "or," but without the conditional.

    (b) Convert the statement $(p \rightarrow q) \rightarrow r$ into an equivalent statement with an "or," but without the conditional.

59. (a) Construct a truth table for the statement $(p \wedge \sim p) \rightarrow q$.

    (b) Based on the truth table for part (a), explain why any conclusion may be reached from a contradictory premise.

60. We saw in this chapter that conjunction is commutative; that is, $p \wedge q \equiv q \wedge p$. But in everyday speech this may not always be the case. Consider the following examples:

    (i) p = Jack and Jill got married, q = Jill became pregnant.

    (ii) p = David became angry, q = Ann left.

    For each example, explain why $p \wedge q$ says something different than $q \wedge p$. Discuss how it can be that the Commutative Law is violated. *Source: Gut Feelings: The Intelligence of the Unconscious.*

61. Psychologist Hugo Mercier of the University of Pennsylvania has said that fewer than 10% of people can correctly determine whether or not the following argument is valid: "No C are B; all B are A; therefore some A are not C." Determine whether or not the argument is valid. Assume that B is not empty. Why does this assumption matter? *Source: Newsweek.*

62. Consider the following statement: If an animal is a raven, it is black. The contrapositive is: If an animal is not black, it is not a raven. If you saw a raven and noticed it is black, that might convince you of the truth of the original statement. If you saw an animal that was green and you saw that it was a frog, that might convince you of the truth of the contrapositive. But the original statement and its contrapositive are logically equivalent, so seeing a green frog should then convince you that ravens are black. Does it? If not, why not? (This is an example of Hempel's paradox, about which philosophers have argued since Carl Gustav Hempel introduced it in 1945.) *Source: Mind.*

63. Read Lewis Carroll's humorous essay "What the Tortoise Said to Achilles," available from numerous sources, such as www.hss.caltech.edu/~fde/papers/Carroll_Tortoise.pdf. In this story, the tortoise tells Achilles that if he accepts premises A and B (which are statements from Euclidean geometry), he will not accept conclusion Z unless he first accepts premise C: If A and B are true, Z must be true. But then he still doesn't accept Z, insisting that he first must accept premise D: If A and B and C are true, Z must be true. After that, he insists on a further premise E: If A and B and C and D are true, Z must be true. He continues to insist on an unending sequence of premises that are necessary before Z can be accepted. Comment on what you think of the tortoise's reasoning and the unending sequence of premises that must be accepted before Z can be accepted. *Source: Mind.*

APPLICATIONS

Business and Economics

Income Tax The following excerpts appear in a guide for preparing income tax reports. *Source: Your Income Tax 2014.*

(a) The tax law provides several tax benefits for people attending school.

(b) If you use the Tax Table, you do not have to compute your tax mathematically.

(c) You may not deduct the expenses of seeking your first job.

(d) Make sure the names used when you and your spouse file your joint return match the names you have provided to the Social Security Administration.

64. Which of these excerpts are statements?

65. Which of these excerpts are compound statements?

66. Write the negation of statement (c).

67. Write statement (b) as an equivalent statement using the connective *or*.

68. Write the contrapositive of statement (b).

Life Sciences

69. Medicine The following statements appear in a home medical reference book. Write each conditional statement in *if . . . then* form. *Source: American College of Physicians Complete Home Medical Guide.*

(a) When you exercise regularly, your heart becomes stronger and more efficient.

(b) All teenagers need to be aware of the risks of drinking and driving.

(c) You may need extra immunizations if you are visiting a country that has a high incidence of infectious diseases.

(d) Food is essential (necessary) for good health.

Social Sciences

70. Law The following statements appear in a guide to common laws. Write the negation of each statement. *Source: Law For Dummies.*

(a) If you can't afford to hire an attorney, the judge will arrange for you to have legal representation.

(b) Your attorney may discover it in the course of working on your case, or the other side may unearth it.

(c) You don't have a Constitutional right to make a phone call from jail, but you may be allowed to make one call.

71. Democratization According to one sociologist, "If, for example, democratization always occurs in the company of widening splits within ruling oligarchies (that is, such splits are active candidates for necessary conditions of democratization), a valid causal story will most likely connect democratization with such splits." Let *w* represent "widening splits occur within ruling oligarchies," *d* represent "democratization occurs," and *v* represent "a valid causal story connects democratization with splits." Represent the sociologist's statement as a statement in logic. *Source: Sociological Theory.*

72. Philosophy In an article in *Skeptical Inquirer*, Ralph Estling said, "Positivists such as [Stephen] Hawking tell us that reality cannot be dealt with . . . [and that] we can only deal with what we can measure in some way. . . . This seems sensible . . . until we watch as our physicists slowly slide down the slippery slopes . . . [and] tell us that only the measurable is real." *Source: Skeptical Inquirer.*

(a) Draw an Euler diagram with three circles showing real things, things we can measure, and things we can deal with. Your diagram should simultaneously illustrate the following statements:

　　i. Real things are not things we can deal with.

　　ii. Only things we can measure are things we can deal with.

　　iii. Only things we can measure are real things.

(b) Using the Euler diagram from part (a), explain why things that we can measure and deal with are not real, assuming the previous statements are true.

(c) Philosopher Timothy Chambers suggests adding the plausible premise, "All things we can measure are things we can deal with." Explain why this premise, added to the previous three, implies that nothing is real. *Source: The Mathematics Teacher.*

General Interest

Scrabble The following excerpts can be found on the box to the game, Scrabble. *Source: Milton Bradley Company.*

(a) Turn all the letter tiles facedown at the side of the board or pour them into the bag or other container, and shuffle.

(b) Any word may be challenged before the next player starts a turn.

(c) If the word challenged is acceptable, the challenger loses his or her next turn.

(d) When the game ends, each player's score is reduced by the sum of his or her unplayed letters.

73. Which of these excerpts are statements?

74. Which of these excerpts are compound statements?

Lewis Carroll The following exercises are from problems by Lewis Carroll. Write each premise in symbols, and then give a conclusion that uses all the premises and yields a valid argument. *Source: The Complete Works of Lewis Carroll.*

75. Let *s* be "the puppy lies still," *g* be "the puppy is grateful to be lent a skipping rope," *l* be "the puppy is lame," and *w* be "the puppy cares to do worsted work."

(a) Puppies that will not lie still are always grateful for the loan of a skipping rope.

(b) A lame puppy would not say "thank you" if you offered to lend it a skipping rope.

(c) None but lame puppies ever care to do worsted work.

(d) Give a conclusion that yields a valid argument.

76. Let o be "the bird is an ostrich," h be "the bird is at least 9 feet high," a be "the bird is in this aviary," m be "the bird belongs to me," and p be "the bird lives on mince pies."

 (a) No birds, except ostriches, are 9 feet high. (*Hint:* Interpret as: If a bird is at least 9 feet high, it is an ostrich.)

 (b) There are no birds in this aviary that belong to any one but me.

 (c) No ostrich lives on mince pies.

 (d) I have no birds less than 9 feet high.

 (e) Give a conclusion that yields a valid argument.

77. Let f be "the kitten loves fish," t be "the kitten is teachable," a be "the kitten has a tail," g be "the kitten will play with a gorilla," w be "the kitten has whiskers," and e be "the kitten has green eyes."

 (a) No kitten that loves fish is unteachable.

 (b) No kitten without a tail will play with a gorilla.

 (c) Kittens with whiskers always love fish.

 (d) No teachable kitten has green eyes.

 (e) No kittens have tails unless they have whiskers. (*Hint:* "($\sim a$) unless b" $\equiv a \to b$)

 (f) Give a conclusion that yields a valid argument.

78. Let u be "the writer understands human nature," c be "the writer is clever," p be "the writer is a true poet," r be "the writer can stir the hearts of men," s be "the writer is Shakespeare," and h be "the writer wrote *Hamlet*."

 (a) All writers who understand human nature are clever.

 (b) No one is a true poet unless he can stir the hearts of men. (*Hint:* "($\sim a$) unless b" $\equiv a \to b$)

 (c) Shakespeare wrote *Hamlet*.

 (d) No writer who does not understand human nature can stir the hearts of men.

 (e) None but a true poet could have written *Hamlet*.

 (f) Give a conclusion that yields a valid argument.

EXTENDED APPLICATION

LOGIC PUZZLES

Some people find that logic puzzles, which appear in periodicals such as *World-Class Logic Problems* (Penny Press) and *Logic Puzzles* (Dell), provide hours of enjoyment. They are based on deductive reasoning, and players answer questions based on clues given. The following explanation on solving such problems appeared in an issue of *World-Class Logic Problems*.

HOW TO SOLVE LOGIC PROBLEMS

Solving logic problems is entertaining and challenging. All the information you need to solve a logic problem is given in the introduction and clues, and in illustrations, when provided. If you've never solved a logic problem before, our sample should help you get started. Fill in the Sample Solving Chart in Figure 19 as you follow our explanation. We use a "•" to signify "Yes" and an "×" to signify "No."

Five couples were married last week, each on a different weekday. From the information provided, determine the woman (one is Cathy) and man (one is Paul) who make up each couple, as well as the day on which each couple was married.

1. Anne was married on Monday, but not to Wally.

2. Stan's wedding was on Wednesday. Rob was married on Friday, but not to Ida.

3. Vern (who married Fran) was married the day after Eve.

Anne was married Monday (1), so put a "•" at the intersection of Anne and Monday. Put "×" in all the other days in Anne's row and all the other names in the Monday column. (Whenever you establish a relationship, as we did here, be sure to place "×" at the intersections of all relationships that become impossible as a result.) Anne wasn't married to Wally (1), so put an "×" at the in-

SAMPLE SOLVING CHART:

FIGURE 19

tersection of Anne and Wally. Stan's wedding was Wednesday (2), so put a "•" at the intersection of Stan and Wednesday (don't forget the "×"s). Stan didn't marry Anne, who was married Monday, so put an "×" at the intersection of Anne and Stan. Rob was married Friday, but not to Ida (2), so put a "•" at the intersection of Rob and Friday, and "×" at the intersections of Rob and Ida and Ida and Friday. Rob also didn't marry Anne, who was married Monday, so put an "×" at the intersection of Anne and Rob. Now your chart should look like Figure 20 on the next page.

Vern married Fran (3), so put a "•" at the intersection of Vern and Fran. This leaves Anne's only possible husband as Paul, so put a "•" at the intersection of Anne and Paul and Paul and Monday. Vern and Fran's wedding was the day after Eve's (3), which wasn't Monday [Anne], so Vern's wasn't Tuesday. It must have been

FIGURE 20

Thursday [see chart], so Eve's was Wednesday (3). Put "•" at the intersections of Vern and Thursday, Fran and Thursday, and Eve and Wednesday. Now your chart should look like Figure 21.

FIGURE 21

The chart shows that Cathy was married Friday, Ida was married Tuesday, and Wally was married Tuesday. Ida married Wally, and Cathy's wedding was Friday, so she married Rob. After this information is filled in, Eve could only have married Stan. You've completed the puzzle, and your chart should now look like Figure 22.

FIGURE 22

In summary: Anne and Paul, Monday; Cathy and Rob, Friday; Eve and Stan, Wednesday; Fran and Vern, Thursday; Ida and Wally, Tuesday.

In some problems, it may be necessary to make a logical guess based on facts you've established. When you do, always look for clues or other facts that disprove it. If you find that your guess is incorrect, eliminate it as a possibility.

EXERCISES

1. ***Water, Water, Everywhere*** After an invigorating workout, five fitness-conscious friends know that nothing is more refreshing than a tall, cool glass of mineral water! Each person (including Annie) has a different, favorite form of daily exercise (one likes to rollerblade), and each drinks a different brand of mineral water (one is Crystal Spring). From the information provided, determine the type of exercise and brand of water each person prefers. *Source: World-Class Logic Problems Special.*

   (a) The one who bicycles in pursuit of fitness drinks Bevé.

   (b) Tim enjoys aerobicizing every morning before work. Ben is neither the one who drinks Sparkling Creek nor the one who imbibes Bevé.

   (c) Page (who is neither the one who jogs nor the one who walks to keep in shape) drinks Purity. Meg drinks Mountain Clear, but not after jogging.

2. ***Let's Get Physical*** The Anytown Community Center, in conjunction with the Board of Education's adult-outreach program, has scheduled a week-long series of lectures this fall on topics in physics. The goals are to increase awareness of the physical sciences and to attract renowned scientists (including Dr. Denton) to the community. Each of the five lectures will be held on a different weekday, and each will feature a different physicist lecturing on a different topic (one is magnetism). So far, the community has shown great interest in their upcoming physical training! From the information provided, determine the physicist who will speak on each weekday and the topic of his or her lecture. *Source: World-Class Logic Problems Special.*

   (a) Dr. Hoo, who is from Yale, will not be lecturing on Thursday. Dr. Zhivago's lecture will be exactly three days after the lecture on chaos theory.

   (b) If Dr. Jay is lecturing on Thursday, then the person giving the kinetic-energy lecture will appear on Tuesday; otherwise, Dr. Jay will speak on Tuesday, and kinetic energy will be the topic of Monday's lecture.

(c) Dr. Know (who is not giving the lecture on quantum mechanics) is not the Harvard physicist who will speak on Monday. The photonics lecture will not be given on either Wednesday or Thursday.

3. ***What's in Store?*** I had a day off from work yesterday, so I figured it was the perfect time to do some shopping. I hit the road shortly after breakfast and visited five stores (one was Bullseye). At each shop, I had intended to buy a different one of five items (a pair of andirons, a Crock-pot, pruning shears, a pair of sneakers, or a toaster oven). Unfortunately, no store had the item I was looking for in stock. The trips weren't a total loss, however, as I purchased a different item (a CD, a fondue pot, a garden gnome, spark plugs, or a winter coat) that had caught my eye in each store. Despite my failure to acquire any of the things I had sought, there were a couple of positive outcomes. I now have some nifty new things that I know I'll enjoy, and I have a shopping list written and ready to go for my next day off! From the information provided, determine the order in which I visited the five stores, as well as the item I sought and the item I bought at each store. *Source: World-Class Logic Problems Special.*

(a) I went to the store where I bought a CD (which isn't where I sought pruning shears) immediately after I visited

(b) PJ Nickle but immediately before I went to the shop where I intended to buy a Crock-pot.

(b) I didn't purchase the fondue pot at Costington's. I went into one store intending to buy a Crock-pot, but came out with a garden gnome instead. I didn't go to PJ Nickle for a pair of andirons.

(c) The store at which I sought a toaster oven (which wasn't the third one I visited) isn't the place where I eventually bought a winter coat. Neither Lacy's nor S-Mart was the fourth shop I visited.

(d) I went to Costington's immediately after I visited the shop where I sought pruning shears (which wasn't S-Mart) but immediately before I went to the store where I purchased a set of spark plugs.

4. ***High Five*** Otis Lifter is the elevator operator at Schwarzenbach Tower, downtown Brownsville's tallest building. Since he works in such a towering edifice, Otis gets a chance to chat with his passengers on the way to their destinations. Five people who always have a friendly word for Otis work on the Schwarzenbach's top floors. Each person works on a different floor, which is home to a different company (one is the Watershed Co.). Each company is in a different business (one is a real-estate agency). Otis is content with his job, but he'll be the first to tell you that, like any profession, it has its ups and downs! From the information provided, can you determine the floor (41st through 45th) to which Otis took each person, as well as the name of his or her company and the type of business it conducts? *Source: World-Class Logic Problems Special.*

(a) Edwina's company is exactly 1 floor above Nelson & Leopold but exactly 1 floor below the accounting firm. Brierwood Ltd. is on the 44th floor.

(b) Zed's company is exactly 1 floor above Ogden's. Keith's business is on the 45th floor. Trish works at the public-relations firm (which is exactly 2 floors above Glyptic).

(c) Glyptic and the Thebes Group are the literary agency and the Web-design firm, in some order. The Web-design firm is not on the 41st floor.

5. *First Ratings* At long last, Macrocosm Industries has released Q Sphere, its new video-game console. To fully demonstrate the Q Sphere's capabilities, each of Macrocosm's five Q Sphere games (including Idle Hands) is a different genre. Anxious to be the first publication to spotlight this new gaming system, *All Game* magazine featured reviews of the Q Sphere games in its latest issue. Each game was played extensively by a different *All Game* staff reviewer (including Chadwick) and given a different rating (from lowest to highest, "don't bother," "just okay," "pretty cool," "almost perfect," or "totally awesome"). In the end, though, true video-game aficionados will want to try all of the Q Sphere games for themselves, despite the ratings! From the information provided, determine the genre of the game reviewed by each *All Game* staff member (identified by first and last names—one surname is Ploof), as well as the rating given to each game. *Source: World-Class Logic Problems Special.*

(a) At least one game was given a lower rating than the sports game (which is called Pitching Duel). The person surnamed Corley reviewed the action game.

(b) The puzzle game's rating was "just okay," which was higher than the rating Darren Castles gave.

(c) King of the Road is the racing game. The person surnamed Munoz (who isn't Milton) gave the "totally awesome" rating.

(d) The person surnamed Gilligan reviewed the simulation game, which isn't Hypnotic Trace (which was rated "almost perfect").

(e) Alise gave one game a "pretty cool" rating. Kourtney spent many hours playing Fiji in order to write her review.

		LAST NAME					GAME					GENRE					RATING				
		CASTLES	CORLEY	GILLIGAN	MUNOZ	PLOOF	FIJI	HYPNOTIC TRACE	IDLE HANDS	KING OF THE ROAD	PITCHING DUEL	ACTION	PUZZLE	RACING	SIMULATION	SPORTS	DON'T BOTHER	JUST OKAY	PRETTY COOL	ALMOST PERFECT	TOTALLY AWESOME
FIRST NAME	ALISE																				
	CHADWICK																				
	DARREN																				
	KOURTNEY																				
	MILTON																				
RATING	DON'T BOTHER																				
	JUST OKAY																				
	PRETTY COOL																				
	ALMOST PERFECT																				
	TOTALLY AWESOME																				
GENRE	ACTION																				
	PUZZLE																				
	RACING																				
	SIMULATION																				
	SPORTS																				
GAME	FIJI																				
	HYPNOTIC																				
	IDLE HANDS																				
	KING OF THE ROAD																				
	PITCHING DUEL																				

DIRECTIONS FOR GROUP PROJECT

Construct your own logic puzzle.

7 Sets and Probability

The study of probability begins with counting. An exercise in Section 2 of this chapter counts trucks carrying different combinations of early, late, and extra late peaches from the orchard to canning facilities. You'll see trees in another context in Section 5, where we use branching tree diagrams to calculate conditional probabilities.

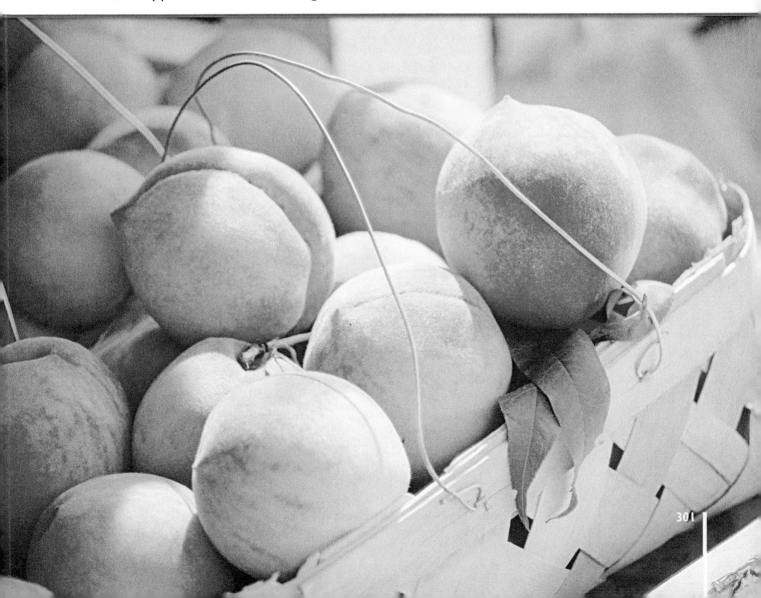

O ur lives are bombarded by seemingly chance events — the chance of rain, the risk of an accident, the possibility the stock market increases, the likelihood of winning the lottery — all whose particular outcome may appear to be quite random. The field of probability attempts to quantify the likelihood of chance events and helps us to prepare for this uncertainty. In short, probability helps us to better understand the world in which we live. In this chapter and the next, we introduce the basic ideas of probability theory and give a sampling of some of its uses. Since the language of sets and set operations is used in the study of probability, we begin there.

7.1 Sets

APPLY IT In how many ways can two candidates win the 50 states plus the District of Columbia in a U.S. presidential election?
Using knowledge of sets, we will answer this question in Exercise 69.

Think of a **set** as a well-defined collection of objects in which it is possible to determine if a given object is included in the collection. A set of coins might include one of each type of coin now put out by the U.S. government. Another set might consist of all the students in your English class. By contrast, a collection of young adults does not constitute a set unless the designation "young adult" is clearly defined. For example, this set might be defined as those aged 18 to 29.

In mathematics, sets often consist of numbers. The set consisting of the numbers 3, 4, and 5 is written

$$\{3, 4, 5\},$$

with set braces, { }, enclosing the numbers belonging to the set. The numbers 3, 4, and 5 are called the **elements** or **members** of this set. To show that 4 is an element of the set $\{3, 4, 5\}$, we use the symbol $\in$ and write

$$4 \in \{3, 4, 5\},$$

read "4 is an element of the set containing 3, 4, and 5." Also, $5 \in \{3, 4, 5\}$.

To show that 8 is *not* an element of this set, place a slash through the symbol:

$$8 \notin \{3, 4, 5\}.$$

Sets often are named with capital letters, so that if

$$B = \{5, 6, 7\},$$

then, for example, $6 \in B$ and $10 \notin B$.

It is possible to have a set with no elements. Some examples are the set of counting numbers less than one, the set of foreign-born presidents of the United States, and the set of men more than 10 feet tall. A set with no elements is called the **empty set** (or **null set**) and is written $\varnothing$.

CAUTION	Be careful to distinguish between the symbols 0, $\varnothing$, $\{0\}$, and $\{\varnothing\}$. The symbol 0 represents a *number*; $\varnothing$ represents a *set* with 0 elements; $\{0\}$ represents a set with one element, 0; and $\{\varnothing\}$ represents a set with one element, $\varnothing$.

We use the symbol $n(A)$ to indicate the *number* of unique elements in a finite set A. For example, if $A = \{a, b, c, d, e\}$, then $n(A) = 5$. Using this notation, we can write the information in the previous Caution as $n(\varnothing) = 0$ and $n(\{0\}) = n(\{\varnothing\}) = 1$.

Two sets are *equal* if they contain the same elements. The sets $\{5, 6, 7\}$, $\{7, 6, 5\}$, and $\{6, 5, 7\}$ all contain exactly the same elements and are equal. In symbols,

$$\{5, 6, 7\} = \{7, 6, 5\} = \{6, 5, 7\}.$$

This means that the ordering of the elements in a set is unimportant. Note that each element of the set is listed only once. Sets that do not contain exactly the same elements are *not equal*. For example, the sets $\{5, 6, 7\}$ and $\{7, 8, 9\}$ do not contain exactly the same elements and, thus, are not equal. To indicate that these sets are not equal, we write

$$\{5, 6, 7\} \neq \{7, 8, 9\}.$$

Sometimes we are interested in a common property of the elements in a set, rather than a list of the elements. This common property can be expressed by using **set-builder notation**, for example,

$$\{x \mid x \text{ has property } P\}$$

(read "the set of all elements x such that x has property P") represents the set of all elements x having some stated property P.

EXAMPLE 1   Sets

Write the elements belonging to each set.

YOUR TURN 1 Write the elements belonging to the set. $\{x \mid x \text{ is a state whose name begins with the letter O}\}$.

(a) $\{x \mid x \text{ is a natural number less than 5}\}$

    SOLUTION The natural numbers less than 5 make up the set $\{1, 2, 3, 4\}$.

(b) $\{x \mid x \text{ is a state that borders Florida}\}$

    SOLUTION The states that border Florida make up the set $\{\text{Alabama, Georgia}\}$.

TRY YOUR TURN 1

The **universal set** for a particular discussion is a set that includes all the objects being discussed. In elementary school arithmetic, for instance, the set of whole numbers might be the universal set, while in a college algebra class the universal set might be the set of real numbers. The universal set will be specified when necessary, or it will be clearly understandable from the context of the problem.

Subsets

Sometimes every element of one set also belongs to another set. For example, if

$$A = \{3, 4, 5, 6\}$$

and

$$B = \{2, 3, 4, 5, 6, 7, 8\},$$

then every element of A is also an element of B. This is an example of the following definition.

> **Subset**
>
> Set A is a **subset** of set B (written $A \subseteq B$) if every element of A is also an element of B. Set A is a *proper subset* (written $A \subset B$) if $A \subseteq B$ and $A \neq B$.

To indicate that A is *not* a subset of B, we write $A \not\subseteq B$.

EXAMPLE 2   Sets

Decide whether the following statements are *true* or *false*.

(a) $\{3, 4, 5, 6\} = \{4, 6, 3, 5\}$

    SOLUTION Both sets contain exactly the same elements, so the sets are equal and the given statement is true. (The fact that the elements are listed in a different order does not matter.)

YOUR TURN 2 Decide if the following statement is *true* or *false*.
{2, 4, 6} ⊆ {6, 2, 4}

(b) {5, 6, 9, 12} ⊆ {5, 6, 7, 8, 9, 10, 11}

SOLUTION The first set is not a subset of the second because it contains an element, 12, that does not belong to the second set. Therefore, the statement is false.

TRY YOUR TURN 2

The empty set, ∅, by default, is a subset of every set A, since it is impossible to find an element of the empty set (it has no elements) that is not an element of the set A. Similarly, A is a subset of itself, since every element of A is also an element of the set A.

Subset Properties
For any set A,

$$\varnothing \subseteq A \quad \text{and} \quad A \subseteq A.$$

EXAMPLE 3 Subsets

List all possible subsets for each set.

(a) {7, 8}

SOLUTION There are 4 subsets of {7, 8}:

$$\varnothing, \quad \{7\}, \quad \{8\}, \quad \text{and} \quad \{7, 8\}.$$

(b) {a, b, c}

SOLUTION There are 8 subsets of {a, b, c}:

$$\varnothing, \quad \{a\}, \quad \{b\}, \quad \{c\}, \quad \{a, b\}, \quad \{a, c\}, \quad \{b, c\}, \quad \text{and} \quad \{a, b, c\}.$$

A good way to find the subsets of {7, 8} and the subsets of {a, b, c} in Example 3 is to use a **tree diagram**—a systematic way of listing all the subsets of a given set. Figure 1 shows tree diagrams for finding the subsets of {7, 8} and {a, b, c}.

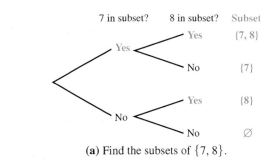

(a) Find the subsets of {7, 8}.

(b) Find the subsets of {a, b, c}.

FIGURE 1

As Figure 1 shows, there are two possibilities for each element (either it's in the subset or it's not), so a set with 2 elements has $2 \cdot 2 = 2^2 = 4$ subsets, and a set with 3 elements has $2^3 = 8$ subsets. This idea can be extended to a set with any finite number of elements, which leads to the following conclusion.

Number of Subsets

A set of k distinct elements has 2^k subsets.

In other words, if $n(A) = k$, then $n(\text{the set of all subsets of } A) = 2^k$.

EXAMPLE 4   Subsets

Find the number of subsets for each set.

(a) $\{3, 4, 5, 6, 7\}$

SOLUTION   This set has 5 elements; thus, it has 2^5 or 32 subsets.

(b) $\{x \mid x \text{ is a day of the week}\}$

SOLUTION   This set has 7 elements and therefore has $2^7 = 128$ subsets.

(c) $\varnothing$

SOLUTION   Since the empty set has 0 elements, it has $2^0 = 1$ subset—itself.

TRY YOUR TURN 3

YOUR TURN 3 Find the number of subsets for the set $\{x \mid x \text{ is a season of the year}\}$.

Figure 2 shows a set A that is a subset of set B. The rectangle and everything inside it represents the universal set, U. Such diagrams, called **Venn diagrams**—after the English logician John Venn (1834–1923), who invented them in 1876—are used to help illustrate relationships among sets. Venn diagrams are very similar to Euler diagrams, described in Section 6.6. Euler diagrams are used in logic to denote variables having a certain property or not, while Venn diagrams are used in the context of sets to denote something being an element of a set or not.

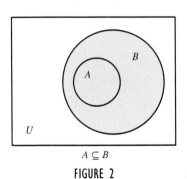

$A \subseteq B$

FIGURE 2

Set Operations

It is possible to form new sets by combining or manipulating one or more existing sets. Given a set A and a universal set U, the set of all elements of U that do *not* belong to A is called the *complement* of set A. For example, if set A is the set of all the female students in a class, and U is the set of all students in the class, then the complement of A would be the set of all students in the class who are not female (that is, who are male). The complement of set A is written A', read "A-prime."

Complement of a Set

Let A be any set, with U representing the universal set. Then the **complement** of A, colored pink in the figure, is

$$A' = \{x \mid x \notin A \text{ and } x \in U\}.$$

(Recall that the rectangle represents the universal set U.)

EXAMPLE 5 **Set Operations**

Let $U = \{1, 2, 3, 4, 5, 6, 7, 8, 9, 10, 11\}$, $A = \{1, 2, 4, 5, 7\}$, and $B = \{2, 4, 5, 7, 9, 11\}$. Find each set.

(a) A'

SOLUTION Set A' contains the elements of U that are not in A.

$$A' = \{3, 6, 8, 9, 10, 11\}$$

(b) $B' = \{1, 3, 6, 8, 10\}$

(c) $\varnothing' = U$ and $U' = \varnothing$

(d) $(A')' = A$

Given two sets A and B, the set of all elements belonging to *both* set A and set B is called the *intersection* of the two sets, written $A \cap B$. For example, the elements that belong to both set $A = \{1, 2, 4, 5, 7\}$ and set $B = \{2, 4, 5, 7, 9, 11\}$ are 2, 4, 5, and 7, so that

$$A \cap B = \{1, 2, 4, 5, 7\} \cap \{2, 4, 5, 7, 9, 11\} = \{2, 4, 5, 7\}.$$

Intersection of Two Sets

The **intersection** of sets A and B, shown in green in the figure, is

$$A \cap B = \{x \mid x \in A \text{ and } x \in B\}.$$

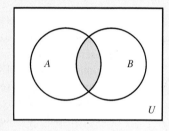

EXAMPLE 6 **Set Operations**

Let $A = \{3, 6, 9\}$, $B = \{2, 4, 6, 8\}$, and the universal set $U = \{0, 1, 2, \ldots, 10\}$. Find each set.

(a) $A \cap B$

SOLUTION

$$A \cap B = \{3, 6, 9\} \cap \{2, 4, 6, 8\} = \{6\}$$

(b) $A \cap B'$

SOLUTION

$$A \cap B' = \{3, 6, 9\} \cap \{0, 1, 3, 5, 7, 9, 10\} = \{3, 9\}$$

TRY YOUR TURN 4

YOUR TURN 4 For the sets in Example 6, find $A' \cap B$.

Two sets that have no elements in common are called *disjoint sets*. For example, there are no elements common to both $\{50, 51, 54\}$ and $\{52, 53, 55, 56\}$, so these two sets are disjoint, and

$$\{50, 51, 54\} \cap \{52, 53, 55, 56\} = \varnothing.$$

This result can be generalized as follows.

Disjoint Sets

For any sets A and B, if A and B are **disjoint sets**, then $A \cap B = \varnothing$.

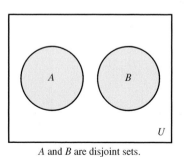

A and B are disjoint sets.

FIGURE 3

Figure 3 shows a pair of disjoint sets.

The set of all elements belonging to set A, to set B, or to both sets is called the *union* of the two sets, written $A \cup B$. For example,

$$\{1, 3, 5\} \cup \{3, 5, 7, 9\} = \{1, 3, 5, 7, 9\}.$$

Union of Two Sets

The **union** of sets A and B, shown in blue in the figure, is

$$A \cup B = \{x \mid x \in A \text{ or } x \in B \text{ (or both)}\}.$$

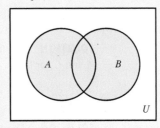

EXAMPLE 7 Union of Sets

Let $A = \{1, 3, 5, 7, 9, 11\}$, $B = \{3, 6, 9, 12\}$, $C = \{1, 2, 3, 4, 5\}$, and the universal set $U = \{0, 1, 2, \ldots, 12\}$. Find each set.

(a) $A \cup B$

SOLUTION Begin by listing the elements of the first set, $\{1, 3, 5, 7, 9, 11\}$. Then include any elements from the second set *that are not already listed*. Doing this gives

$$A \cup B = \{1, 3, 5, 7, 9, 11\} \cup \{3, 6, 9, 12\} = \{1, 3, 5, 7, 9, 11, 6, 12\}$$
$$= \{1, 3, 5, 6, 7, 9, 11, 12\}.$$

(b) $(A \cup B) \cap C'$

SOLUTION Begin with the expression in parentheses, which we calculated in part (a), and then intersect this with C'.

$$(A \cup B) \cap C' = \{1, 3, 5, 6, 7, 9, 11, 12\} \cap \{0, 6, 7, 8, 9, 10, 11, 12\}$$
$$= \{6, 7, 9, 11, 12\} \qquad \text{TRY YOUR TURN 5}$$

YOUR TURN 5 For the sets in Example 7, find $A \cup (B \cap C')$.

NOTE
1. As Example 7 shows, when forming sets, do not list the same element more than once. In our final answer, we listed the elements in numerical order to make it easier to see what elements are in the set, but the set is the same, regardless of the order of the elements.
2. As shown in the definitions, an element is in the *intersection* of sets A and B if it is in A *and* B. On the other hand, an element is in the *union* of sets A and B if it is in A *or* B (or both).
3. In mathematics, "A *or* B" implies A or B, or both. Since "or" includes the possibility of both, we will usually omit the words "or both".

EXAMPLE 8 Stocks

The following table gives the 52-week low and high prices, the closing price, and the change from the previous day for six stocks in the Standard & Poor's 100 on May 20, 2014. *Source: New York Stock Exchange.*

New York Stock Exchange				
Stock	Low	High	Close	Change
AT&T	31.74	37.17	35.22	−0.28
Coca-Cola	36.83	43.05	40.74	+0.16
Costco	107.38	126.12	114.62	−0.51
McDonald's	92.22	103.78	102.47	+0.94
Pepsico	77.01	87.68	85.89	+0.24
Walt Disney	60.41	83.65	82.12	+1.27

Let the universal set U consist of the six stocks listed in the table. Let A contain all stocks with a high price greater than \$80, B all stocks with a closing price between \$40 and \$105, C all stocks with a positive price change, and D all stocks with a low price less than \$40. Find the following.

(a) A'

SOLUTION Set A' contains all the listed stocks that are not in set A, or those with a high price less than or equal to \$80, so

$$A' = \{\text{AT\&T, Coca-Cola}\}.$$

(b) $A \cap C$

SOLUTION The intersection of A and C will contain those stocks that are in both sets A and C, or those with a high price greater than \$80 *and* a positive price change.

$$A \cap C = \{\text{McDonald's, Pepsico, Walt Disney}\}$$

(c) $B \cup D$

SOLUTION The union of B and D contains all stocks with a closing price between \$40 and \$105 *or* a low price less than \$40.

$$B \cup D = \{\text{AT\&T, Coca-Cola, McDonald's, Pepsico, Walt Disney}\}$$

EXAMPLE 9 **Employment**

A department store classifies credit applicants by gender, marital status, and employment status. Let the universal set be the set of all applicants, M be the set of male applicants, S be the set of single applicants, and E be the set of employed applicants. Describe each set in words.

(a) $M \cap E$

SOLUTION The set $M \cap E$ includes all applicants who are both male *and* employed; that is, employed male applicants.

(b) $M' \cup S$

SOLUTION This set includes all applicants who are female (not male) *or* single. *All* female applicants and *all* single applicants are in this set.

(c) $M' \cap S'$

SOLUTION These applicants are female *and* married (not single); thus, $M' \cap S'$ is the set of all married female applicants.

(d) $M \cup E'$

SOLUTION $M \cup E'$ is the set of applicants that are male *or* unemployed. The set includes *all* male applicants and *all* unemployed applicants.

7.1 EXERCISES

In Exercises 1–10, write true or false for each statement.

1. $3 \in \{2, 5, 7, 9, 10\}$

2. $6 \in \{-2, 6, 9, 5\}$

3. $9 \notin \{2, 1, 5, 8\}$

4. $3 \notin \{7, 6, 5, 4\}$

5. $\{2, 5, 8, 9\} = \{2, 5, 9, 8\}$

6. $\{3, 7, 12, 14\} = \{3, 7, 12, 14, 0\}$

7. {all whole numbers greater than 7 and less than 10} $= \{8, 9\}$

8. $\{x \mid x \text{ is an odd integer}; 6 \leq x \leq 18\} = \{7, 9, 11, 15, 17\}$

9. $0 \in \varnothing$

10. $\varnothing \in \{\varnothing\}$

Let $A = \{2, 4, 6, 10, 12\}$, $B = \{2, 4, 8, 10\}$, $C = \{4, 8, 12\}$, $D = \{2, 10\}$, $E = \{6\}$, and $U = \{2, 4, 6, 8, 10, 12, 14\}$. Insert $\subseteq$ or $\nsubseteq$ to make the statement true.

11. $A \_\_ U$

12. $E \_\_ A$

13. $A \_\_ E$

14. $B \_\_ C$

15. $\varnothing \_\_ A$

16. $\{0, 2\} \_\_ D$

17. $D \_\_ B$

18. $A \_\_ C$

19. Repeat Exercises 11–18 except insert $\subset$ or $\not\subset$ to make the statement true.

20. What is set-builder notation? Give an example.

Insert a number in each blank to make the statement true, using the sets for Exercises 11–18.

21. There are exactly ___ subsets of A.

22. There are exactly ___ subsets of B.

23. There are exactly ___ subsets of C.

24. There are exactly ___ subsets of D.

Insert ∩ or ∪ to make each statement true.

25. $\{5, 7, 9, 19\}$ ___ $\{7, 9, 11, 15\} = \{7, 9\}$

26. $\{8, 11, 15\}$ ___ $\{8, 11, 19, 20\} = \{8, 11\}$

27. $\{2, 1, 7\}$ ___ $\{1, 5, 9\} = \{1, 2, 5, 7, 9\}$

28. $\{6, 12, 14, 16\}$ ___ $\{6, 14, 19\} = \{6, 12, 14, 16, 19\}$

29. $\{3, 5, 9, 10\}$ ___ $\varnothing = \varnothing$

30. $\{3, 5, 9, 10\}$ ___ $\varnothing = \{3, 5, 9, 10\}$

31. $\{1, 2, 4\}$ ___ $\{1, 2, 4\} = \{1, 2, 4\}$

32. $\{0, 10\}$ ___ $\{10, 0\} = \{0, 10\}$

33. Describe the intersection and union of sets. How do they differ?

34. Is it possible for two nonempty sets to have the same intersection and union? If so, give an example.

Let $U = \{1, 2, 3, 4, 5, 6, 7, 8, 9\}$, $X = \{2, 4, 6, 8\}$, $Y = \{2, 3, 4, 5, 6\}$, and $Z = \{1, 2, 3, 8, 9\}$. List the members of each set, using set braces.

35. $X \cap Y$ **36.** $X \cup Y$

37. X' **38.** Y'

39. $X' \cap Y'$ **40.** $X' \cap Z$

41. $Y \cap (X \cup Z)$ **42.** $X' \cap (Y' \cup Z)$

43. $(X \cap Y') \cup (Z' \cap Y')$ **44.** $(X \cap Y) \cup (X' \cap Z)$

45. In Example 6, what set do you get when you calculate $(A \cap B) \cup (A \cap B')$?

46. Explain in words why $(A \cap B) \cup (A \cap B') = A$.

Let $U = \{$all students in this school$\}$, $M = \{$all students taking this course$\}$, $N = \{$all students taking accounting$\}$, and $P = \{$all students taking zoology$\}$. Describe each set in words.

47. M' **48.** $M \cup N$

49. $N \cap P$ **50.** $N' \cap P'$

51. Refer to the sets listed for Exercises 11–18. Which pairs of sets are disjoint?

52. Refer to the sets listed for Exercises 35–44. Which pairs are disjoint?

Refer to Example 8 in the text. Describe each set in Exercises 53–56 in words; then list the elements of each set.

53. B' **54.** $A \cap B$

55. $(A \cap B)'$ **56.** $(C \cup D)'$

57. Let $A = \{1, 2, 3, \{3\}, \{1, 4, 7\}\}$. Answer each of the following as *true* or *false*.

(a) $1 \in A$ (b) $\{3\} \in A$ (c) $\{2\} \in A$

(d) $4 \in A$ (e) $\{\{3\}\} \subset A$

(f) $\{1, 4, 7\} \in A$ (g) $\{1, 4, 7\} \subseteq A$

58. Let $B = \{a, b, c, \{d\}, \{e, f\}\}$. Answer each of the following as *true* or *false*.

(a) $a \in B$ (b) $\{b, c, d\} \subset B$ (c) $\{d\} \in B$

(d) $\{d\} \subseteq B$ (e) $\{e, f\} \in B$

(f) $\{a, \{e, f\}\} \subset B$ (g) $\{e, f\} \subset B$

APPLICATIONS

Business and Economics

Mutual Funds The tables below show five of the largest holdings of four major mutual funds on May 21, 2014. *Sources: fidelity.com, janus.com, vanguard.com, weitzinvestments.com.*

Vanguard 500	Fidelity New Millenium Fund
Apple	AIG
Berkshire Hathaway	Google
Google	Microsoft
Microsoft	Verizon
Wells Fargo	Wells Fargo

Janus Perkins Large Cap Value	Weitz Value Fund
AIG	Apache
Berkshire Hathaway	Berkshire Hathaway
Citigroup	DIRECTV
Pfizer	Texas Instruments
Wells Fargo	Wells Fargo

Let U be the smallest possible set that includes all the corporations listed, and $V, F, J,$ and W be the set of top holdings for each mutual fund, respectively. Find each set:

59. $V \cap J$ **60.** $V \cap (F \cup W)$

61. $(J \cup F)'$ **62.** $J' \cap W'$

63. **Sales Calls** Suppose that Carolyn Gogolin has appointments with 9 potential customers. Carolyn will be ecstatic if all 9 of these potential customers decide to make a purchase from her. Of course, in sales there are no guarantees. How many different sets of customers may place an order with Carolyn? (*Hint:* Each set of customers is a subset of the original set of 9 customers.)

Life Sciences

Health The following table shows some symptoms of an overactive thyroid and an underactive thyroid. *Source: The Merck Manual of Diagnosis and Therapy.*

Underactive Thyroid	Overactive Thyroid
Sleepiness, s	Insomnia, i
Dry hands, d	Moist hands, m
Intolerance of cold, c	Intolerance of heat, h
Goiter, g	Goiter, g

Let U be the smallest possible set that includes all the symptoms listed, N be the set of symptoms for an underactive thyroid, and O be the set of symptoms for an overactive thyroid. Find each set.

64. O'

65. N'

66. $N \cap O$

67. $N \cup O$

68. $N \cap O'$

Social Sciences

69. APPLY IT Electoral College U.S. presidential elections are decided by the Electoral College, in which each of the 50 states, plus the District of Columbia, gives all of its votes to a candidate.* Ignoring the number of votes each state has in the Electoral College, but including all possible combinations of states that could be won by either candidate, how many outcomes are possible in the Electoral College if there are two candidates? (*Hint:* The states that can be won by a candidate form a subset of all the states.)

General Interest

70. Musicians A concert featured a cellist, a flutist, a harpist, and a vocalist. Throughout the concert, different subsets of the four musicians performed together, with at least two musicians playing each piece. How many subsets of at least two are possible?

Television Cable Services The following table lists some of the most popular cable television networks. Use this information for Exercises 71–76. *Source: The World Almanac and Book of Facts 2014.*

Network	Subscribers (in millions)	Launch	Content
The Discovery Channel	99.1	1985	Nonfiction, nature, science
TNT	99.7	1988	Movies, sports, original programming
USA Network	99.0	1980	Sports, family entertainment
The Learning Channel (TLC)	98.5	1980	Original programming, family entertainment
TBS Superstation	99.7	1976	Movies, sports, original programming

*The exceptions are Maine and Nebraska, which allocate their electoral college votes according to the winner in each congressional district.

List the elements of the following sets. For exercises 74–76, describe each set in words.

71. F, the set of networks that were launched before 1985.

72. G, the set of networks that feature sports.

73. H, the set of networks that have more than 99.5 million viewers.

74. $F \cap H$ **75.** $G \cup H$ **76.** G'

77. Games In David Gale's game of Subset Takeaway, the object is for each player, at his or her turn, to pick a nonempty proper subset of a given set subject to the condition that no subset chosen earlier by either player can be a subset of the newly chosen set. The winner is the last person who can make a legal move. Consider the set $A = \{1, 2, 3\}$. Suppose Joe and Dorothy are playing the game and Dorothy goes first. If she chooses the proper subset $\{1\}$, then Joe cannot choose any subset that includes the element 1. Joe can, however, choose $\{2\}$ or $\{3\}$ or $\{2, 3\}$. Develop a strategy for Joe so that he can always win the game if Dorothy goes first. *Source: Scientific American.*

States In the following list of states, let $A = \{$states whose name contains the letter $e\}$, let $B = \{$states with a population of more than 4,000,000$\}$, and $C = \{$states with an area greater than 40,000 square miles$\}$. *Source: The World Almanac and Book of Facts 2014.*

State	Population (1000s)	Area (sq. mi.)
Alabama	4822	52,420
Alaska	731	665,384
Colorado	5187	104,094
Florida	19,318	65,758
Hawaii	1392	10,932
Indiana	6537	36,420
Kentucky	4380	40,408
Maine	1329	35,380
Nebraska	1856	77,348
New Jersey	8865	8723

78. (a) Describe in words the set $A \cup (B \cap C)'$.

　　(b) List all elements in the set $A \cup (B \cap C)'$.

79. (a) Describe in words the set $(A \cup B)' \cap C$.

　　(b) List all elements in the set $(A \cup B)' \cap C$.

YOUR TURN ANSWERS

1. $\{$Ohio, Oklahoma, Oregon$\}$

2. True

3. $2^4 = 16$ subsets

4. $\{2, 4, 8\}$

5. $\{1, 3, 5, 6, 7, 9, 11, 12\}$

7.2 Applications of Venn Diagrams

APPLY IT   The responses to a survey of 100 households show that 76 have a DVD player, 21 have a Blu-ray player, and 12 have both. How many have neither a DVD player nor Blu-ray player?

In Example 3 we show how a Venn diagram can be used to sort out this information to answer the question.

One set leads to 2 regions
(numbering is arbitrary).

FIGURE 4

Venn diagrams were used in the previous section to illustrate set union and intersection. The rectangular region of a Venn diagram represents the universal set U. Including only a single set A inside the universal set, as in Figure 4, divides U into two regions. Region 1 represents those elements of U outside set A (that is, the elements in A'), and region 2 represents those elements belonging to set A. (The numbering of these regions is arbitrary.)

The Venn diagram in Figure 5(a) shows two sets inside U. These two sets divide the universal set into four regions. As labeled in Figure 5(a), region 1 represents the set whose elements are outside both set A and set B. Region 2 shows the set whose elements belong to A and not to B. Region 3 represents the set whose elements belong to both A and B. Which set is represented by region 4? (Again, the labeling is arbitrary.)

Two other situations can arise when representing two sets by Venn diagrams. If it is known that $A \cap B = \varnothing$, then the Venn diagram is drawn as in Figure 5(b). If it is known that $A \subseteq B$, then the Venn diagram is drawn as in Figure 5(c). For the material presented throughout this chapter we will refer only to Venn diagrams like the one in Figure 5(a), and note that some of the regions of the Venn diagram may be equal to the empty (or null) set.

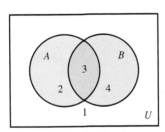

Two sets lead to 4 regions
(numbering is arbitrary).

(a)

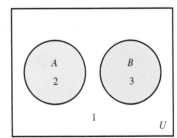

Two sets lead to 3 regions
(numbering is arbitrary).

(b)

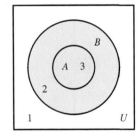

Two sets lead to 3 regions
(numbering is arbitrary).

(c)

FIGURE 5

EXAMPLE 1   **Venn Diagrams**

Draw Venn diagrams similar to Figure 5(a) and shade the regions representing each set.

(a) $A' \cap B$

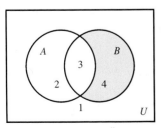

FIGURE 6

SOLUTION   Set A' contains all the elements outside set A. As labeled in Figure 5(a), A' is represented by regions 1 and 4. Set B is represented by regions 3 and 4. The intersection of sets A' and B, the set $A' \cap B$, is given by the region common to both sets. The result is the set represented by region 4, which is blue in Figure 6. When looking for the intersection, remember to choose the area that is in one region *and* the other region.

In addition to the fact that region 4 in Figure 6 is $A' \cap B$, notice that region 1 is $A' \cap B'$, region 2 is $A \cap B'$, and region 3 is $A \cap B$.

(b) $A' \cup B'$

YOUR TURN 1 Draw a Venn diagram and shade the region representing $A \cup B'$.

SOLUTION Again, set A' is represented by regions 1 and 4, and set B' by regions 1 and 2. To find $A' \cup B'$, identify the region that represents the set of all elements in A', B', or both. The result, which is blue in Figure 7, includes regions 1, 2, and 4. When looking for the union, remember to choose the area that is in one region *or* the other region (or both). **TRY YOUR TURN 1**

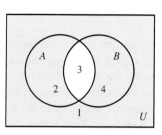

FIGURE 7

FIGURE 8

Three sets lead to 8 regions.

Venn diagrams also can be drawn with three sets inside U. These three sets divide the universal set into eight regions, which can be numbered (arbitrarily) as in Figure 8.

EXAMPLE 2 Venn Diagram

In a Venn diagram, shade the region that represents $A' \cup (B \cap C')$.

YOUR TURN 2 Draw a Venn diagram and shade the region representing $A' \cap (B \cup C)$.

SOLUTION First find $B \cap C'$. Set B is represented by regions 3, 4, 7, and 8, and set C' by regions 1, 2, 3, and 8. The overlap of these regions (regions 3 and 8) represents the set $B \cap C'$. Set A' is represented by regions 1, 6, 7, and 8. The union of the set represented by regions 3 and 8 and the set represented by regions 1, 6, 7, and 8 is the set represented by regions 1, 3, 6, 7, and 8, which are blue in Figure 9. **TRY YOUR TURN 2**

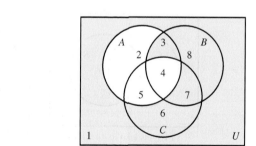

FIGURE 9

Applications Venn diagrams can be used to analyze many applications, as illustrated in the following examples.

EXAMPLE 3 Entertainment Technology

A researcher collecting data on 100 households finds that

  76 have a DVD player;

  21 have a Blu-ray player; and

  12 have both.

The researcher wants to answer the following questions.

(a) How many do not have a DVD player?

(b) How many have neither a DVD player nor a Blu-ray player?

(c) How many have a Blu-ray player but not a DVD player?

APPLY IT

SOLUTION A Venn diagram like the one in Figure 10 will help sort out this information. In Figure 10(a), we put the number 12 in the region common to both a DVD player and a Blu-ray player, because 12 households have both. Of the 21 with a Blu-ray player, $21 - 12 = 9$ have no DVD player, so in Figure 10(b) we put 9 in the region for a Blu-ray player but no DVD player. Similarly, $76 - 12 = 64$ households have a DVD player but not a Blu-ray player, so we put 64 in that region. Finally, the diagram shows that $100 - 64 - 12 - 9 = 15$ households have neither a DVD player nor a Blu-ray player. Now we can answer the questions:

(a) $15 + 9 = 24$ do not have a DVD player.

(b) 15 have neither.

(c) 9 have a Blu-ray player but not a DVD player.

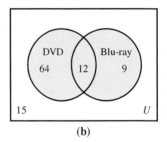

(a)   (b)

FIGURE 10

EXAMPLE 4 **Magazines**

A survey of 77 freshman business students at a large university produced the following results.

> 25 of the students read *Bloomberg Businessweek*;
>
> 19 read *The Wall Street Journal*;
>
> 27 do not read *Fortune*;
>
> 11 read *Bloomberg Businessweek* but not *The Wall Street Journal*;
>
> 11 read *The Wall Street Journal* and *Fortune*;
>
> 13 read *Bloomberg Businessweek* and *Fortune*;
>
> 9 read all three.

Use this information to answer the following questions.

(a) How many students read none of the publications?

(b) How many read only *Fortune*?

(c) How many read *Bloomberg Businessweek* and *The Wall Street Journal*, but not *Fortune*?

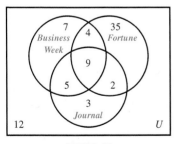

FIGURE 11

SOLUTION Since 9 students read all three publications, begin by placing 9 in the area that belongs to all three regions, as shown in Figure 11. Of the 13 students who read *Bloomberg Businessweek* and *Fortune*, 9 also read *The Wall Street Journal*. Therefore, only $13 - 9 = 4$ read just *Bloomberg Businessweek* and *Fortune*. Place the number 4 in the area of Figure 11 common only to *Bloomberg Businessweek* and *Fortune* readers.

In the same way, place $11 - 9 = 2$ in the region common only to *Fortune* and *The Wall Street Journal*. Of the 11 students who read *Bloomberg Businessweek* but not *The Wall Street Journal*, 4 read *Fortune*, so place $11 - 4 = 7$ in the region for those who read only *Bloomberg Businessweek*.

The data show that 25 students read *Bloomberg Businessweek*. However, $7 + 4 + 9 = 20$ readers have already been placed in the region representing *Bloomberg Businessweek*. The balance of this region will contain only $25 - 20 = 5$ students. These students read *Bloomberg Businessweek* and *The Wall Street Journal* but not *Fortune*. In the same way, $19 - (5 + 9 + 2) = 3$ students read only *The Wall Street Journal*.

YOUR TURN 3 One hundred students were asked which fast food restaurants they had visited in the past month. The results are as follows:

47 ate at McDonald's;

46 ate at Taco Bell;

44 ate at Wendy's;

17 ate at McDonald's and Taco Bell;

19 ate at Taco Bell and Wendy's;

22 ate at Wendy's and McDonald's;

13 ate at all three.

Determine how many ate only at Taco Bell.

Using the fact that 27 of the 77 students do not read *Fortune*, we know that 50 do read *Fortune*. We already have $4 + 9 + 2 = 15$ students in the region representing *Fortune*, leaving $50 - 15 = 35$ who read only *Fortune*.

A total of $7 + 4 + 35 + 5 + 9 + 2 + 3 = 65$ students are placed in the three circles in Figure 11. Since 77 students were surveyed, $77 - 65 = 12$ students read none of the three publications, and 12 is placed outside all three regions.

Now Figure 11 can be used to answer the questions asked above.

(a) There are 12 students who read none of the three publications.

(b) There are 35 students who read only *Fortune*.

(c) The overlap of the regions representing readers of *Bloomberg Businessweek* and *The Wall Street Journal* shows that 5 students read *Bloomberg Businessweek* and *The Wall Street Journal* but not *Fortune*.   **TRY YOUR TURN 3** ▬

CAUTION A common error in solving problems of this type is to make a circle represent one set and another circle represent its complement. In Example 4, with one circle representing those who read *Bloomberg Businessweek*, we did not draw another for those who do not read *Bloomberg Businessweek*. An additional circle is not only unnecessary (because those not in one set are automatically in the other) but very confusing, because the region outside or inside both circles must be empty. Similarly, if a problem involves men and women, do not draw one circle for men and another for women. Draw one circle; if you label it "women," for example, then men are automatically those outside the circle.

EXAMPLE 5 **Utility Maintenance**

Jeff Friedman is a section chief for an electric utility company. The employees in his section cut down trees, climb poles, and splice wire. Friedman reported the following information to the management of the utility.

"Of the 100 employees in my section,

45 can cut trees;

50 can climb poles;

57 can splice wire;

22 can climb poles but can't cut trees;

20 can climb poles and splice wire;

25 can cut trees and splice wire;

14 can cut trees and splice wire but can't climb poles;

9 can't do any of the three (management trainees)."

The data supplied by Friedman lead to the numbers shown in Figure 12. Add the numbers from all of the regions to get the total number of employees:

$$9 + 3 + 14 + 23 + 11 + 9 + 17 + 13 = 99.$$

Friedman claimed to have 100 employees, but his data indicated only 99. Management decided that Friedman didn't qualify as a section chief, and he was reassigned as a night-shift meter reader in Guam. (*Moral:* He should have taken this course.)   ▬

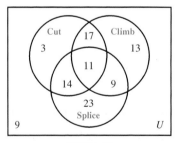

FIGURE 12

In all the examples above, we started with a piece of information specifying the relationship with all the categories. This is usually the best way to begin solving problems of this type.

As we saw in the previous section, we use the symbol $n(A)$ to indicate the *number* of elements in a finite set A. The following statement about the number of elements in the union of two sets will be used later in our study of probability.

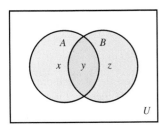

FIGURE 13

Union Rule for Sets

$$n(A \cup B) = n(A) + n(B) - n(A \cap B)$$

To prove this statement, let $x + y$ represent $n(A)$, y represent $n(A \cap B)$, and $y + z$ represent $n(B)$, as shown in Figure 13. Then

$$n(A \cup B) = x + y + z,$$
$$n(A) + n(B) - n(A \cap B) = (x + y) + (y + z) - y = x + y + z,$$
so
$$n(A \cup B) = n(A) + n(B) - n(A \cap B).$$

YOUR TURN 4 A group of students are sitting in the lounge. All are texting or listening to music or both. Eleven are listening to music and 15 are texting. Eight are doing both. How many students are in the lounge?

EXAMPLE 6 School Activities

A group of 10 students meet to plan a school function. All are majoring in accounting or economics or both. Five of the students are economics majors and 7 are majors in accounting. How many major in both subjects?

SOLUTION Let A represent the set of accounting majors and B represent the set of economics majors. Use the union rule, with $n(A) = 5$, $n(B) = 7$, and $n(A \cup B) = 10$. Find $n(A \cap B)$.

$$n(A \cup B) = n(A) + n(B) - n(A \cap B)$$
$$10 = 5 + 7 - n(A \cap B),$$
so
$$n(A \cap B) = 5 + 7 - 10 = 2. \qquad \text{TRY YOUR TURN 4}$$

When A and B are disjoint, then $n(A \cap B) = 0$, so the union rule simplifies to $n(A \cup B) = n(A) + n(B)$.

> **CAUTION** The rule $n(A \cup B) = n(A) + n(B)$ is valid only when A and B are disjoint. When A and B are *not* disjoint, use the rule $n(A \cup B) = n(A) + n(B) - n(A \cap B)$.

EXAMPLE 7 Endangered Species

The following table gives the number of threatened and endangered animal species in the world as of May, 2014. *Source: U.S. Fish and Wildlife Service.*

Endangered and Threatened Species			
	Endangered (E)	Threatened (T)	Totals
Amphibians and reptiles (A)	111	56	167
Arachnids and insects (I)	94	10	104
Birds (B)	291	33	324
Clams, crustaceans, corals and snails (C)	134	30	164
Fishes (F)	94	70	164
Mammals (M)	326	40	366
Totals	1050	239	1289

Using the letters given in the table to denote each set, find the number of species in each of the following sets.

(a) $E \cap B$

SOLUTION The set $E \cap B$ consists of all species that are endangered *and* are birds. From the table, we see that there are 291 such species.

(b) $E \cup B$

SOLUTION The set $E \cup B$ consists of all species that are endangered *or* are birds. We include all 1050 endangered species, plus the 33 bird species who are threatened but not endangered, for a total of 1083. Alternatively, we could use the formula $n(E \cup B) = n(E) + n(B) - n(E \cap B) = 1050 + 324 - 291 = 1083$.

(c) $(F \cup M) \cap T'$

SOLUTION Begin with the set $F \cup M$, which is all species that are fish or mammals. This consists of the four categories with 94, 70, 326, and 40 species. Of this set, take those that are *not* threatened, for a total of $94 + 326 = 420$ species. This is the number of species of fish and mammals in the table that are not threatened. ▬

EXAMPLE 8 Online Activities

Suppose that a group of 150 students have done at least one of these activities online: purchasing an item, banking, and watching a video. In addition,

> 90 students have made an online purchase;
>
> 50 students have banked online;
>
> 70 students have watched an online video;
>
> 15 students have made an online purchase and watched an online video;
>
> 12 have banked online and watched an online video; and
>
> 10 students have done all three.

How many students have made an online purchase and banked online?

SOLUTION Let P represent the set of students who have made a purchase online, B the set who have banked online, and V the set who have watched a video online. Since 10 students did all three activities, begin by placing 10 in the area that belongs to all three regions, as shown in Figure 14. Of the 15 students who belong in sets P and V, 10 also belong to set B. Thus, only $15 - 10 = 5$ students were in the area of Figure 14 common only to sets P and V. Likewise, there are $12 - 10 = 2$ students who belong to only sets B and V. Since there are already $5 + 10 + 2 = 17$ students in set V, there are $70 - 17 = 53$ students in only set V.

We cannot use the information about set P, since there are two regions in P for which we have no information. Similarly, we cannot use the information about set B. In such cases, we label a region with the variable x. Here we place x in the region common only to P and B, as shown in Figure 14.

Of the 90 students in set P, the number who are only in set P must be $90 - x - 10 - 5 = 75 - x$, and this expression is placed in the appropriate region in Figure 14. Similarly, the number who are in only set B is $50 - x - 10 - 2 = 38 - x$. Notice that because all 150 students participated in at least one activity, there are no elements in the region outside the three circles.

Now that the diagram is filled out, we can determine the value of x by recalling that the total number of students was 150. Thus,

$$(75 - x) + 5 + x + 10 + (38 - x) + 2 + 53 = 150.$$

Simplifying, we have $183 - x = 150$, implying that $x = 33$. The number of students who made an online purchase and banked online is

$$33 + 10 = 43. \qquad ▬$$

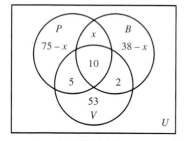

FIGURE 14

7.2 WARM-UP EXERCISES

Let $U = \{1, 2, 3, 4, 5, 6, 7, 8, 9, 10\}, A = \{1, 3, 5, 7, 9\}$, $B = \{1, 2, 3, 4, 5\}$ and $C = \{1, 10\}$. **List the members of each set.**

W1. $(A \cap B)' \cup C$ *(Sec. 7.1)*

W2. $A \cap (B' \cup C)$ *(Sec. 7.1)*

7.2 EXERCISES

Sketch a Venn diagram like the one in the figure, and use shading to show each set.

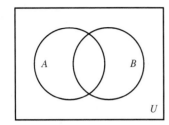

1. $B \cap A'$ **2.** $A \cup B'$

3. $A' \cup B$ **4.** $A' \cap B'$

5. $B' \cup (A' \cap B')$ **6.** $(A \cap B) \cup B'$

7. U' **8.** $\varnothing'$

9. Three sets divide the universal set into at most ___ regions.

10. What does the notation $n(A)$ represent?

Sketch a Venn diagram like the one shown, and use shading to show each set.

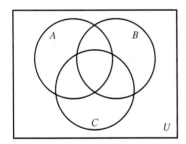

11. $(A \cap B) \cap C$ **12.** $(A \cap C') \cup B$

13. $A \cap (B \cup C')$ **14.** $A' \cap (B \cap C)$

15. $(A' \cap B') \cap C$ **16.** $(A \cap B') \cap C$

17. $(A \cap B') \cup C'$ **18.** $A' \cap (B' \cup C)$

19. $(A \cup B') \cap C$ **20.** $A' \cup (B' \cap C')$

Use the union rule to answer the following questions.

21. If $n(A) = 5$, $n(B) = 12$, and $n(A \cap B) = 4$, what is $n(A \cup B)$?

22. If $n(A) = 15$, $n(B) = 30$, and $n(A \cup B) = 33$, what is $n(A \cap B)$?

23. Suppose $n(B) = 9$, $n(A \cap B) = 5$, and $n(A \cup B) = 22$. What is $n(A)$?

24. Suppose $n(A \cap B) = 5$, $n(A \cup B) = 38$, and $n(A) = 13$. What is $n(B)$?

Draw a Venn diagram and use the given information to fill in the number of elements for each region.

25. $n(U) = 41, n(A) = 16, n(A \cap B) = 12, n(B') = 20$

26. $n(A) = 28, n(B) = 12, n(A \cup B) = 32, n(A') = 19$

27. $n(A \cup B) = 24, n(A \cap B) = 6, n(A) = 11,$
$n(A' \cup B') = 25$

28. $n(A') = 31, n(B) = 25, n(A' \cup B') = 46, n(A \cap B) = 12$

29. $n(A) = 28, n(B) = 34, n(C) = 25, n(A \cap B) = 14,$
$n(B \cap C) = 15, n(A \cap C) = 11, n(A \cap B \cap C) = 9,$
$n(U) = 59$

30. $n(A) = 54, n(A \cap B) = 22, n(A \cup B) = 85,$
$n(A \cap B \cap C) = 4, n(A \cap C) = 15, n(B \cap C) = 16,$
$n(C) = 44, n(B') = 63$

31. $n(A \cap B) = 6, n(A \cap B \cap C) = 4, n(A \cap C) = 7,$
$n(B \cap C) = 4, n(A \cap C') = 11, n(B \cap C') = 8,$
$n(C) = 15, n(A' \cap B' \cap C') = 5$

32. $n(A) = 13, n(A \cap B \cap C) = 4, n(A \cap C) = 6,$
$n(A \cap B') = 6, n(B \cap C) = 6, n(B \cap C') = 11,$
$n(B \cup C) = 22, n(A' \cap B' \cap C') = 5$

In Exercises 33–36, show that the statement is true by drawing Venn diagrams and shading the regions representing the sets on each side of the equals sign.*

33. $(A \cup B)' = A' \cap B'$

34. $(A \cap B)' = A' \cup B'$

35. $A \cap (B \cup C) = (A \cap B) \cup (A \cap C)$

36. $A \cup (B \cap C) = (A \cup B) \cap (A \cup C)$

37. Use the union rule of sets to prove that $n(A \cup B \cup C) = n(A) + n(B) + n(C) - n(A \cap B) - n(A \cap C) - n(B \cap C) + n(A \cap B \cap C)$. (*Hint:* Write $A \cup B \cup C$ as $A \cup (B \cup C)$ and use the formula from Exercise 35.)

38. In Figure 8, let $U = \{$all humans who have ever lived$\}$, $A = \{$men$\}$, $B = \{$Americans$\}$, and $C = \{$politicians$\}$. For each of the eight regions in Figure 8, write the name of one person who belongs in that region. Many answers are possible.

39. Repeat Exercise 38, letting $U = \{$all countries of the world$\}$, $A = \{$countries in the Northern Hemisphere$\}$, $B = \{$countries with Spanish as the primary language$\}$, and $C = \{$countries bordering the Pacific Ocean$\}$. For each of the eight regions in Figure 8, write the name of one country that belongs in that region. Many answers are possible.

---

*The statements in Exercises 33 and 34 are known as De Morgan's Laws. They are named for the English mathematician Augustus De Morgan (1806–1871). They are analogous to De Morgan's Laws for logic seen in the previous chapter.

Business and Economics

Use Venn diagrams to answer the following questions.

40. Cooking Preferences Jeff Friedman, of Example 5 in the text, was again reassigned, this time to the home economics department of the electric utility. He interviewed 140 people in a suburban shopping center to discover some of their cooking habits. He obtained the following results:

> 58 use microwave ovens;
> 63 use electric ranges;
> 58 use gas ranges;
> 19 use microwave ovens and electric ranges;
> 17 use microwave ovens and gas ranges;
> 4 use both gas and electric ranges;
> 1 uses all three;
> 2 use none of the three.

Should he be reassigned one more time? Why or why not?

41. Harvesting Fruit Toward the middle of the harvesting season, peaches for canning come in three types, early, late, and extra late, depending on the expected date of ripening. During a certain week, the following data were recorded at a fruit delivery station:

> 34 trucks went out carrying early peaches;
> 61 carried late peaches;
> 50 carried extra late;
> 25 carried early and late;
> 30 carried late and extra late;
> 8 carried early and extra late;
> 6 carried all three;
> 9 carried only figs (no peaches at all).

(a) How many trucks carried only late variety peaches?

(b) How many carried only extra late?

(c) How many carried only one type of peach?

(d) How many trucks (in all) went out during the week?

42. Cola Consumption Market research showed that the adult residents of a certain small town in Georgia fit the following categories of cola consumption. (We assume here that no one drinks both regular cola and diet cola.)

Age	Drink Regular Cola (R)	Drink Diet Cola (D)	Drink No Cola (N)	Totals
21–25 (Y)	40	15	15	70
26–35 (M)	30	30	20	80
Over 35 (O)	10	50	10	70
Totals	80	95	45	220

Using the letters given in the table, find the number of people in each set.

(a) $Y \cap R$

(b) $M \cap D$

(c) $M \cup (D \cap Y)$

(d) $Y' \cap (D \cup N)$

(e) $O' \cup N$

(f) $M' \cap (R' \cap N')$

(g) Describe the set $M \cup (D \cap Y)$ in words.

43. Investment Habits The following table shows the results of a survey taken by a bank in a medium-sized town in Tennessee. The survey asked questions about the investment habits of bank customers. (We assume here that no one invests in more than one type of investment.)

Age	Stocks (S)	Bonds (B)	Savings Accounts (A)	Totals
18–29 (Y)	6	2	15	23
30–49 (M)	14	5	14	33
50 or over (O)	32	20	12	64
Totals	52	27	41	120

Using the letters given in the table, find the number of people in each set.

(a) $Y \cap B$

(b) $M \cup A$

(c) $Y \cap (S \cup B)$

(d) $O' \cup (S \cup A)$

(e) $(M' \cup O') \cap B$

(f) Describe the set $Y \cap (S \cup B)$ in words.

44. Investment Survey Most mathematics professors love to invest their hard-earned money. A recent survey of 150 math professors revealed that

> 111 invested in stocks;
> 98 invested in bonds;
> 100 invested in certificates of deposit;
> 80 invested in stocks and bonds;
> 83 invested in bonds and certificates of deposit;
> 85 invested in stocks and certificates of deposit;
> 9 did not invest in any of the three.

How many mathematics professors invested in stocks and bonds and certificates of deposit?

Life Sciences

45. Genetics After a genetics experiment on 50 pea plants, the number of plants having certain characteristics was tallied, with the following results.

> 22 were tall;
> 25 had green peas;
> 39 had smooth peas;
> 9 were tall and had green peas;
> 20 had green peas and smooth peas;
> 6 had all three characteristics;
> 4 had none of the characteristics.

(a) Find the number of plants that were tall and had smooth peas.

(b) How many plants were tall and had peas that were neither smooth nor green?

(c) How many plants were not tall but had peas that were smooth and green?

46. Blood Antigens Human blood can contain the A antigen, the B antigen, both the A and B antigens, or neither antigen. A third antigen, called the Rh antigen, is important in human reproduction, and again may or may not be present in an individual.

Blood is called type A-positive if the individual has the A and Rh but not the B antigen. A person having only the A and B antigens is said to have type AB-negative blood. A person having only the Rh antigen has type O-positive blood. Other blood types are defined in a similar manner. Identify the blood types of the individuals in regions (a)–(h) below.

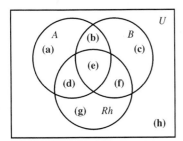

47. Blood Antigens (Use the diagram from Exercise 46.) In a certain hospital, the following data were recorded.

25 patients had the A antigen;
8 had the A and not the B antigen;
27 had the B antigen;
22 had the B and Rh antigens;
30 had the Rh antigen;
12 had none of the antigens;
16 had the A and Rh antigens;
15 had all three antigens.

How many patients

(a) were represented?

(b) had exactly one antigen?

(c) had exactly two antigens?

(d) had O-positive blood?

(e) had AB-positive blood?

(f) had B-negative blood?

(g) had O-negative blood?

(h) had A-positive blood?

48. Mortality The table lists the number of deaths in the United States during 2010 according to race and gender. Use this information and the letters given to find the number of people in each set. *Source: National Vital Statistics Reports.*

	White (W)	Black (B)	American Indian (I)	Asian or Pacific Islander (A)
Female (F)	1,063,235	141,157	7049	24,562
Male (M)	1,051,514	145,802	8516	26,600

(a) F

(b) $F \cap (I \cup A)$

(c) $M \cup B$

(d) $W' \cup I' \cup A'$

(e) In words, describe the set in part (b).

49. Hockey The table lists the number of head and neck injuries for 319 ice hockey players wearing either a full shield or half shield in the Canadian Inter-University Athletics Union during one season. Using the letters given in the table, find the number of injuries in each set. *Source: JAMA.*

	Half Shield (H)	Full Shield (F)
Head and Face Injuries (A)	95	34
Concussions (B)	41	38
Neck Injuries (C)	9	7
Other Injuries (D)	202	150

(a) $A \cap F$

(b) $C \cap (H \cup F)$

(c) $D \cup F$

(d) $B' \cap C'$

50. Lyme Disease Scientists have found a way to distinguish chronic-fatigue syndrome (CFS) from post-treatment Lyme disease by different proteins in a patient's spinal fluid. In a study of 4365 patients,

1605 had the protein for normal patients, CFS, and post-treatment Lyme disease;
1910 had the protein for CFS and Lyme;
738 had the protein for CFS only;
2783 had the protein for CFS;
1771 had the normal protein as well as the one for Lyme;
2768 had the protein for Lyme;
2630 had the normal protein.

Source: Science News.

(a) How many had the protein for Lyme only?

(b) How many had the normal protein only?

(c) How many had none of the proteins?

Social Sciences

51. Military The number of female military personnel in March 2013 is given in the following table. Use this information and the letters given to find the number of female military personnel in each set. *Source: Department of Defense.*

	Army (A)	Air Force (B)	Navy (C)	Marines (D)	Totals
Officers (O)	16,007	12,663	8893	1403	38,966
Enlisted (E)	55,016	48,924	47,195	12,907	164,042
Cadets & Midshipmen (M)	738	872	968	0	2578
Totals	71,761	62,459	57,056	14,310	205,586

(a) $A \cup B$

(b) $E \cup (C \cup D)$

(c) $O' \cap M'$

U.S. Population The projected U.S. population in 2020 (in millions) by age and race or ethnicity is given in the following table. Use this information in Exercises 52–57. *Source: U.S. Bureau of the Census.*

	Non-Hispanic White (A)	Hispanic (B)	Black (C)	Asian (D)	American Indian (E)
Under 45 (F)	110.6	37.6	30.2	13.1	2.2
45–64 (G)	55.3	10.3	9.9	4.3	0.6
65 and over (H)	41.4	4.7	5.0	2.2	0.3
Totals	207.3	52.6	45.1	19.6	3.1

Using the letters given in the table, find the number of people in each set.

52. $G \cup B$

53. $A \cap F$

54. $F \cap (B \cup H)$

55. $G \cup (C \cap H)$

56. $G' \cap (A' \cap C')$

57. $H \cup D$

Marital Status The following table gives the population breakdown (in millions) of the U.S. population in 2010 based on marital status and race or ethnic origin. *Source: U.S. Census Bureau.*

	White (W)	Black (B)	Hispanic (H)	Asian or Pacific Islander (A)
Never Married (N)	45.1	11.7	10.9	2.7
Married (M)	109.4	10.6	17.1	7.0
Widowed (I)	11.8	1.8	1.2	0.5
Divorced/ Separated (D)	19.4	3.2	2.6	0.5

Find the number of people in each set. Describe each set in words.

58. $N \cap (B \cup H)$

59. $(M \cup I) \cap A$

60. $(D \cup W) \cap A'$

61. $M' \cap (B \cup A)$

General Interest

62. Native American Ceremonies At a pow-wow in Arizona, 75 Native American families from all over the Southwest came to participate in the ceremonies. A coordinator of the pow-wow took a survey and found that

> 15 families brought food, costumes, and crafts;
> 25 families brought food and crafts;
> 42 families brought food;
> 35 families brought crafts;
> 14 families brought crafts but not costumes;
> 10 families brought none of the three items;
> 18 families brought costumes but not crafts.

(a) How many families brought costumes and food?

(b) How many families brought costumes?

(c) How many families brought food, but not costumes?

(d) How many families did not bring crafts?

(e) How many families brought food or costumes?

63. Poultry Analysis A chicken farmer surveyed his flock with the following results. The farmer had

> 9 fat red roosters;
> 13 thin brown hens;
> 15 red roosters;
> 11 thin red chickens (hens and roosters);
> 17 red hens;
> 56 fat chickens (hens and roosters);
> 41 roosters;
> 48 hens.

Assume all chickens are thin or fat, red or brown, and hens (female) or roosters (male). How many chickens were

(a) in the flock? (b) red?

(c) fat roosters? (d) fat hens?

(e) thin and brown? (f) red and fat?

YOUR TURN ANSWERS

1.

2.

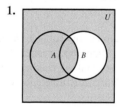

3. 23 **4.** 18

7.3 Introduction to Probability

APPLY IT   What is the probability that a randomly selected person in the United States is Hispanic? That the person is Black?
After introducing probability, we will answer these questions in Exercise 58.

If you go to a supermarket and buy 5 pounds of peaches at 99 cents per pound, you can easily find the *exact* price of your purchase: $4.95. On the other hand, the produce manager of the market is faced with the problem of ordering peaches. The manager may have a good estimate of the number of pounds of peaches that will be sold during the day, but it is impossible to predict the *exact* amount. The number of pounds that customers will purchase during a day is *random*: The quantity cannot be predicted exactly. A great many problems that come up in applications of mathematics involve random phenomena—those for which exact prediction is impossible. The best that we can do is determine the *probability* of the possible outcomes.

Sample Spaces   In probability, an **experiment** is an activity or occurrence with an observable result. Each repetition of an experiment is called a **trial**. The possible results of each trial are called **outcomes**. The set of all possible outcomes for an experiment is the **sample space** for that experiment. A sample space for the experiment of tossing a coin is made up of the outcomes heads (*h*) and tails (*t*). If *S* represents this sample space, then

$$S = \{h, t\}.$$

EXAMPLE 1   **Sample Spaces**

Give the sample space for each experiment.

(a) A spinner like the one in Figure 15 is spun.

SOLUTION   The three outcomes are 1, 2, or 3, so the sample space is

$$S = \{1, 2, 3\}.$$

(b) For the purposes of a public opinion poll, respondents are classified as young, middle-aged, or senior, and as male or female.

SOLUTION   A sample space for this poll could be written as a set of ordered pairs:

$$S = \{(\text{young, male}), (\text{young, female}), (\text{middle-aged, male}),$$
$$(\text{middle-aged, female}), (\text{senior, male}), (\text{senior, female})\}.$$

(c) An experiment consists of studying the numbers of boys and girls in families with exactly 3 children. Let *b* represent *boy* and *g* represent *girl*.

SOLUTION   A three-child family can have 3 boys, written *bbb*, 3 girls, *ggg*, or various combinations, such as *bgg*. A sample space with four outcomes (not equally likely) is

$$S_1 = \{3 \text{ boys}, 2 \text{ boys and } 1 \text{ girl}, 1 \text{ boy and } 2 \text{ girls}, 3 \text{ girls}\}.$$

Notice that a family with 3 boys or 3 girls can occur in just one way, but a family of 2 boys and 1 girl or 1 boy and 2 girls can occur in more than one way. If the *order* of the births is considered, so that *bgg* is different from *gbg* or *ggb*, for example, another sample space is

$$S_2 = \{bbb, bbg, bgb, gbb, bgg, gbg, ggb, ggg\}.$$

The second sample space, S_2, has equally likely outcomes if we assume that boys and girls are equally likely. This assumption, while not quite true, is approximately true, so we will use it throughout this book. The outcomes in S_1 are not equally likely, since there is more than one way to get a family with 2 boys and 1 girl (*bbg*, *bgb*, or *gbb*) or a family with 2 girls and 1 boy (*ggb*, *gbg*, or *bgg*), but only one way to get 3 boys (*bbb*) or 3 girls (*ggg*).

FIGURE 15

YOUR TURN 1   Two coins are tossed, and a head or a tail is recorded for each coin. Give a sample space where each outcome is equally likely.

TRY YOUR TURN 1

CAUTION An experiment may have more than one sample space, as shown in Example 1(c). The most convenient sample spaces have equally likely outcomes, but it is not always possible to choose such a sample space.

Events

An **event** is a subset of a sample space. If the sample space for tossing a coin is $S = \{h, t\}$, then one event is $E = \{h\}$, which represents the outcome "heads."

An ordinary die is a cube whose six different faces show the following numbers of dots: 1, 2, 3, 4, 5, and 6. If the die is fair (not "loaded" to favor certain faces over others), then any one of the faces is equally likely to occur when the die is rolled. The sample space for the experiment of rolling a single fair die is $S = \{1, 2, 3, 4, 5, 6\}$. Some possible events are listed below.

The die shows an even number: $E_1 = \{2, 4, 6\}$.

The die shows a 1: $E_2 = \{1\}$.

The die shows a number less than 5: $E_3 = \{1, 2, 3, 4\}$.

The die shows a multiple of 3: $E_4 = \{3, 6\}$.

Using the notation introduced earlier in this chapter, notice that $n(S) = 6, n(E_1) = 3$, $n(E_2) = 1, n(E_3) = 4$, and $n(E_4) = 2$.

EXAMPLE 2 Events

For the sample space S_2 in Example 1(c), write the following events.

(a) Event H: the family has exactly two girls

SOLUTION Families with three children can have exactly two girls with either bgg, gbg, or ggb, so event H is

$$H = \{bgg, gbg, ggb\}.$$

(b) Event K: the three children are the same sex

SOLUTION Two outcomes satisfy this condition: all boys or all girls.

$$K = \{bbb, ggg\}$$

(c) Event J: the family has three girls

SOLUTION Only ggg satisfies this condition, so

$$J = \{ggg\}. \qquad \text{TRY YOUR TURN 2}$$

YOUR TURN 2 Two coins are tossed, and a head or a tail is recorded for each coin. Write the event E: the coins show exactly one head.

In Example 2(c), event J had only one possible outcome, ggg. Such an event, with only one possible outcome, is a **simple event**. If event E equals the sample space S, then E is called a **certain event**. If event $E = \varnothing$, then E is called an **impossible event**.

EXAMPLE 3 Events

Suppose a coin is flipped until both a head and a tail appear, or until the coin has been flipped four times, whichever comes first. Write each of the following events in set notation.

(a) The coin is flipped exactly three times.

SOLUTION This means that the first two flips of the coin did not include both a head and a tail, so they must both be heads or both be tails. Because the third flip is the last one, it must show the side of the coin not yet seen. Thus the event is

$$\{hht, tth\}.$$

(b) The coin is flipped at least three times.

SOLUTION In addition to the outcomes listed in part (a), there is also the possibility that the coin is flipped four times, which happens only when the first three flips are all heads or all tails. Thus the event is

$$\{hht, tth, hhhh, hhht, tttt, ttth\}.$$

(c) The coin is flipped at least two times.

SOLUTION This event consists of the entire sample space:

$$S = \{ht, th, hht, tth, hhhh, hhht, tttt, ttth\}.$$

This is an example of a certain event.

(d) The coin is flipped fewer than two times.

SOLUTION The coin cannot be flipped fewer than two times under the rules described, so the event is the empty set $\varnothing$. This is an example of an impossible event. ▬▬▬

Since events are sets, we can use set operations to find unions, intersections, and complements of events. A summary of the set operations for events is given below.

Set Operations for Events

Let E and F be events for a sample space S.

$E \cap F$ occurs when both E **and** F occur;

$E \cup F$ occurs when E **or** F **or both** occur;

E' occurs when E does **not** occur.

� EXAMPLE 4   Minimum-Wage Workers

A study of workers earning the minimum wage grouped such workers into various categories, which can be interpreted as events when a worker is selected at random. Consider the following events:

   E: worker is under 20;

   F: worker is white;

   G: worker is female.

Describe the following events in words. *Source: Economic Policy Institute.*

(a) E'

SOLUTION E' is the event that the worker is 20 or over.

(b) $F \cap G'$

SOLUTION $F \cap G'$ is the event that the worker is white and not a female, that is, the worker is a white male.

(c) $E \cup G$

SOLUTION $E \cup G$ is the event that the worker is under 20 or is female. Note that this event includes all workers under 20, both male and female, and all female workers of any age. **TRY YOUR TURN 3** ▬▬▬

YOUR TURN 3 In Example 4, describe the following event in words: $E' \cap F'$. ▬▬▬

Two events that cannot both occur at the same time, such as rolling an even number and an odd number with a single roll of a die, are called *mutually exclusive events*.

Mutually Exclusive Events

Events E and F are **mutually exclusive events** if $E \cap F = \varnothing$.

Any event E and its complement E' are mutually exclusive. By definition, mutually exclusive events are disjoint sets.

$E \cap G = \varnothing$

FIGURE 16

EXAMPLE 5 **Mutually Exclusive Events**

Let $S = \{1, 2, 3, 4, 5, 6\}$, the sample space for tossing a single die. Let $E = \{4, 5, 6\}$, and let $G = \{1, 2\}$. Then E and G are mutually exclusive events, since they have no outcomes in common: $E \cap G = \varnothing$. See Figure 16.

Probability   For sample spaces with *equally likely* outcomes, the probability of an event is defined as follows.

Basic Probability Principle

Let S be a sample space of equally likely outcomes, and let event E be a subset of S. Then the **probability** that event E occurs is

$$P(E) = \frac{n(E)}{n(S)}.$$

By this definition, the probability of an event is a number that indicates the relative likelihood of the event.

CAUTION   The basic probability principle only applies when the outcomes are equally likely.

EXAMPLE 6 **Basic Probabilities**

Suppose a single fair die is rolled. Use the sample space $S = \{1, 2, 3, 4, 5, 6\}$ and give the probability of each event.

(a) E: the die shows an even number

SOLUTION   Here, $E = \{2, 4, 6\}$, a set with three elements. Since S contains six elements,

$$P(E) = \frac{3}{6} = \frac{1}{2}.$$

(b) F: the die shows a number less than 10

SOLUTION   Event F is a certain event, with

$$F = \{1, 2, 3, 4, 5, 6\},$$

so

$$P(F) = \frac{6}{6} = 1.$$

YOUR TURN 4   In Example 6, find the probability of event H: The die shows a number less than 5.

(c) G: the die shows an 8

SOLUTION   This event is impossible, so

$$P(G) = 0.$$ TRY YOUR TURN 4

A standard deck of 52 cards has four suits: hearts (♥), clubs (♣), diamonds (♦), and spades (♠), with 13 cards in each suit. The hearts and diamonds are red, and the spades and clubs are black. Each suit has an ace (A), a king (K), a queen (Q), a jack (J), and cards numbered from 2 to 10. The jack, queen, and king are called *face cards* and for many purposes can be thought of as having values 11, 12, and 13, respectively. The ace can be thought of as the low card (value 1) or the high card (value 14). See Figure 17. We will refer to this standard deck of cards often in our discussion of probability.

FIGURE 17

EXAMPLE 7 Playing Cards

If a single playing card is drawn at random from a standard 52-card deck, find the probability of each event.

(a) Drawing an ace

SOLUTION There are 4 aces in the deck. The event "drawing an ace" is

$$\{\text{heart ace, diamond ace, club ace, spade ace}\}.$$

Therefore,

$$P(\text{ace}) = \frac{4}{52} = \frac{1}{13}.$$

(b) Drawing a face card

SOLUTION Since there are 12 face cards (three in each of the four suits),

$$P(\text{face card}) = \frac{12}{52} = \frac{3}{13}.$$

(c) Drawing a spade

SOLUTION The deck contains 13 spades, so

$$P(\text{spade}) = \frac{13}{52} = \frac{1}{4}.$$

(d) Drawing a spade or a heart

SOLUTION Besides the 13 spades, the deck contains 13 hearts, so

$$P(\text{spade or heart}) = \frac{26}{52} = \frac{1}{2}.$$

YOUR TURN 5 Find the probability of drawing a jack or a king.

TRY YOUR TURN 5

In the preceding examples, the probability of each event was a number between 0 and 1. The same thing is true in general. Any event E is a subset of the sample space S, so $0 \le n(E) \le n(S)$. Since $P(E) = n(E)/n(S)$, it follows that $0 \le P(E) \le 1$. Note that a certain event has probability 1 and an impossible event has probability 0, as seen in Example 6.

> For any event E, $\quad 0 \le P(E) \le 1.$

Empirical Probability

In many real-life problems, it is not possible to establish exact probabilities for events. Instead, useful approximations are often found by drawing on past experience. The next example shows one approach to such **empirical probabilities**.

EXAMPLE 8 Injuries

The following table lists the estimated number of injuries in the United States associated with recreation equipment. *Source: National Safety Council.*

Recreation Equipment Injuries	
Equipment	Number of Injuries
Bicycles	515,871
Skateboards	143,682
Trampolines	107,345
Playground climbing equipment	77,845
Swings or swing sets	59,144

Find the probability that a randomly selected person whose injury is associated with recreation equipment was hurt on a trampoline.

SOLUTION We first find the total number of injuries. Verify that the amounts in the table sum to 903,887. The probability is then found by dividing the number of people injured on trampolines by the total number of people injured. Thus,

$$P(\text{Trampolines}) = \frac{107,345}{903,887} \approx 0.1188.$$

7.3 EXERCISES

1. What is meant by a "fair" coin or die?

2. What is the sample space for an experiment?

Write sample spaces for the experiments in Exercises 3–10.

3. A month of the year is chosen for a wedding.

4. A day in April is selected for a bicycle race.

5. A student is asked how many questions she answered correctly on a recent 80-question test.

6. A person is asked the number of hours (to the nearest hour) he watched television yesterday.

7. The management of an oil company must decide whether to go ahead with a new oil shale plant or to cancel it.

8. A record is kept each day for three days about whether a particular stock goes up or down.

9. A coin is tossed, and a die is rolled.

10. A box contains five balls, numbered 1, 2, 3, 4, and 5. A ball is drawn at random, the number on it recorded, and the ball replaced. The box is shaken, a second ball is drawn, and its number is recorded.

11. Define an event.

12. What is a simple event?

For the experiments in Exercises 13–18, write out the sample space *S*, choosing an *S* with equally likely outcomes, if possible. Then give the value of *n*(*S*) and tell whether the outcomes in *S* are equally likely. Finally, write the indicated events in set notation.

13. A committee of 2 people is selected at random from 5 executives: Alam, Bartolini, Chinn, Dickson, and Ellsberg.

    (a) Chinn is on the committee.

    (b) Dickson and Ellsberg are not both on the committee.

    (c) Both Alam and Chinn are on the committee.

14. Five states are being considered as the location for three new high-energy physics laboratories: California (CA), Colorado (CO), New Jersey (NJ), New York (NY), and Utah (UT). Three states will be chosen at random. Write elements of the sample space in the form (CA, CO, NJ).

    (a) All three states border an ocean.

    (b) Exactly two of the three states border an ocean.

    (c) Exactly one of the three states is west of the Mississippi River.

15. Slips of paper marked with the numbers 1, 2, 3, 4, and 5 are placed in a box. After being mixed, two slips are drawn simultaneously.

    (a) Both slips are marked with even numbers.

    (b) One slip is marked with an odd number and the other is marked with an even number.

    (c) Both slips are marked with the same number.

16. An unprepared student takes a three-question, true/false quiz in which he guesses the answers to all three questions, so each answer is equally likely to be correct or wrong.

    (a) The student gets three answers wrong.

    (b) The student gets exactly two answers correct.

    (c) The student gets only the first answer correct.

17. A coin is flipped until two heads appear, up to a maximum of four flips. (If three tails are flipped, the coin is still tossed a fourth time to complete the experiment).

    (a) The coin is tossed four times.

    (b) Exactly two heads are tossed.

    (c) No heads are tossed.

18. One jar contains four balls, labeled 1, 2, 3, and 4. A second jar contains five balls, labeled 1, 2, 3, 4, and 5. An experiment consists of taking one ball from the first jar, and then taking a ball from the second jar.

    (a) The number on the first ball is even.

    (b) The number on the second ball is even.

    (c) The sum of the numbers on the two balls is 5.

    (d) The sum of the numbers on the two balls is 1.

A single fair die is rolled. Find the probabilities of each event.

19. Getting a 2

20. Getting an odd number

21. Getting a number less than 5

22. Getting a number greater than 2

23. Getting a 3 or a 4

24. Getting any number except 3

A card is drawn from a well-shuffled deck of 52 cards. Find the probability of drawing the following.

25. A 9

26. A black card

27. A black 9

28. A heart

29. The 9 of hearts

30. A face card

31. A 2 or a queen

32. A black 7 or a red 8

33. A red card or a 10

34. A spade or a king

A jar contains 3 white, 4 orange, 5 yellow, and 8 black marbles. If a marble is drawn at random, find the probability that it is the following.

35. White

36. Orange

37. Yellow

38. Black

39. Not black

40. Orange or yellow

Which of Exercises 41–48 are examples of empirical probability?

41. The probability of heads on 5 consecutive tosses of a coin

42. The probability that a freshman entering college will graduate with a degree

43. The probability that a person is allergic to penicillin

44. The probability of drawing an ace from a standard deck of 52 cards

45. The probability that a person will get lung cancer from smoking cigarettes

46. A weather forecast that predicts a 70% chance of rain tomorrow

47. A gambler's claim that on a roll of a fair die, $P(\text{even}) = 1/2$

48. A surgeon's prediction that a patient has a 90% chance of a full recovery

49. The student sitting next to you in class concludes that the probability of the ceiling falling down on both of you before class ends is 1/2, because there are two possible outcomes—the ceiling will fall or not fall. What is wrong with this reasoning?

50. The following puzzler was given on the *Car Talk* radio program.

    "Three different numbers are chosen at random, and one is written on each of three slips of paper. The slips are then placed face down on the table. The objective is to choose the slip upon which is written the largest number. Here are the rules: You can turn over any slip of paper and look at the amount written on it. If for any reason you think this is the largest, you're done; you keep it. Otherwise you discard it and turn over a second slip. Again, if you think this is the one with the biggest number, you keep that one and the game is over. If you don't, you discard that one too . . . . The chance of getting the highest number is one in three. Or is it? Is there a strategy by which you can improve the odds?" *Source: Car Talk*.

    The answer to the puzzler is that you can indeed improve the probability of getting the highest number by the following strategy. Pick one of the slips of paper, and after looking at the number, throw it away. Then pick a second slip; if it has a larger number than the first slip, stop. If not, pick the third slip. Find the probability of winning with this strategy.*

APPLICATIONS

Business and Economics

51. Survey of Workers The management of a firm wishes to check on the opinions of its assembly line workers. Before the workers are interviewed, they are divided into various categories. Define events E, F, and G as follows.

E: worker is female
F: worker has worked less than 5 years
G: worker contributes to a voluntary retirement plan

Describe each event in words.

(a) E' (b) $E \cap F$ (c) $E \cup G'$

(d) F' (e) $F \cup G$ (f) $F' \cap G'$

52. Brand Choice A study considers consumers' choices between two brands, A and B, based on the proportion of unique features in each brand. Suppose that the number of features of brand A is a and of brand B is b, and that c is the number of common features. Show that

$$P(A) = \frac{a - c}{a + b - 2c} \quad \text{and} \quad P(B) = \frac{b - c}{a + b - 2c}.$$

Source: Marketing Science.

53. Investment Survey Exercise 44 of the previous section presented a survey of 150 mathematics professors. Use the information given in that exercise to find each probability.

(a) A randomly chosen professor invested in stocks and bonds and certificates of deposit.

(b) A randomly chosen professor invested in only bonds.

54. Labor Force The 2012 and the 2022 (projected) civilian labor forces by age are given in the following table. *Source: Bureau of Labor Statistics.*

Age (in years)	2012 (in millions)	2022 (in millions)
16 to 24	21.3	18.5
25 to 54	101.3	103.2
55 and over	32.4	41.8
Total	155.0	163.5

(a) In 2012, find the probability that a member of the civilian labor force is age 55 or older.

*This is a special case of the famous Googol problem. For more details, see "Recognizing the Maximum of a Sequence" by John P. Gilbert and Frederick Mosteller, *Journal of the American Statistical Association*, Vol. 61, No. 313, March 1966, pp. 35–73.

(b) In 2022, find the probability that a member of the civilian labor force is age 55 or over.

(c) What do these projections imply about the future civilian labor force?

Life Sciences

55. Medical Survey For a medical experiment, people are classified as to whether they smoke, have a family history of heart disease, or are overweight. Define events E, F, and G as follows.

E: person smokes
F: person has a family history of heart disease
G: person is overweight

Describe each event in words.

(a) G' (b) $F \cap G$ (c) $E \cup G'$

56. Medical Survey Refer to Exercise 55. Describe each event in words.

(a) $E \cup F$ (b) $E' \cap F$ (c) $F' \cup G'$

57. Causes of Death There were 2,468,435 U.S. deaths in 2010. They are listed according to cause in the following table. If a randomly selected person died in 2010, use this information to find the following probabilities. *Source: Centers for Disease Control and Prevention.*

Cause	Number of Deaths
Heart disease	597,689
Cancer	574,743
Chronic lower respiratory disease	138,080
Cerebrovascular disease	129,476
Accidents	120,859
Alzheimer's disease	83,494
Diabetes mellitus	69,071
Influenza and pneumonia	50,097
All other causes	704,926

(a) The probability that the cause of death was heart disease

(b) The probability that the cause of death was cancer or heart disease

(c) The probability that the cause of death was not an accident and was not diabetes mellitus

Social Sciences

58. APPLY IT U.S. Population The projected U.S. population (in thousands) by race in 2020 and 2050 is given in the table. *Source: Bureau of the Census.*

Race	2020	2050
White	207,393	207,901
Hispanic	52,652	96,508
Black	41,538	53,555
Asian and Pacific Islander	18,557	32,432
Other	2602	3535

Find the probability that a randomly selected person in the given year is of the race specified.

(a) Hispanic in 2020

(b) Hispanic in 2050

(c) Black in 2020

(d) Black in 2050

59. **Congressional Service** The following table gives the number of years of service of senators in the 113th Congress of the United States of America. Find the probability that a randomly selected senator of the 113th Congress had served 20–29 years when Congress convened. *Source: Infoplease.com.*

Years of Service	Number of Senators
0–9	60
10–19	24
20–29	11
30–39	5

60. **Civil War** Estimates of the Union Army's strength and losses for the battle of Gettysburg are given in the following table, where *strength* is the number of soldiers immediately preceding the battle and *loss* indicates a soldier who was killed, wounded, captured, or missing. *Source: Regimental Strengths and Losses of Gettysburg.*

Unit	Strength	Loss
I Corps (Reynolds)	12,222	6059
II Corps (Hancock)	11,347	4369
III Corps (Sickles)	10,675	4211
V Corps (Sykes)	10,907	2187
VI Corps (Sedgwick)	13,596	242
XI Corps (Howard)	9188	3801
XII Corps (Slocum)	9788	1082
Cavalry (Pleasonton)	11,851	610
Artillery (Tyler)	2376	242
Total	91,950	22,803

(a) Find the probability that a randomly selected Union soldier was from the XI Corps.

(b) Find the probability that a soldier was lost in the battle.

(c) Find the probability that a I Corps soldier was lost in the battle.

(d) Which group had the highest probability of not being lost in the battle?

(e) Which group had the highest probability of loss?

(f) Explain why these probabilities vary.

61. **Civil War** Estimates of the Confederate Army's strength and losses for the battle of Gettysburg are given in the following table, where *strength* is the number of soldiers immediately preceding the battle and *loss* indicates a soldier who was killed, wounded, captured, or missing. *Source: Regimental Strengths and Losses at Gettysburg.*

Unit	Strength	Loss
I Corps (Longstreet)	20,706	7661
II Corps (Ewell)	20,666	6603
III Corps (Hill)	22,083	8007
Cavalry (Stuart)	6621	286
Total	70,076	22,557

(a) Find the probability that a randomly selected Confederate soldier was from the III Corps.

(b) Find the probability that a confederate soldier was lost in the battle.

(c) Find the probability that a I Corps soldier was lost in the battle.

(d) Which group had the highest probability of not being lost in the battle?

(e) Which group had the highest probability of loss?

General Interest

62. **Native American Ceremonies** Exercise 62 of the previous section presented a survey of families participating in a pow-wow in Arizona. Use the information given in that exercise to find each probability.

(a) A randomly chosen family brought costumes and food.

(b) A randomly chosen family brought crafts, but neither food nor costumes.

(c) A randomly chosen family brought food or costumes.

63. **Poultry Analysis** Exercise 63 of the previous section described a flock of chickens. See the information given in that exercise to find each of the following probabilities.

(a) A randomly chosen chicken was a fat red rooster.

(b) A randomly chosen chicken was a rooster.

(c) A randomly chosen chicken was red.

YOUR TURN ANSWERS

1. $S = \{HH, HT, TH, TT\}$ 2. $E = \{HT, TH\}$
3. $E' \cap F'$ is the event that the worker is 20 or over and is not white.
4. $P(H) = \dfrac{4}{6} = \dfrac{2}{3}.$
5. $P(\text{jack or a king}) = 8/52 = 2/13.$

7.4 Basic Concepts of Probability

APPLY IT What is the probability that a dollar of consumer debt is held by a finance company or credit union?

We will determine this probability in Example 8. But first we need to develop additional rules for calculating probability, beginning with the probability of a union of two events.

The Union Rule To determine the probability of the union of two events E and F in a sample space S, use the union rule for sets,

$$n(E \cup F) = n(E) + n(F) - n(E \cap F),$$

which was proved in Section 7.2. Assuming that the events in the sample space S are equally likely, divide both sides by $n(S)$, so that

$$\frac{n(E \cup F)}{n(S)} = \frac{n(E)}{n(S)} + \frac{n(F)}{n(S)} - \frac{n(E \cap F)}{n(S)}$$

$$P(E \cup F) = P(E) + P(F) - P(E \cap F).$$

Although our derivation is valid only for sample spaces with equally likely events, the result is valid for any events E and F from any sample space, and is called the **union rule for probability**.

> **Union Rule for Probability**
> For any events E and F from a sample space S,
> $$P(E \cup F) = P(E) + P(F) - P(E \cap F).$$

EXAMPLE 1 Probabilities with Playing Cards

If a single card is drawn from an ordinary deck of cards, find the probability that it will be a red or a face card.

SOLUTION Let R represent the event "red card" and F the event "face card." There are 26 red cards in the deck, so $P(R) = 26/52$. There are 12 face cards in the deck, so $P(F) = 12/52$. Since there are 6 red face cards in the deck, $P(R \cap F) = 6/52$. By the union rule, the probability of the card being red or a face card is

$$P(R \cup F) = P(R) + P(F) - P(R \cap F)$$
$$= \frac{26}{52} + \frac{12}{52} - \frac{6}{52} = \frac{32}{52} = \frac{8}{13}.$$ TRY YOUR TURN 1

YOUR TURN 1 In Example 1, find the probability of an ace or a club.

EXAMPLE 2 Probabilities with Dice

Suppose two fair dice are rolled. Find each probability.

(a) The first die shows a 2, or the sum of the results is 6 or 7.

SOLUTION The sample space for the throw of two dice is shown in Figure 18 on the next page, where 1-1 represents the event "the first die shows a 1 and the second die shows a 1," 1-2 represents "the first die shows a 1 and the second die shows a 2," and so on. Let A represent the event "the first die shows a 2," and B represent the event "the sum of the results is 6 or 7." These events are indicated in Figure 18. From the diagram, event A has 6 elements, B has 11 elements, the intersection of A and B has 2 elements, and the sample space has 36 elements. Thus,

$$P(A) = \frac{6}{36}, \quad P(B) = \frac{11}{36}, \quad \text{and} \quad P(A \cap B) = \frac{2}{36}.$$

FIGURE 18

By the union rule,

$$P(A \cup B) = P(A) + P(B) - P(A \cap B)$$

$$P(A \cup B) = \frac{6}{36} + \frac{11}{36} - \frac{2}{36} = \frac{15}{36} = \frac{5}{12}.$$

(b) The sum of the results is 11, or the second die shows a 5.

SOLUTION $P(\text{sum is } 11) = 2/36$, $P(\text{second die shows a } 5) = 6/36$, and $P(\text{sum is } 11 \text{ and second die shows a } 5) = 1/36$, so

$$P(\text{sum is } 11 \text{ or second die shows a } 5) = \frac{2}{36} + \frac{6}{36} - \frac{1}{36} = \frac{7}{36}.$$

YOUR TURN 2 In Example 2, find the probability that the sum is 8, or both die show the same number.

TRY YOUR TURN 2

> **CAUTION** You may wonder why we did not use $S = \{2, 3, 4, 5, \ldots, 12\}$ as the sample space in Example 2. Remember, we prefer to use a sample space with equally likely outcomes. The outcomes in set S above are not equally likely—a sum of 2 can occur in just one way, a sum of 3 in two ways, a sum of 4 in three ways, and so on, as shown in Figure 18.

If events E and F are mutually exclusive, then $E \cap F = \varnothing$ by definition; hence, $P(E \cap F) = 0$. In this case the union rule simplifies to $P(E \cup F) = P(E) + P(F)$.

> **CAUTION** The rule $P(E \cup F) = P(E) + P(F)$ is valid only when E and F are mutually exclusive. When E and F are *not* mutually exclusive, use the rule $P(E \cup F) = P(E) + P(F) - P(E \cap F)$.

The Complement Rule

By the definition of E', for any event E from a sample space S,

$$E \cup E' = S \qquad \text{and} \qquad E \cap E' = \varnothing.$$

Since $E \cap E' = \varnothing$, events E and E' are mutually exclusive, so that

$$P(E \cup E') = P(E) + P(E').$$

However, $E \cup E' = S$, the sample space, and $P(S) = 1$. Thus

$$P(E \cup E') = P(E) + P(E') = 1.$$

Rearranging these terms gives the following useful rule for complements.

Complement Rule

$$P(E) = 1 - P(E') \qquad \text{and} \qquad P(E') = 1 - P(E).$$

EXAMPLE 3 Complement Rule

If a fair die is rolled, what is the probability that any number but 5 will come up?

SOLUTION If E is the event that 5 comes up, then E' is the event that any number but 5 comes up. Since $P(E) = 1/6$, we have $P(E') = 1 - 1/6 = 5/6$.

EXAMPLE 4 Complement Rule

If two fair dice are rolled, find the probability that the sum of the numbers rolled is greater than 3. Refer to Figure 18.

SOLUTION To calculate this probability directly, we must find the probabilities that the sum is 4, 5, 6, 7, 8, 9, 10, 11, or 12 and then add them. It is much simpler to first find the probability of the complement, the event that the sum is less than or equal to 3.

$$P(\text{sum} \le 3) = P(\text{sum is 2}) + P(\text{sum is 3})$$
$$= \frac{1}{36} + \frac{2}{36}$$
$$= \frac{3}{36} = \frac{1}{12}$$

YOUR TURN 3 Find the probability that when two fair dice are rolled, the sum is less than 11.

Now use the fact that $P(E) = 1 - P(E')$ to get

$$P(\text{sum} > 3) = 1 - P(\text{sum} \le 3)$$
$$= 1 - \frac{1}{12} = \frac{11}{12}.$$

TRY YOUR TURN 3

Odds Sometimes probability statements are given in terms of **odds**, a comparison of $P(E)$ with $P(E')$. For example, suppose $P(E) = 4/5$. Then $P(E') = 1 - 4/5 = 1/5$. These probabilities predict that E will occur 4 out of 5 times and E' will occur 1 out of 5 times. Then we say the *odds in favor* of E are 4 to 1.

> **Odds**
> The **odds in favor** of an event E are defined as the ratio of $P(E)$ to $P(E')$, or
> $$\frac{P(E)}{P(E')}, \text{ where } P(E') \ne 0.$$

EXAMPLE 5 Odds in Favor of Rain

Suppose the weather forecaster says that the probability of rain tomorrow is 1/3. Find the odds in favor of rain tomorrow.

SOLUTION Let E be the event "rain tomorrow." Then E' is the event "no rain tomorrow." Since $P(E) = 1/3$, $P(E') = 2/3$. By the definition of odds, the odds in favor of rain are

$$\frac{1/3}{2/3} = \frac{1}{2}, \qquad \text{written} \qquad \text{1 to 2, or 1:2.}$$

YOUR TURN 4 If the probability of snow tomorrow is 3/10, find the odds in favor of snow tomorrow.

On the other hand, the odds that it will *not* rain, or the *odds against* rain, are

$$\frac{2/3}{1/3} = \frac{2}{1}, \qquad \text{written} \qquad \text{2 to 1, or 2:1.}$$

TRY YOUR TURN 4

If the odds in favor of an event are, say, 3 to 5, then the probability of the event is 3/8, while the probability of the complement of the event is 5/8. (Odds of 3 to 5 indicate

3 outcomes in favor of the event out of a total of 8 possible outcomes.) This example suggests the following generalization.

> If the odds favoring event E are m to n, then
>
> $$P(E) = \frac{m}{m + n} \quad \text{and} \quad P(E') = \frac{n}{m + n}.$$

EXAMPLE 6 Package Delivery

The odds that a particular package will be delivered on time are 25 to 2.

(a) Find the probability that the package will be delivered on time.

SOLUTION Odds of 25 to 2 show 25 favorable chances out of $25 + 2 = 27$ chances altogether:

$$P(\text{package will be delivered on time}) = \frac{25}{25 + 2} = \frac{25}{27}.$$

(b) Find the odds against the package being delivered on time.

SOLUTION Using the complement rule, there is a 2/27 chance that the package will not be delivered on time. So the odds against the package being delivered on time are

$$\frac{P(\text{package will not be delivered on time})}{P(\text{package will be delivered on time})} = \frac{2/27}{25/27} = \frac{2}{25},$$

or 2:25.

YOUR TURN 5 If the odds that a package will be delivered on time are 17 to 3, find the probability that the package will not be delivered on time.

TRY YOUR TURN 5

EXAMPLE 7 Odds in Horse Racing

If the odds in favor of a particular horse's winning a race are 5 to 7, what is the probability that the horse will win the race?

SOLUTION The odds indicate chances of 5 out of 12 ($5 + 7 = 12$) that the horse will win, so

$$P(\text{winning}) = \frac{5}{12}.$$

YOUR TURN 6 If the odds against a particular horse winning a race are 7 to 3, what is the probability the horse will win the race?

Race tracks generally give odds *against* a horse winning. In this case, the track would give the odds as 7 to 5. Of course, race tracks, casinos, and other gambling establishments need to give odds that are more favorable to the house than those representing the actual probabilities, because they need to make a profit.

TRY YOUR TURN 6

Probability Distribution
A table listing each possible outcome of an experiment and its corresponding probability is called a **probability distribution**. The assignment of probabilities may be done in any reasonable way (on an empirical basis, as in the next example, or by theoretical reasoning, as in Section 7.3), provided that it satisfies the following conditions.

Properties of Probability
Let S be a sample space consisting of n distinct outcomes, $s_1, s_2, \ldots, s_n$. An acceptable probability assignment consists of assigning to each outcome s_i a number p_i (the probability of s_i) according to these rules.

1. The probability of each outcome is a number between 0 and 1, inclusive.

$$0 \le p_1 \le 1, \quad 0 \le p_2 \le 1, \ldots, \quad 0 \le p_n \le 1$$

2. The sum of the probabilities of all possible outcomes is 1.

$$p_1 + p_2 + p_3 + \cdots + p_n = 1$$

EXAMPLE 8 Consumer Credit

The following table lists the major holders of U.S. consumer credit (in billions of dollars) in 2012. *Source: The World Almanac and Book of Facts 2014.*

Consumer Credit	
Holder	Amount
Depository institutions	1218.6
Finance companies	680.7
Credit unions	243.6
Federal government	526.8
Nonfinancial business	48.5
Pools of securitized assets	49.9

(a) Construct a probability distribution for the probability that a dollar of consumer credit is held by each type of holder.

SOLUTION We first find the total amount of credit and then divide the amount held by each type of holder by the total. Verify that the amounts in the table sum to 2768.1. The probability that a dollar of consumer credit is held by a depository institution, for example, is $P(\text{depository institution}) = 1218.6/2768.1 \approx 0.4402$. Similarly, we could divide each amount by 2768.1, with the results (rounded to four decimal places) shown in the following table.

Consumer Credit	
Holder	Probability
Depository institutions	0.4402
Finance companies	0.2459
Credit unions	0.0880
Federal government	0.1903
Nonfinancial business	0.0175
Pools of securitized assets	0.0180

Verify that this distribution satisfies the conditions for probability. Each probability is between 0 and 1, so the first condition holds. The probabilities in this table sum to 0.9999. In theory, to satisfy the second condition, they should total 1.0000, but this does not always occur when the individual numbers are rounded.

(b) Find the probability that a dollar of consumer debt is held by a finance company or credit union.

APPLY IT

SOLUTION The categories in the table are mutually exclusive simple events. Thus, to find the probability that a dollar of consumer debt is held by a finance company or credit union, we use the union rule to calculate

$$P(\text{finance company or credit union}) = 0.2459 + 0.0880 = 0.3339.$$

We could get this same result by summing the amount held by finance companies and credit unions, and dividing the total by 2768.1.

Thus, about one-third of all consumer debt is held by finance companies and credit unions.

Probability distributions are discussed further in the next chapter.

EXAMPLE 9 Clothing

Susan is a college student who receives heavy sweaters from her aunt at the first sign of cold weather. Susan has determined that the probability that a sweater is the wrong size is 0.47, the probability that it is a loud color is 0.59, and the probability that it is both the wrong size and a loud color is 0.31.

(a) Find the probability that the sweater is the correct size and not a loud color.

SOLUTION   Let W represent the event "wrong size," and L represent "loud color." Place the given information on a Venn diagram, starting with 0.31 in the intersection of the regions W and L (see Figure 19). As stated earlier, event W has probability 0.47. Since 0.31 has already been placed inside the intersection of W and L,

$$0.47 - 0.31 = 0.16$$

goes inside region W, but outside the intersection of W and L, that is, in the region $W \cap L'$. In the same way,

$$0.59 - 0.31 = 0.28$$

goes inside the region for L, and outside the overlap, that is, in the region $L \cap W'$.

   Using regions W and L, the event we want is $W' \cap L'$. From the Venn diagram in Figure 19, the labeled regions have a total probability of

$$0.16 + 0.31 + 0.28 = 0.75.$$

Since the entire region of the Venn diagram must have probability 1, the region outside W and L, or $W' \cap L'$, has probability

$$1 - 0.75 = 0.25.$$

The probability is 0.25 that the sweater is the correct size and not a loud color.

(b) Find the probability that the sweater is the correct size or is not loud.

SOLUTION   The corresponding region, $W' \cup L'$, has probability

$$0.25 + 0.16 + 0.28 = 0.69.$$

Alternatively, we could write $W' \cup L' = (W \cap L)'$ using one of De Morgan's Laws. (See Exercises 33 and 34 in Section 7.2.) Then we can use the complement rule to get $P((W \cap L)') = 1 - P(W \cap L) = 1 - 0.31 = 0.69.$

The figure at the left:

W	L
0.16	0.31	0.28
	0.25

FIGURE 19

7.4 WARM-UP EXERCISES

A card is drawn from a well-shuffled deck of 52 cards. Find the probabilities of the following.

W1. A heart or a queen   *(Sec. 7.3)*

W2. A black card or an ace   *(Sec. 7.3)*

7.4 EXERCISES

1. Define mutually exclusive events in your own words.

2. Explain the union rule for mutually exclusive events.

Decide whether the events in Exercises 3–8 are mutually exclusive.

3. Owning a dog and owning an MP3 player

4. Being a business major and being from Texas

5. Being retired and being 70 years old

6. Being a teenager and being 70 years old

7. Being one of the ten tallest people in the United States and being under 4 feet tall

8. Being male and being a nurse

Two dice are rolled. Find the probabilities of rolling the given sums.

9. (a) 2   **(b)** 4   **(c)** 5   **(d)** 6

10. (a) 8   **(b)** 9   **(c)** 10   **(d)** 13

11. (a) 9 or more   **(b)** Less than 7
   (c) Between 5 and 8 (exclusive)

12. (a) Not more than 5
   (b) Not less than 8
   (c) Between 3 and 7 (exclusive)

Two dice are rolled. Find the probabilities of the following events.

13. The first die is 3 or the sum is 8.

14. The second die is 5 or the sum is 10.

One card is drawn from an ordinary deck of 52 cards. Find the probabilities of drawing the following cards.

15. (a) A 9 or 10 (b) A red card or a 3

 (c) A 9 or a black 10 (d) A heart or a black card

 (e) A face card or a diamond

16. (a) Less than a 4 (count aces as ones)

 (b) A diamond or a 7 (c) A black card or an ace

 (d) A heart or a jack (e) A red card or a face card

Kristina Karganova invites 13 relatives to a party: her mother, 2 aunts, 3 uncles, 2 brothers, 1 male cousin, and 4 female cousins. If the chances of any one guest arriving first are equally likely, find the probabilities that the first guest to arrive is as follows.

17. (a) A brother or an uncle

 (b) A brother or a cousin

 (c) A brother or her mother

18. (a) An uncle or a cousin

 (b) A male or a cousin

 (c) A female or a cousin

The numbers 1, 2, 3, 4, and 5 are written on slips of paper, and 2 slips are drawn at random one at a time without replacement. Find the probabilities in Exercises 19 and 20.

19. (a) The sum of the numbers is 9.

 (b) The sum of the numbers is 5 or less.

 (c) The first number is 2 or the sum is 6.

20. (a) Both numbers are even.

 (b) One of the numbers is even or greater than 3.

 (c) The sum is 5 or the second number is 2.

Use Venn diagrams to work Exercises 21 and 22.

21. Suppose $P(E) = 0.26$, $P(F) = 0.41$, and $P(E \cap F) = 0.16$. Find the following.

 (a) $P(E \cup F)$ (b) $P(E' \cap F)$

 (c) $P(E \cap F')$ (d) $P(E' \cup F')$

22. Let $P(Z) = 0.42$, $P(Y) = 0.35$, and $P(Z \cup Y) = 0.59$. Find each probability.

 (a) $P(Z' \cap Y')$ (b) $P(Z' \cup Y')$

 (c) $P(Z' \cup Y)$ (d) $P(Z \cap Y')$

23. Three unusual dice, A, B, and C, are constructed such that die A has the numbers 3, 3, 4, 4, 8, 8; die B has the numbers 1, 1, 5, 5, 9, 9; and die C has the numbers 2, 2, 6, 6, 7, 7.

 (a) If dice A and B are rolled, find the probability that B beats A, that is, the number that appears on die B is greater than the number that appears on die A.

 (b) If dice B and C are rolled, find the probability that C beats B.

 (c) If dice A and C are rolled, find the probability that A beats C.

 (d) Which die is better? Explain.

24. In the "Ask Marilyn" column of *Parade* magazine, a reader wrote about the following game: You and I each roll a die. If your die is higher than mine, you win. Otherwise, I win. The reader thought that the probability that each player wins is 1/2. Is this correct? If not, what is the probability that each player wins? *Source: Parade magazine.*

25. Define what is meant by odds.

26. On page 134 of Roger Staubach's autobiography, *First Down, Lifetime to Go*, Staubach makes the following statement regarding his experience in Vietnam:

 "Odds against a direct hit are very low but when your life is in danger, you don't worry too much about the odds."

 Is this wording consistent with our definition of odds, for and against? How could it have been said so as to be technically correct? *Source: First Down, Lifetime to Go.*

A single fair die is rolled. Find the odds in favor of getting the results in Exercises 27–30.

27. 3   **28.** 4, 5, or 6

29. 2, 3, 4, or 5   **30.** Some number less than 6

31. A marble is drawn from a box containing 3 yellow, 4 white, and 11 blue marbles. Find the odds in favor of drawing the following.

 (a) A yellow marble (b) A blue marble

 (c) A white marble (d) Not drawing a white marble

32. Two dice are rolled. Find the odds of rolling the following. (Refer to Figure 18.)

 (a) A sum of 3 (b) A sum of 7 or 11

 (c) A sum less than 5 (d) Not a sum of 6

33. What is a probability distribution?

34. What conditions must hold for a probability distribution to be acceptable?

An experiment is conducted for which the sample space is $S = \{s_1, s_2, s_3, s_4, s_5\}$. Which of the probability assignments in Exercises 35–40 are possible for this experiment? If an assignment is not possible, tell why.

35.

Outcomes	s_1	s_2	s_3	s_4	s_5
Probabilities	0.09	0.32	0.21	0.25	0.13

36.

Outcomes	s_1	s_2	s_3	s_4	s_5
Probabilities	0.92	0.03	0	0.02	0.03

37.

Outcomes	s_1	s_2	s_3	s_4	s_5
Probabilities	1/3	1/4	1/6	1/8	1/10

38.

Outcomes	s_1	s_2	s_3	s_4	s_5
Probabilities	1/5	1/3	1/4	1/5	1/10

39.

Outcomes	s_1	s_2	s_3	s_4	s_5
Probabilities	0.64	−0.08	0.30	0.12	0.02

40.

Outcomes	s_1	s_2	s_3	s_4	s_5
Probabilities	0.05	0.35	0.5	0.2	−0.3

One way to solve a probability problem is to repeat the experiment many times, keeping track of the results. Then the probability can be approximated using the basic definition of the probability of an event E: $P(E) = n(E)/n(S)$, where E occurs $n(E)$ times out of $n(S)$ trials of an experiment. This is called the Monte Carlo method of finding probabilities. If physically repeating the experiment is too tedious, it may be simulated using a random-number generator, available on most computers and scientific or graphing calculators. To simulate a coin toss or the roll of a die on the TI-84 Plus C, change the setting to display 0 digits, and enter `rand` or `rand*6+.5`, respectively. For a coin toss, interpret 0 as a head and 1 as a tail. In either case, the ENTER key can be pressed repeatedly to perform multiple simulations.

41. Suppose two dice are rolled. Use the Monte Carlo method with at least 50 repetitions to approximate the following probabilities. Compare with the results of Exercise 11.

  (a) P(the sum is 9 or more)

  (b) P(the sum is less than 7)

42. Suppose two dice are rolled. Use the Monte Carlo method with at least 50 repetitions to approximate the following probabilities. Compare with the results of Exercise 12.

  (a) P(the sum is not more than 5)

  (b) P(the sum is not less than 8)

43. Suppose three dice are rolled. Use the Monte Carlo method with at least 100 repetitions to approximate the following probabilities.

  (a) P(the sum is 5 or less)

  (b) P(neither a 1 nor a 6 is rolled)

44. Suppose a coin is tossed 5 times. Use the Monte Carlo method with at least 50 repetitions to approximate the following probabilities.

  (a) P(exactly 4 heads)   (b) P(2 heads and 3 tails)

45. The following description of the classic "Linda problem" appeared in the *New Yorker*:

  "In this experiment, subjects are told, 'Linda is thirty-one years old, single, outspoken, and very bright. She majored in philosophy. As a student, she was deeply concerned with issues of discrimination and social justice and also participated in antinuclear demonstrations.' They are then asked to rank the probability of several possible descriptions of Linda today. Two of them are 'bank teller' and 'bank teller and active in the feminist movement.'"

  Many people rank the second event as more likely. Explain why this violates basic concepts of probability. *Source: New Yorker.*

46. You are given $P(A \cup B) = 0.7$ and $P(A \cup B') = 0.9$. Determine $P(A)$. Choose one of the following. *Source: Society of Actuaries.*

  (a) 0.2   (b) 0.3   (c) 0.4   (d) 0.6   (e) 0.8

APPLICATIONS

Business and Economics

47. Defective Merchandise Suppose that 8% of a certain batch of calculators have a defective case, and that 11% have defective batteries. Also, 3% have both a defective case and defective batteries. A calculator is selected from the batch at random. Find the probability that the calculator has a good case and good batteries.

48. Profit The probability that a company will make a profit this year is 0.74.

  (a) Find the probability that the company will not make a profit this year.

  (b) Find the odds against the company making a profit.

49. Mobile Web Usage A survey asking mobile phone users how long they would wait for a page to load found the following results. *Source: Kissmetrics.*

Time (Seconds)	Percentage
< 1	3%
1–5	16%
6–10	30%
11–15	16%
16–20	15%
> 20	20%

Find the probabilities that a person would wait the following amounts.

  (a) No more than 10 seconds

  (b) At least 6 seconds

  (c) Between 6 and 20 seconds

  (d) Between 1 and 15 seconds

50. Employment The table shows the projected probabilities of a worker employed by different occupational groups in 2018. *Source: U.S. Department of Labor.*

Occupation	Probability
Management and business	0.1047
Professional	0.2182
Service	0.2024
Sales	0.1015
Office and administrative support	0.1560
Farming, fishing, forestry	0.0061
Construction	0.0531
Production	0.0585
Other	0.0995

If a worker in 2018 is selected at random, find the following.

  (a) The probability that the worker is in sales or service

  (b) The probability that the worker is not in construction

  (c) The odds in favor of the worker being in production

51. Labor Force The following table gives the 2018 projected civilian labor force probability distribution by age and gender. *Source: U.S. Department of Labor.*

Age	Male	Female	Total
16–24	0.066	0.061	0.127
25–54	0.343	0.291	0.634
55 and over	0.122	0.117	0.239
Total	0.531	0.469	1.000

Find the probability that a randomly selected worker is the following.

(a) Female and 16 to 24 years old

(b) 16 to 54 years old

(c) Male or 25 to 54 years old

(d) Female or 16 to 24 years old

Life Sciences

52. Body Types A study on body types gave the following results: 45% were short; 25% were short and overweight; and 24% were not short and not overweight. Find the probabilities that a person is the following.

(a) Overweight

(b) Short, but not overweight

(c) Overweight, but not short

53. Color Blindness Color blindness is an inherited characteristic that is more common in males than in females. If M represents male and C represents red-green color blindness, we use the relative frequencies of the incidences of males and red-green color blindness as probabilities to get

$P(C) = 0.039, P(M \cap C) = 0.035, P(M \cup C) = 0.491.$

Find the following probabilities. *Source: Parsons' Diseases of the Eye.*

(a) $P(C')$

(b) $P(M)$

(c) $P(M')$

(d) $P(M' \cap C')$

(e) $P(C \cap M')$

(f) $P(C \cup M')$

54. Genetics Gregor Mendel, an Austrian monk, was the first to use probability in the study of genetics. In an effort to understand the mechanism of character transmittal from one generation to the next in plants, he counted the number of occurrences of various characteristics. Mendel found that the flower color in certain pea plants obeyed this scheme:

Pure red crossed with pure white produces red.

From its parents, the red offspring received genes for both red (R) and white (W), but in this case red is *dominant* and white *recessive*, so the offspring exhibits the color red. However, the offspring still carries both genes, and when two such offspring are crossed, several things can happen in the third generation.

The table below, which is called a *Punnett square*, shows the equally likely outcomes.

		Second Parent	
		R	W
First Parent	R	RR	RW
	W	WR	WW

Use the fact that red is dominant over white to find the following. Assume that there are an equal number of red and white genes in the population.

(a) P(a flower is red)

(b) P(a flower is white)

55. Genetics Mendel found no dominance in snapdragons, with one red gene and one white gene producing pink-flowered offspring. These second-generation pinks, however, still carry one red and one white gene, and when they are crossed, the next generation still yields the Punnett square from Exercise 54. Find each probability.

(a) P(red)   (b) P(pink)   (c) P(white)

(Mendel verified these probability ratios experimentally and did the same for many characteristics other than flower color. His work, published in 1866, was not recognized until 1890.)

56. Genetics In most animals and plants, it is very unusual for the number of main parts of the organism (such as arms, legs, toes, or flower petals) to vary from generation to generation. Some species, however, have *meristic variability,* in which the number of certain body parts varies from generation to generation. One researcher studied the front feet of certain guinea pigs and produced the following probabilities.

$$P(\text{only four toes, all perfect}) = 0.77$$
$$P(\text{one imperfect toe and four good ones}) = 0.13$$
$$P(\text{exactly five good toes}) = 0.10$$

Find the probability of each event. *Source: Genetics.*

(a) No more than four good toes

(b) Five toes, whether perfect or not

57. Doctor Visit The probability that a visit to a primary care physician's (PCP) office results in neither lab work nor referral to a specialist is 35%. Of those coming to a PCP's office, 30% are referred to specialists and 40% require lab work. Determine the probability that a visit to a PCP's office results in both lab work and referral to a specialist. Choose one of the following. (*Hint:* Use the union rule for probability.) *Source: Society of Actuaries.*

(a) 0.05   (b) 0.12   (c) 0.18

(d) 0.25   (e) 0.35

58. Shoulder Injuries Among a large group of patients recovering from shoulder injuries, it is found that 22% visit both a physical therapist and a chiropractor, whereas 12% visit neither of these. The probability that a patient visits a chiropractor exceeds by 0.14 the probability that a patient visits a physical therapist. Determine the probability that a randomly chosen member of this group visits a physical therapist. Choose one of the following. (*Hint:* Use the union rule for probability, and let $x = P$(patient visits a physical therapist).) *Source: Society of Actuaries.*

(a) 0.26   (b) 0.38   (c) 0.40

(d) 0.48   (e) 0.62

59. Health Plan An insurer offers a health plan to the employees of a large company. As part of this plan, the individual employees may choose exactly two of the supplementary coverages A, B, and C, or they may choose no supplementary coverage. The proportions of the company's employees that choose coverages A, B, and C are 1/4, 1/3, and 5/12, respectively. Determine the probability that a randomly chosen employee will choose no supplementary coverage. Choose one of the following. (*Hint:* Draw a Venn diagram with three sets, and let $x = P(A \cap B)$. Use the fact that 4 of the 8 regions in the Venn diagram have a probability of 0.) *Source: Society of Actuaries.*

(a) 0   (b) 47/144   (c) 1/2

(d) 97/144   (e) 7/9

Social Sciences

60. Presidential Candidates In 2002, *The New York Times* columnist William Safire gave the following odds against various prominent Democrats receiving their party's presidential nomination in 2004.

> Al Gore: 2 to 1
> Tom Daschle: 4 to 1
> John Kerry: 4 to 1
> Chris Dodd: 4 to 1
> Joe Lieberman: 5 to 1
> Joe Biden: 5 to 1
> Pat Leahy: 6 to 1
> Russell Feingold: 8 to 1
> John Edwards: 9 to 1
> Dick Gephardt: 15 to 1

John Allen Paulos observed that there is something wrong with those odds. Translate these odds into probabilities of winning the nomination, and then explain why these are not possible. *Sources: The New York Times and ABC News.*

61. Earnings The following data were gathered for 130 adult U.S. workers: 55 were women; 3 women earned more than \$40,000; and 62 men earned \$40,000 or less. Find the probability that an individual is

(a) a woman earning \$40,000 or less;

(b) a man earning more than \$40,000;

(c) a man or is earning more than \$40,000;

(d) a woman or is earning \$40,000 or less.

62. Expenditures for Music A survey of 100 people about their music expenditures gave the following information: 38 bought rock music; 20 were teenagers who bought rock music; and 26 were teenagers. Find the probabilities that a person is

(a) a teenager who buys nonrock music;

(b) someone who buys rock music or is a teenager;

(c) not a teenager;

(d) not a teenager, but a buyer of rock music.

63. Refugees In a refugee camp in southern Mexico, it was found that 90% of the refugees came to escape political oppression, 80% came to escape abject poverty, and 70% came to escape both. What is the probability that a refugee in the camp was not poor nor seeking political asylum?

64. Community Activities At the first meeting of a committee to plan a local Lunar New Year celebration, the persons attending are 3 Chinese men, 4 Chinese women, 3 Vietnamese women, 2 Vietnamese men, 4 Korean women, and 2 Korean men. A chairperson is selected at random. Find the probabilities that the chairperson is the following.

(a) Chinese

(b) Korean or a woman

(c) A man or Vietnamese

(d) Chinese or Vietnamese

(e) Korean and a woman

65. Elections If the odds that a given candidate will win an election are 3 to 2, what is the probability that the candidate will lose?

66. Military There were 205,586 female military personnel in March 2013 in various ranks and military branches, as listed in the table. *Source: Department of Defense.*

	Army (A)	Air Force (B)	Navy (C)	Marines (D)
Officers (O)	16,007	12,663	8893	1403
Enlisted (E)	55,016	48,924	47,195	12,907
Cadets & Midshipmen (M)	738	872	968	0

(a) Convert the numbers in the table to probabilities.

(b) Find the probability that a randomly selected woman is in the Army.

(c) Find the probability that a randomly selected woman is an officer in the Navy or Marine Corps.

(d) $P(A \cup B)$ (e) $P(E \cup (C \cup D))$

67. Perceptions of Threat Research has been carried out to measure the amount of intolerance that citizens of Russia have for left-wing Communists and right-wing Fascists, as indicated in the table below. Note that the numbers are given as percents and each row sums to 100 (except for rounding). *Source: Political Research Quarterly.*

	Russia				
	None at All	Don't Know	Not Very Much	Somewhat	Extremely
Left-Wing Communists	47.8	6.7	31.0	10.5	4.1
Right-Wing Fascists	3.0	3.2	7.1	27.1	59.5

(a) Find the probability that a randomly chosen citizen of Russia would be somewhat or extremely intolerant of right-wing Fascists.

(b) Find the probability that a randomly chosen citizen of Russia would be completely tolerant of left-wing Communists.

(c) Compare your answers to parts (a) and (b) and provide possible reasons for these numbers.

68. Perceptions of Threat Research has been carried out to measure the amount of intolerance that U.S. citizens have for left-wing Communists and right-wing Fascists, as indicated in the table. Note that the numbers are given as percents and each row sums to 100 (except for rounding). *Source: Political Research Quarterly*.

	United States				
	None at All	Don't Know	Not Very Much	Somewhat	Extremely
Left-Wing Communists	13.0	2.7	33.0	34.2	17.1
Right-Wing Fascists	10.1	3.3	20.7	43.1	22.9

(a) Find the probability that a randomly chosen U.S. citizen would have at least some intolerance of right-wing Fascists.

(b) Find the probability that a randomly chosen U.S. citizen would have at least some intolerance of left-wing Communists.

(c) Compare your answers to parts (a) and (b) and provide possible reasons for these numbers.

(d) Compare these answers to the answers to Exercise 67.

General Interest

69. Olympics In recent winter Olympics, each part of the women's figure skating program has 12 judges, but the scores of only 9 of the judges are randomly selected for the final results. As we will see in the next chapter, there are 220 possible ways for the 9 judges whose scores are counted to be selected. *The New York Times* examined those 220 possibilities for the short program in the 2006 Olympics, based on the published scores of the judges, and listed what the results would have been for each, as shown below. *Source: The New York Times*.

(a) The winner of the short program was Sasha Cohen. For a random combination of 9 judges, what is the probability of that outcome?

(b) The second place finisher in the short program was Irina Slutskaya. For a random combination of 9 judges, what is the probability of that outcome?

(c) The third place finisher in the short program was Shizuka Arakawa. For a random combination of 9 judges, what is the probability of that outcome? Do not include outcomes that include a tie.

Outcome	1. Slutskaya 2. Cohen 3. Arakawa	1. Slutskaya 2. Arakawa 3. Cohen	1. Slutskaya 2, 3. Arakawa and Cohen tied	1. Cohen 2. Slutskaya 3. Arakawa	1. Cohen 2. Arakawa 3. Slutskaya
Number of Possible Judging Combinations	92	33	3	67	25

70. Book of Odds The following table gives the probabilities that a particular event will occur. Convert each probability to the odds in favor of the event. *Source: The Book of Odds*.

Event	Probability for the Event
An NFL pass will be intercepted.	0.03
A U.S. president owned a dog during his term in office.	0.65
A woman owns a pair of high heels.	0.61
An adult smokes.	0.21
A flight is canceled.	0.02

71. Book of Odds The following table gives the odds that a particular event will occur. Convert each odd to the probability that the event will occur. *Source: The Book of Odds*.

Event	Odds for the Event
A Powerball entry will win the jackpot.	1 to 195,199,999
An adult will be struck by lightning during a year.	1 to 835,499
An adult will file for personal bankruptcy during a year.	1 to 157.6
A person collects stamps.	1 to 59.32

YOUR TURN ANSWERS

1. 16/52 = 4/13

2. 10/36 = 5/18

3. 33/36 = 11/12

4. 3 to 7 or 3:7

5. 3/20

6. 3/10

7.5 Conditional Probability; Independent Events

APPLY IT **What is the probability that a broker who uses research picks stocks that go up?**

The manager for a brokerage firm has noticed that some of the firm's stockbrokers have selected stocks based on the firm's research, while other brokers tend to follow their own instincts. To see whether the research department performs better than the brokers' instincts, the manager surveyed 100 brokers, with results as shown in the following table.

	Results of Stockbroker Survey		
	Picked Stocks That Went Up (A)	Didn't Pick Stocks That Went Up (A')	Totals
Used Research (B)	30	15	45
Didn't Use Research (B')	30	25	55
Totals	60	40	100

Letting A represent the event "picked stocks that went up," and letting B represent the event "used research," we can find the following probabilities.

$$P(A) = \frac{60}{100} = 0.6 \qquad P(A') = \frac{40}{100} = 0.4$$

$$P(B) = \frac{45}{100} = 0.45 \qquad P(B') = \frac{55}{100} = 0.55$$

APPLY IT To answer the question asked at the beginning of this section, suppose we want to find the probability that a broker using research will pick stocks that go up. From the table, of the 45 brokers who use research, 30 picked stocks that went up, with

$$P(\text{broker who uses research picks stocks that go up}) = \frac{30}{45} \approx 0.6667.$$

This is a different number than the probability that a broker picks stocks that go up, 0.6, since we have additional information (the broker uses research) that has *reduced the sample space.* In other words, we found the probability that a broker picks stocks that go up, A, given the additional information that the broker uses research, B. This is called the *conditional probability* of event A, given that event B has occurred. It is written $P(A|B)$ and read as "the probability of A given B." In this example,

$$P(A|B) = \frac{30}{45}.$$

To generalize this result, assume that E and F are two events for a particular experiment and that all events in the sample space S are equally likely. We want to find $P(E|F)$, the probability that E occurs given F has occurred. Since we assume that F has occurred, reduce the sample space to F: Look only at the elements inside F. See Figure 20. Of those $n(F)$ elements, there are $n(E \cap F)$ elements where E also occurs. This makes

$$P(E|F) = \frac{n(E \cap F)}{n(F)}.$$

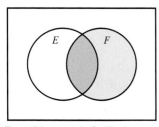

Event F has a total of $n(F)$ elements.

FIGURE 20

This equation can also be written as the quotient of two probabilities. Divide numerator and denominator by $n(S)$ to get

$$P(E|F) = \frac{n(E \cap F)/n(S)}{n(F)/n(S)} = \frac{P(E \cap F)}{P(F)}.$$

This last result motivates the definition of conditional probability.

Conditional Probability
The **conditional probability** of event E given event F, written $P(E\,|\,F)$, is

$$P(E\,|\,F) = \frac{P(E \cap F)}{P(F)}, \quad \text{where } P(F) \neq 0.$$

Although the definition of conditional probability was motivated by an example with equally likely outcomes, it is valid in all cases. However, for *equally likely outcomes*, conditional probability can be found by directly applying the definition, or by first reducing the sample space to event F, and then finding the number of outcomes in F that are also in event E. Thus,

$$P(E\,|\,F) = \frac{n(E \cap F)}{n(F)}.$$

In the preceding example, the conditional probability could have also been found using the definition of conditional probability:

$$P(A\,|\,B) = \frac{P(A \cap B)}{P(B)} = \frac{30/100}{45/100} = \frac{30}{45} = \frac{2}{3}.$$

EXAMPLE 1 Stocks

Use the information given in the chart at the beginning of this section to find the following probabilities.

(a) $P(B\,|\,A)$

SOLUTION This represents the probability that the broker used research, given that the broker picked stocks that went up. Reduce the sample space to A. Then find $n(A \cap B)$ and $n(A)$.

$$P(B\,|\,A) = \frac{P(B \cap A)}{P(A)} = \frac{n(A \cap B)}{n(A)} = \frac{30}{60} = \frac{1}{2}$$

If a broker picked stocks that went up, then the probability is $1/2$ that the broker used research.

(b) $P(A'\,|\,B)$

SOLUTION In words, this is the probability that a broker picks stocks that do not go up, even though he used research.

$$P(A'\,|\,B) = \frac{n(A' \cap B)}{n(B)} = \frac{15}{45} = \frac{1}{3}$$

(c) $P(B'\,|\,A')$

SOLUTION Here, we want the probability that a broker who picked stocks that did not go up did not use research.

$$P(B'\,|\,A') = \frac{n(B' \cap A')}{n(A')} = \frac{25}{40} = \frac{5}{8} \qquad \text{TRY YOUR TURN 1} \ ▪$$

Venn diagrams are useful for illustrating problems in conditional probability. A Venn diagram for Example 1, in which the probabilities are used to indicate the number in the set defined by each region, is shown in Figure 21. In the diagram, $P(B\,|\,A)$ is found by reducing the sample space to just set A. Then $P(B\,|\,A)$ is the ratio of the number in that part of set B that is also in A to the number in set A, or $0.3/0.6 = 0.5$.

YOUR TURN 1 In Example 1, find $P(A\,|\,B')$.

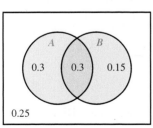

$P(A) = 0.3 + 0.3 = 0.6$

FIGURE 21

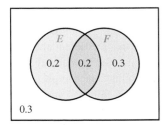

FIGURE 22

YOUR TURN 2 Given $P(E) = 0.56$, $P(F) = 0.64$, and $P(E \cup F) = 0.80$, find $P(E \mid F)$.

EXAMPLE 2 Conditional Probabilities

Given $P(E) = 0.4$, $P(F) = 0.5$, and $P(E \cup F) = 0.7$, find $P(E|F)$.

SOLUTION Find $P(E \cap F)$ first. By the union rule,

$$P(E \cup F) = P(E) + P(F) - P(E \cap F)$$
$$0.7 = 0.4 + 0.5 - P(E \cap F)$$
$$P(E \cap F) = 0.2.$$

$P(E|F)$ is the ratio of the probability of that part of E that is in F to the probability of F, or

$$P(E|F) = \frac{P(E \cap F)}{P(F)} = \frac{0.2}{0.5} = \frac{2}{5}.$$ **TRY YOUR TURN 2**

The Venn diagram in Figure 22 illustrates Example 2.

EXAMPLE 3 Tossing Coins

Two fair coins were tossed, and it is known that at least one was a head. Find the probability that both were heads.

SOLUTION At first glance, the answer may appear to be 1/2, but this is not the case. The sample space has four equally likely outcomes, $S = \{hh, ht, th, tt\}$. Because of the condition that at least one coin was a head, the sample space is reduced to $\{hh, ht, th\}$. Since only one outcome in this reduced sample space is 2 heads,

$$P(2 \text{ heads} \mid \text{at least 1 head}) = \frac{1}{3}.$$

Alternatively, we could use the conditional probability definition. Define two events:

$$E_1 = \text{at least 1 head} = \{hh, ht, th\}$$

and

$$E_2 = 2 \text{ heads} = \{hh\}.$$

YOUR TURN 3 In Example 3, find the probability of exactly one head, given that there is at least one tail.

Since there are four equally likely outcomes, $P(E_1) = 3/4$ and $P(E_1 \cap E_2) = 1/4$. Therefore,

$$P(E_2|E_1) = \frac{P(E_2 \cap E_1)}{P(E_1)} = \frac{1/4}{3/4} = \frac{1}{3}.$$ **TRY YOUR TURN 3**

EXAMPLE 4 Playing Cards

Two cards are drawn from a standard deck, one after another without replacement. Find the probability that the second card is red, given that the first card is red.

SOLUTION According to the conditional probability formula,

$$P(\text{second card is red} \mid \text{first card is red})$$
$$= \frac{P(\text{second card is red and the first card is red})}{P(\text{first card is red})}.$$

We will soon see how to compute probabilities such as the one in the numerator. But there is a much simpler way to calculate this conditional probability. We only need to observe that with one red card gone, there are 51 cards left, 25 of which are red, so

$$P(\text{second card is red} \mid \text{first card is red}) = \frac{25}{51}.$$

It is important not to confuse $P(A|B)$ with $P(B|A)$. For example, in a criminal trial, a prosecutor may point out to the jury that the probability of the defendant's DNA profile matching that of a sample taken at the scene of the crime, given that the defendant is innocent, $P(D|I)$, is very small. What the jury must decide, however, is the probability that the defendant is innocent, given that the defendant's DNA profile matches the sample, $P(I|D)$. Confusing the two is an error sometimes called "the prosecutor's fallacy," and the 1990 conviction of a rape suspect in England was overturned by a panel of judges, who ordered a retrial, because the fallacy made the original trial unfair. *Source: New Scientist.*

In the next section, we will see how to compute $P(A|B)$ when we know $P(B|A)$.

Product Rule

If $P(E) \neq 0$ and $P(F) \neq 0$, then the definition of conditional probability shows that

$$P(E|F) = \frac{P(E \cap F)}{P(F)} \quad \text{and} \quad P(F|E) = \frac{P(F \cap E)}{P(E)}.$$

Using the fact that $P(E \cap F) = P(F \cap E)$, and solving each of these equations for $P(E \cap F)$, we obtain the following rule.

Product Rule of Probability

If E and F are events, then $P(E \cap F)$ may be found by either of these formulas.

$$P(E \cap F) = P(F) \cdot P(E|F) \quad \text{or} \quad P(E \cap F) = P(E) \cdot P(F|E)$$

The product rule gives a method for finding the probability that events E and F both occur, as illustrated by the next few examples.

EXAMPLE 5   Business Majors

In a class with 2/5 women and 3/5 men, 25% of the women are business majors. Find the probability that a student chosen from the class at random is a female business major.

SOLUTION   Let B and W represent the events "business major" and "woman," respectively. We want to find $P(B \cap W)$. By the product rule,

$$P(B \cap W) = P(W) \cdot P(B|W).$$

Using the given information, $P(W) = 2/5 = 0.4$ and $P(B|W) = 0.25$. Thus,

$$P(B \cap W) = 0.4(0.25) = 0.10. \quad \text{TRY YOUR TURN 4} \blacksquare$$

> **YOUR TURN 4** At a local college, 4/5 of the students live on campus. Of those who live on campus, 25% have cars on campus. Find the probability that a student lives on campus and has a car.

The next examples show how a tree diagram is used with the product rule to find the probability of a sequence of events.

EXAMPLE 6   Advertising

A company needs to hire a new director of advertising. It has decided to try to hire either person A or B, who are assistant advertising directors for its major competitor. To decide between A and B, the company does research on the campaigns managed by either A or B (no campaign is managed by both) and finds that A is in charge of twice as many advertising campaigns as B. Also, A's campaigns have satisfactory results 3 out of 4 times, while B's campaigns have satisfactory results only 2 out of 5 times. Suppose one of the competitor's advertising campaigns (managed by A or B) is selected randomly.

We can represent this situation using a tree diagram as follows. Let A denote the event "Person A manages the job" and B the event "person B manages the job." Notice that A and

B are complementary events. Since A does twice as many jobs as B, we have $P(A) = 2/3$ and $P(B) = 1/3$, as noted on the first-stage branches of the tree in Figure 23.

Let S be the event "satisfactory results" and U the event "unsatisfactory results." When A manages the job, the probability of satisfactory results is 3/4 and of unsatisfactory results 1/4 as noted on the second-stage branches. Similarly, the probabilities when B manages the job are noted on the remaining second-stage branches. The composite branches labeled 1 to 4 represent the four mutually exclusive possibilities for the managing and outcome of the selected campaign.

(a) Find the probability that A is in charge of the selected campaign and that it produces satisfactory results.

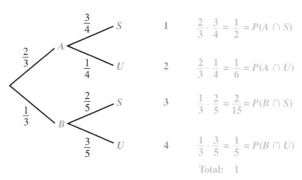

FIGURE 23

SOLUTION We are asked to find $P(A \cap S)$. We know that when A does the job, the probability of success is 3/4, that is, $P(S|A) = 3/4$. Hence, by the product rule,

$$P(A \cap S) = P(A) \cdot P(S|A) = \frac{2}{3} \cdot \frac{3}{4} = \frac{1}{2}.$$

The event $A \cap S$ is represented by branch 1 of the tree, and, as we have just seen, its probability is the product of the probabilities of the pieces that make up that branch.

(b) Find the probability that B runs the campaign and that it produces satisfactory results.

SOLUTION We must find $P(B \cap S)$. The event is represented by branch 3 of the tree, and, as before, its probability is the product of the probabilities of the pieces of that branch:

$$P(B \cap S) = P(B) \cdot P(S|B) = \frac{1}{3} \cdot \frac{2}{5} = \frac{2}{15}.$$

(c) What is the probability that the selected campaign is satisfactory?

SOLUTION The event S is the union of the mutually exclusive events $A \cap S$ and $B \cap S$, which are represented by branches 1 and 3 of the diagram. By the union rule,

$$P(S) = P(A \cap S) + P(B \cap S) = \frac{1}{2} + \frac{2}{15} = \frac{19}{30}.$$

Thus, the probability of an event that appears on several branches is the sum of the probabilities of each of these branches.

(d) What is the probability that the selected campaign is unsatisfactory?

SOLUTION $P(U)$ can be read from branches 2 and 4 of the tree.

$$P(U) = \frac{1}{6} + \frac{1}{5} = \frac{11}{30}$$

Alternatively, since U is the complement of S,

$$P(U) = 1 - P(S) = 1 - \frac{19}{30} = \frac{11}{30}. \quad \text{TRY YOUR TURN 5} \blacksquare$$

YOUR TURN 5 In Example 6, what is the probability that A is in charge of the selected campaign and that it produces unsatisfactory results?

EXAMPLE 7 Environmental Inspections

The Environmental Protection Agency is considering inspecting 6 plants for environmental compliance: 3 in Chicago, 2 in Los Angeles, and 1 in New York. Due to a lack of inspectors, they decide to inspect two plants selected at random, one this month and one next month, with each plant equally likely to be selected, but no plant selected twice. What is the probability that 1 Chicago plant and 1 Los Angeles plant are selected?

SOLUTION A tree diagram showing the various possible outcomes is given in Figure 24. In this diagram, the events of inspecting a plant in Chicago, Los Angeles, and New York are represented by C, LA, and NY, respectively. For the first inspection, $P(\text{C first}) = 3/6 = 1/2$ because 3 of the 6 plants are in Chicago, and all plants are equally likely to be selected. Likewise, $P(\text{LA first}) = 1/3$ and $P(\text{NY first}) = 1/6$.

For the second inspection, we first note that one plant has been inspected and, therefore, removed from the list, leaving 5 plants. For example, $P(\text{LA second}|\text{C first}) = 2/5$, since 2 of the 5 remaining plants are in Los Angeles. The remaining second inspection probabilities are calculated in the same manner.

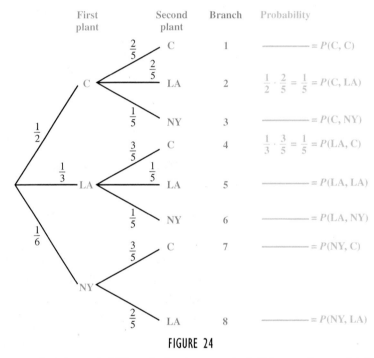

FIGURE 24

We want to find the probability of selecting exactly 1 Chicago plant and 1 Los Angeles plant. This event can occur in two ways: inspecting Chicago this month and Los Angeles next month (branch 2 of the tree diagram), or inspecting Los Angeles this month and Chicago next month (branch 4). For branch 2,

$$P(\text{C first}) \cdot P(\text{LA second}|\text{C first}) = \frac{1}{2} \cdot \frac{2}{5} = \frac{1}{5}.$$

For branch 4, where Los Angeles is inspected first,

$$P(\text{LA first}) \cdot P(\text{C second}|\text{LA first}) = \frac{1}{3} \cdot \frac{3}{5} = \frac{1}{5}.$$

Since the two events are mutually exclusive, the final probability is the sum of these two probabilities.

$$P(1\,\text{C}, 1\,\text{LA}) = P(\text{C first}) \cdot P(\text{LA second}|\text{C first})$$
$$+ P(\text{LA first}) \cdot P(\text{C second}|\text{LA first})$$
$$= \frac{2}{5}$$

YOUR TURN 6 In Example 7, what is the probability that 1 New York plant and 1 Chicago plant are selected?

TRY YOUR TURN 6

The product rule is often used with *stochastic processes*, which are mathematical models that evolve over time in a probabilistic manner. For example, selecting factories at random for inspection is such a process, in which the probabilities change with each successive selection.

EXAMPLE 8 Playing Cards

Two cards are drawn from a standard deck, one after another without replacement.

(a) Find the probability that the first card is a heart and the second card is red.

SOLUTION Start with the tree diagram in Figure 25. On the first draw, since there are 13 hearts among the 52 cards, the probability of drawing a heart is $13/52 = 1/4$. On the second draw, since a (red) heart has been drawn already, there are 25 red cards in the remaining 51 cards. Thus, the probability of drawing a red card on the second draw, given that the first is a heart, is $25/51$. By the product rule of probability,

$$P(\text{heart first and red second})$$
$$= P(\text{heart first}) \cdot P(\text{red second} \mid \text{heart first})$$
$$= \frac{1}{4} \cdot \frac{25}{51} = \frac{25}{204} \approx 0.123.$$

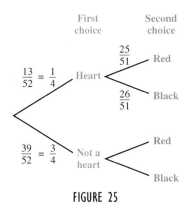

FIGURE 25

(b) Find the probability that the second card is red.

SOLUTION To solve this, we need to fill out the bottom branch of the tree diagram in Figure 25. Unfortunately, if the first card is not a heart, it is not clear how to find the probability that the second card is red, because it depends upon whether the first card is red or black. One way to solve this problem would be to divide the bottom branch into two separate branches: diamond and black card (club or spade).

There is a simpler way, however, since we don't care whether or not the first card is a heart, as we did in part (a). Instead, we'll consider whether the first card is red or black and then do the same for the second card. The result, with the corresponding probabilities, is in Figure 26. The probability that the second card is red is found by multiplying the probabilities along the two branches and adding.

$$P(\text{red second}) = \frac{1}{2} \cdot \frac{25}{51} + \frac{1}{2} \cdot \frac{26}{51}$$
$$= \frac{1}{2}$$

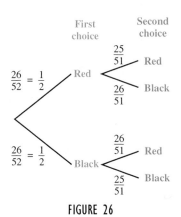

FIGURE 26

The probability is 1/2, exactly the same as the probability that any card is red. If we know nothing about the first card, there is no reason for the probability of the second card to be anything other than 1/2.

Independent Events

Suppose, in Example 8(a), that we draw the two cards *with* replacement rather than without replacement (that is, we put the first card back before drawing the second card). If the first card is a heart, then the probability of drawing a red card on the second draw is 26/52, rather than 25/51, because there are still 52 cards in the deck, 26 of them red. In this case, $P(\text{red second} \mid \text{heart first})$ is the same as $P(\text{red second})$. The value of the second card is not affected by the value of the first card. We say that the event that the second card is red is *independent* of the event that the first card is a heart, since the knowledge of the first card does not influence what happens to the second card. On the other hand, when we draw without replacement, the events that the first card is a heart and that the second card is red are *dependent* events. The fact that the first card is a heart means there is one less red card in the deck, influencing the probability that the second card is red.

As another example, consider tossing a fair coin twice. If the first toss shows heads, the probability that the next toss is heads is still 1/2. Coin tosses are independent events, since the outcome of one toss does not influence the outcome of the next toss. Similarly, rolls of a fair die are independent events.

On the other hand, the events "the milk is old" and "the milk is sour" are dependent events; if the milk is old, there is an increased chance that it is sour. Also, in the example at the beginning of this section, the events A (broker picked stocks that went up) and B (broker used research) are dependent events, because information about the use of research affected the probability of picking stocks that go up. That is, $P(A|B)$ is different from $P(A)$.

If events E and F are independent, then the knowledge that E has occurred gives no (probability) information about the occurrence or nonoccurrence of event F. That is, $P(F)$ is exactly the same as $P(F|E)$, or

$$P(F|E) = P(F).$$

This, in fact, is the formal definition of independent events.

Independent Events
Events E and F are **independent events** if

$$P(F|E) = P(F) \quad \text{or} \quad P(E|F) = P(E).$$

If the events are not independent, they are **dependent events**.

Notice that the mathematical definition of independence does not always correspond to the intuitive definition of independence. For example, you may think that whether you like a movie and your friend likes a movie are independent, since it is possible that you like the movie and your friend doesn't, or vice versa. In fact, if your taste in movies is similar to your friend's, the fact that you like the movie might increase the probability that your friend likes the movie. If your tastes are very different, it is possible that your liking the movie makes it less likely that your friend likes it. In either of these cases, the events are dependent. Only if your liking the movie tells nothing about whether your friend will like it are the events independent.

When E and F are independent events, then $P(F|E) = P(F)$ and the product rule becomes

$$P(E \cap F) = P(E) \cdot P(F|E) = P(E) \cdot P(F).$$

Conversely, if this equation holds, then it follows that $P(F) = P(F|E)$. Consequently, we have this useful fact:

Product Rule for Independent Events
Events E and F are independent events if and only if

$$P(E \cap F) = P(E) \cdot P(F).$$

EXAMPLE 9 Calculator

A calculator requires a keystroke assembly and a logic circuit. Assume that 99% of the keystroke assemblies are satisfactory and 97% of the logic circuits are satisfactory. Find the probability that a finished calculator will be satisfactory.

SOLUTION If the failure of a keystroke assembly and the failure of a logic circuit are independent events, then

$P(\text{satisfactory calculator})$

$\quad = P(\text{satisfactory keystroke assembly}) \cdot P(\text{satisfactory logic circuit})$

$\quad = (0.99)(0.97) \approx 0.96.$

(The probability of a defective calculator is $1 - 0.96 = 0.04$.)   TRY YOUR TURN 7

YOUR TURN 7 The probability that you roll a five on a single die is 1/6. Find the probability you roll two five's in a row.

CAUTION | It is common for students to confuse the ideas of *mutually exclusive* events and *independent* events. Events E and F are mutually exclusive if $E \cap F = \varnothing$. For example, if a family has exactly one child, the only possible outcomes are $B = \{\text{boy}\}$ and $G = \{\text{girl}\}$. These two events are mutually exclusive. The events are *not* independent, however, since $P(G|B) = 0$ (if a family with only one child has a boy, the probability it has a girl is then 0). Since $P(G|B) \neq P(G)$, the events are not independent.

Of all the families with exactly two children, the events $G_1 = \{\text{first child is a girl}\}$ and $G_2 = \{\text{second child is a girl}\}$ are independent, since $P(G_2|G_1)$ equals $P(G_2)$. However, G_1 and G_2 are not mutually exclusive, since $G_1 \cap G_2 = \{\text{both children are girls}\} \neq \varnothing$.

To show that two events E and F are independent, show that $P(F|E) = P(F)$ or that $P(E|F) = P(E)$ or that $P(E \cap F) = P(E) \cdot P(F)$. Another way is to observe that knowledge of one outcome does not influence the probability of the other outcome, as we did for coin tosses.

NOTE   In some cases, it may not be apparent from the physical description of the problem whether two events are independent or not. For example, it is not obvious whether the event that a baseball player gets a hit tomorrow is independent of the event that he got a hit today. In such cases, it is necessary to calculate whether $P(F|E) = P(F)$ or, equivalently, whether $P(E \cap F) = P(E) \cdot P(F)$.

EXAMPLE 10   Snow in Manhattan

On a typical January day in Manhattan the probability of snow is 0.10, the probability of a traffic jam is 0.80, and the probability of snow or a traffic jam (or both) is 0.82. Are the event "it snows" and the event "a traffic jam occurs" independent?

YOUR TURN 8 The probability that you do your math homework is 0.8, the probability that you do your history assignment is 0.7, and the probability of you doing your math homework or your history assignment is 0.9. Are the events "do your math homework" and "do your history assignment" independent?

SOLUTION   Let S represent the event "it snows" and T represent the event "a traffic jam occurs." We must determine whether

$$P(T|S) = P(T) \qquad \text{or} \qquad P(S|T) = P(S).$$

We know $P(S) = 0.10$, $P(T) = 0.8$, and $P(S \cup T) = 0.82$. We can use the union rule (or a Venn diagram) to find $P(S \cap T) = 0.08$, $P(T|S) = 0.8$, and $P(S|T) = 0.1$. Since

$$P(T|S) = P(T) = 0.8 \qquad \text{and} \qquad P(S|T) = P(S) = 0.1,$$

the events "it snows" and "a traffic jam occurs" are independent.   TRY YOUR TURN 8

Although we showed $P(T|S) = P(T)$ and $P(S|T) = P(S)$ in Example 10, only one of these results is needed to establish independence. It is also important to note that independence of events does not necessarily follow intuition; it is established from the mathematical definition of independence.

── 7.5 WARM-UP EXERCISES ──────────────────────

Two dice are rolled. Find the probabilities of the following.

W1. The first die is 5 or the sum is 9.   *(Sec. 7.4)*

W2. The second die is 6 or the sum is 11.   *(Sec. 7.4)*

7.5 EXERCISES

If a single fair die is rolled, find the probabilities of the following results.

1. A 2, given that the number rolled was odd

2. A 4, given that the number rolled was even

3. An even number, given that the number rolled was 6

4. An odd number, given that the number rolled was 6

If two fair dice are rolled, find the probabilities of the following results.

5. A sum of 8, given that the sum is greater than 7

6. A sum of 6, given that the roll was a "double" (two identical numbers)

7. A double, given that the sum was 9

8. A double, given that the sum was 8

If two cards are drawn without replacement from an ordinary deck, find the probabilities of the following results.

9. The second is a heart, given that the first is a heart.

10. The second is black, given that the first is a spade.

11. The second is a face card, given that the first is a jack.

12. The second is an ace, given that the first is not an ace.

13. A jack and a 10 are drawn.

14. An ace and a 4 are drawn.

15. Two black cards are drawn.

16. Two hearts are drawn.

17. In your own words, explain how to find the conditional probability $P(E|F)$.

18. In your own words, define independent events.

Decide whether the following pairs of events are dependent or independent.

19. A red die and a green die are rolled. A is the event that the red die comes up even, and B is the event that the green die comes up even.

20. C is the event that it rains more than 10 days in Chicago next June, and D is the event that it rains more than 15 days.

21. E is the event that a resident of Texas lives in Dallas, and F is the event that a resident of Texas lives in either Dallas or Houston.

22. A coin is flipped. G is the event that today is Tuesday, and H is the event that the coin comes up heads.

In the previous section, we described an experiment in which the numbers 1, 2, 3, 4, and 5 are written on slips of paper, and 2 slips are drawn at random one at a time without replacement. Find each probability in Exercises 23 and 24.

23. The probability that the first number is 3, given the following.

    (a) The sum is 7.   (b) The sum is 8.

24. The probability that the sum is 8, given the following.

    (a) The first number is 5.   (b) The first number is 4.

25. Suppose two dice are rolled. Let A be the event that the sum of the two dice is 7. Find an event B related to numbers on the dice such that A and B are

    (a) independent;   (b) dependent.

26. Your friend asks you to explain how the product rule for independent events differs from the product rule for dependent events. How would you respond?

27. Another friend asks you to explain how to tell whether two events are dependent or independent. How would you reply? (Use your own words.)

28. A student reasons that the probability in Example 3 of both coins being heads is just the probability that the other coin is a head, that is, 1/2. Explain why this reasoning is wrong.

29. Let A and B be independent events with $P(A) = \dfrac{1}{4}$ and $P(B) = \dfrac{1}{5}$. Find $P(A \cap B)$ and $P(A \cup B)$.

30. If A and B are events such that $P(A) = 0.5$ and $P(A \cup B) = 0.7$, find $P(B)$ when

    (a) A and B are mutually exclusive;

    (b) A and B are independent.

31. The following problem, submitted by Daniel Hahn of Blairstown, Iowa, appeared in the "Ask Marilyn" column of *Parade* magazine.

    "You discover two booths at a carnival. Each is tended by an honest man with a pair of covered coin shakers. In each shaker is a single coin, and you are allowed to bet upon the chance that both coins in that booth's shakers are heads after the man in the booth shakes them, does an inspection, and can tell you that at least one of the shakers contains a head. The difference is that the man in the first booth always looks inside both of his shakers, whereas the man in the second booth looks inside only one of the shakers. Where will you stand the best chance?" *Source: Parade magazine.*

32. The following question was posed in *Chance News* by Craig Fox and Yoval Rotenstrich. You are playing a game in which a fair coin is flipped and a fair die is rolled. You win a prize if both the coin comes up heads and a 6 is rolled on the die. Now suppose the coin is tossed and the die is rolled, but you are not allowed to see either result. You are told, however, that either the head or the 6 occurred. You are then offered the chance to cancel the game and play a new game in which a die is rolled (there is no coin), and you win a prize if a 6 is rolled. *Source: Chance News.*

    (a) Is it to your advantage to switch to the new game, or to stick with the original game? Answer this question by calculating your probability of winning in each case.

    (b) Many people erroneously think that it's better to stick with the original game. Discuss why this answer might seem intuitive, but why it is wrong.

33. Suppose a male defendant in a court trial has a mustache, beard, tattoo, and an earring. Suppose, also, that an eyewitness has identified the perpetrator as someone with these characteristics. If the respective probabilities for the male population in this region are 0.35, 0.30, 0.10, and 0.05, is it fair to multiply these probabilities together to conclude that the probability that a person having these characteristics is 0.000525, or 21 in 40,000, and thus decide that the defendant must be guilty?

34. In a two-child family, if we assume that the probabilities of a male child and a female child are each 0.5, are the events *all children are the same sex* and *at most one male* independent? Are they independent for a three-child family?

35. Laura Johnson, a game show contestant, could win one of two prizes: a shiny new Porsche or a shiny new penny. Laura is given two boxes of marbles. The first box has 50 pink marbles in it and the second box has 50 blue marbles in it. The game show host will pick someone from the audience to be blindfolded and then draw a marble from one of the two boxes. If a pink marble is drawn, she wins the Porsche. Otherwise, Laura wins the penny. Can Laura increase her chances of winning by redistributing some of the marbles from one box to the other? Explain. *Source: Car Talk.*

APPLICATIONS

Business and Economics

Banking The Midtown Bank has found that most customers at the tellers' windows either cash a check or make a deposit. The following table indicates the transactions for one teller for one day.

	Cash Check	No Check	Totals
Make Deposit	60	20	80
No Deposit	30	10	40
Totals	90	30	120

Letting C represent "cashing a check" and D represent "making a deposit," express each probability in words and find its value.

36. $P(C|D)$ **37.** $P(D'|C)$ **38.** $P(C'|D')$

39. $P(C'|D)$ **40.** $P[(C \cap D)']$

41. Airline Delays During March 2014, the major U.S. airline with the fewest delays was Delta, for which 84.32% of their flights arrived on time. Assume that the event that a given flight arrives on time is independent of the event that another flight arrives on time. *Source: U.S. Department of Transportation.*

(a) Jessica Cipperly plans to take four separate flights for her publisher next month on Delta. Assuming that the airline has the same on-time performance as in March 2014, what is the probability that all four flights arrive on time?

(b) Discuss how realistic it is to assume that the on-time arrivals of the different flights are independent.

42. Backup Computers Corporations where a computer is essential to day-to-day operations, such as banks, often have a second backup computer in case the main computer fails. Suppose there is a 0.003 chance that the main computer will fail in a given time period and a 0.005 chance that the backup computer will fail while the main computer is being repaired. Assume these failures represent independent events, and find the fraction of the time that the corporation can assume it will have computer service. How realistic is our assumption of independence?

43. ATM Transactions Among users of automated teller machines (ATMs), 92% use ATMs to withdraw cash, and 32% use them to check their account balance. Suppose that 96% use ATMs to either withdraw cash or check their account balance (or both). Given a woman who uses an ATM to check her account balance, what is the probability that she also uses an ATM to get cash? *Source: Chicago Tribune.*

Quality Control A bicycle factory runs two assembly lines, A and B. If 95% of line A's products pass inspection, while only 85% of line B's products pass inspection, and 60% of the factory's bikes come off assembly line A (the rest off B), find the probabilities that one of the factory's bikes did not pass inspection and came off the following.

44. Assembly line A   **45.** Assembly line B

46. Find the probability that one of the factory's bikes did not pass inspection.

Life Sciences

47. Genetics Both of a certain pea plant's parents had a gene for red and a gene for white flowers. (See Exercise 54 in Section 7.4.) If the offspring has red flowers, find the probability that it combined a gene for red and a gene for white (rather than 2 for red).

48. Medical Experiment A medical experiment showed that the probability that a new medicine is effective is 0.75, the probability that a patient will have a certain side effect is 0.4, and the probability that both events occur is 0.3. Decide whether these events are dependent or independent.

Genetics Assuming that boy and girl babies are equally likely, fill in the remaining probabilities on the tree diagram below and use that information to find the probability that a family with three children has all girls, given the following.

49. The first is a girl.   **50.** The third is a girl.

51. The second is a girl.   **52.** At least 2 are girls.

53. At least 1 is a girl.

Color Blindness The following table shows frequencies for red-green color blindness, where M represents "person is male" and C represents "person is color-blind." Use this table to find the following probabilities. (See Exercise 53, Section 7.4.)

	M	M'	Totals
C	0.035	0.004	0.039
C'	0.452	0.509	0.961
Totals	0.487	0.513	1.000

54. $P(M)$

55. $P(C)$

56. $P(M \cap C)$

57. $P(M \cup C)$

58. $P(M|C)$

59. $P(C|M)$

60. $P(M'|C)$

61. Are the events C and M, described above, dependent? What does this mean?

62. **Color Blindness** A scientist wishes to determine whether there is a relationship between color blindness (C) and deafness (D).

(a) Suppose the scientist found the probabilities listed in the table. What should the findings be? (See Exercises 54–61.)

(b) Explain what your answer tells us about color blindness and deafness.

	D	D'	Totals
C	0.0008	0.0392	0.0400
C'	0.0192	0.9408	0.9600
Totals	0.0200	0.9800	1.0000

63. **Overweight** According to a recent report, 68.3% of men and 64.1% of women in the United States were overweight. Given that 49.3% of Americans are men and 50.7% are women, find the probability that a randomly selected American fits the following description. *Source: JAMA.*

(a) An overweight man   (b) Overweight

(c) Are the events "male" and "overweight" independent?

Hockey The table below lists the number of head and neck injuries for 319 ice hockey players' exposures wearing either a full shield or half shield in the Canadian Inter-University Athletics Union. For a randomly selected injury, find each probability. *Source: JAMA.*

64. $P(A)$

65. $P(C|F)$

66. $P(A|H)$

67. $P(B'|H')$

	Half Shield (H)	Full Shield (F)	Totals
Head and Face Injuries (A)	95	34	129
Concussions (B)	41	38	79
Neck Injuries (C)	9	7	16
Other Injuries (D)	202	150	352
Totals	347	229	576

68. Are the events A and H independent events?*

69. **Blood Pressure** A doctor is studying the relationship between blood pressure and heartbeat abnormalities in her patients. She tests a random sample of her patients and notes their blood pressures (high, low, or normal) and their heartbeats (regular or irregular). She finds that:

(i) 14% have high blood pressure.

(ii) 22% have low blood pressure.

(iii) 15% have an irregular heartbeat.

(iv) Of those with an irregular heartbeat, one-third have high blood pressure.

(v) Of those with normal blood pressure, one-eighth have an irregular heartbeat.

What portion of the patients selected have a regular heartbeat and low blood pressure? Choose one of the following. (*Hint:* Make a table similar to the one for Exercises 54–61.) *Source: Society of Actuaries.*

(a) 2%   (b) 5%   (c) 8%   (d) 9%   (e) 20%

70. **Breast Cancer** To explain why the chance of a woman getting breast cancer in the next year goes up each year, while the chance of a woman getting breast cancer in her lifetime goes down, Ruma Falk made the following analogy. Suppose you are looking for a letter that you may have lost. You have 8 drawers in your desk. There is a probability of 0.1 that the letter is in any one of the 8 drawers and a probability of 0.2 that the letter is not in any of the drawers. *Source: Chance News.*

(a) What is the probability that the letter is in drawer 1?

(b) Given that the letter is not in drawer 1, what is the probability that the letter is in drawer 2?

(c) Given that the letter is not in drawer 1 or 2, what is the probability that the letter is in drawer 3?

(d) Given that the letter is not in drawers 1–7, what is the probability that the letter is in drawer 8?

(e) Based on your answers to parts (a)–(d), what is happening to the probability that the letter is in the next drawer?

(f) What is the probability that the letter is in some drawer?

(g) Given that the letter is not in drawer 1, what is the probability that the letter is in some drawer?

(h) Given that the letter is not in drawer 1 or 2, what is the probability that the letter is in some drawer?

(i) Given that the letter is not in drawers 1–7, what is the probability that the letter is in some drawer?

(j) Based on your answers to parts (f)–(i), what is happening to the probability that the letter is in some drawer?

71. **Twins** A 1920 study of 17,798 pairs of twins found that 5844 consisted of two males, 5612 consisted of two females, and 6342 consisted of a male and a female. Of course, all of the

*We are assuming here and in other exercises that the events consist entirely of the numbers given in the table. If the numbers are interpreted as a sample of all people fitting the description of the events, then testing for independence is more complicated, requiring a technique from statistics known as a *contingency table*.

mixed-gender pairs were not identical twins. The same-gender pairs may or may not have been identical twins. The goal here is to use the data to estimate p, the probability that a pair of twins is identical.

(a) Use the data to find the proportion of twins who were male.

(b) Denoting your answer from part (a) by $P(B)$, show that the probability that a pair of twins consists of two males is

$$pP(B) + (1 - p)(P(B))^2.$$

(*Hint:* Draw a tree diagram. The first set of branches should be identical and not identical. Then note that if one member of a pair of identical twins is male, the other must also be male.)

(c) Using your answers from parts (a) and (b), plus the fact that 5844 of the 17,798 twin pairs consisted of two males, find an estimate for the value of p.

(d) Find an expression, similar to the one in part (b), for the probability that a pair of twins is female.

(e) Using your answers from parts (a) and (d), plus the fact that 5612 of the 17,798 twin pairs were female, find an estimate for the value of p.

(f) Find an expression, similar to those in parts (b) and (d), for the probability that a pair of twins consists of one male and one female.

(g) Using your answers from parts (a) and (f), plus the fact that 6342 of the 17,798 twin pairs consisted of one male and one female, find an estimate for the value of p.

Social Sciences

72. Working Women A survey has shown that 52% of the women in a certain community work outside the home. Of these women, 64% are married, while 86% of the women who do not work outside the home are married. Find the probabilities that a woman in that community can be categorized as follows.

(a) Married

(b) A single woman working outside the home

(c) Are the events that a woman is married and that she works outside the home independent? Explain.

73. Cigarette Smokers The following table gives a recent estimate (in millions) of the smoking status among persons 25 years of age and over and their highest level of education. *Source: National Health Interview Survey.*

Education	Current Smoker	Former Smoker	Non-Smoker	Total
Less than a high school diploma	7.90	6.66	14.12	28.68
High school diploma or GED	14.38	13.09	25.70	53.17
Some college	12.41	13.55	28.65	54.61
Bachelor's degree or higher	4.97	12.87	38.34	56.18
Total	39.66	46.17	106.81	192.64

(a) Find the probability that a person is a current smoker.

(b) Find the probability that a person has less than a high school diploma.

(c) Find the probability that a person is a current smoker and has less than a high school diploma.

(d) Find the probability that a person is a current smoker, given that the person has less than a high school diploma.

(e) Are the events "current smoker" and "less than a high school diploma" independent events?

Physical Sciences

74. Rain Forecasts In a letter to the journal *Nature*, Robert A. J. Matthews gives the following table of outcomes of forecast and weather over 1000 1-hour walks, based on the United Kingdom's Meteorological office's 83% accuracy in 24-hour forecasts. *Source: Nature.*

	Rain	No Rain	Totals
Forecast of Rain	66	156	222
Forecast of No Rain	14	764	778
Totals	80	920	1000

(a) Verify that the probability that the forecast called for rain, given that there was rain, is indeed 83%. Also verify that the probability that the forecast called for no rain, given that there was no rain, is also 83%.

(b) Calculate the probability that there was rain, given that the forecast called for rain.

(c) Calculate the probability that there was no rain, given that the forecast called for no rain.

(d) Observe that your answer to part (c) is higher than 83% and that your answer to part (b) is much lower. Discuss which figure best describes the accuracy of the weather forecast in recommending whether or not you should carry an umbrella.

75. Earthquakes There are seven geologic faults (and possibly more) capable of generating a magnitude 6.7 earthquake in the region around San Francisco. Their probabilities of rupturing by the year 2032 are 27%, 21%, 11%, 10%, 4%, 3%, and 3%. *Source: Science News.*

(a) Calculate the probability that at least one of these faults erupts by the year 2032, assuming that these are independent events.

(b) Scientists forecast a 62% chance of an earthquake with magnitude at least 6.7 in the region around San Francisco by the year 2032. Compare this with your answer from part (a). Consider the realism of the assumption of independence. Also consider the role of roundoff. For example, the probability of 10% for one of the faults is presumably rounded to the nearest percent, with the actual probability between 9.5% and 10.5%.

76. Reliability The probability that a key component of a space rocket will fail is 0.03.

   (a) How many such components must be used as backups to ensure that the probability of at least one of the components working is 0.999999 or more?

   (b) Is it reasonable to assume independence here?

General Interest

77. Titanic The table at the bottom of the page lists the number of passengers who were on the *Titanic* and the number of passengers who survived, according to class of ticket. Use this information to determine the following (round answers to four decimal places). *Source: The Mathematics Teacher.*

   (a) What is the probability that a randomly selected passenger was second class?

   (b) What is the overall probability of surviving?

   (c) What is the probability of a first-class passenger surviving?

   (d) What is the probability of a child who was also in the third class surviving?

   (e) Given that the survivor is from first class, what is the probability that she was a woman?

   (f) Given that a man has survived, what is the probability that he was in third class?

   (g) Are the events third-class survival and man survival independent events? What does this imply?

78. Real Estate A real estate agent trying to sell you an attractive beachfront house claims that it will not collapse unless it is subjected simultaneously to extremely high winds and extremely high waves. According to weather service records, there is a 0.001 probability of extremely high winds, and the same for extremely high waves. The real estate agent claims, therefore, that the probability of both occurring is $(0.001)(0.001) = 0.000001$. What is wrong with the agent's reasoning?

79. Age and Loans Suppose 20% of the population are 65 or over, 26% of those 65 or over have loans, and 53% of those under 65 have loans. Find the probabilities that a person fits into the following categories.

   (a) 65 or over and has a loan

   (b) Has a loan

   (c) Are the events that a person is 65 or over and that the person has a loan independent? Explain.

80. Women Joggers In a certain area, 15% of the population are joggers and 40% of the joggers are women. If 55% of those who do not jog are women, find the probabilities that an individual from that community fits the following descriptions.

   (a) A woman jogger

   (b) A man who is not a jogger

   (c) A woman

   (d) Are the events that a person is a woman and a person is a jogger independent? Explain.

81. Diet Soft Drinks Two-thirds of the population are on a diet at least occasionally. Of this group, 4/5 drink diet soft drinks, while 1/2 of the rest of the (nondieting) population drink diet soft drinks. Find the probabilities that a person fits into the following categories.

   (a) Drinks diet soft drinks

   (b) Diets, but does not drink diet soft drinks

82. Driver's License Test The Motor Vehicle Department has found that the probability of a person passing the test for a driver's license on the first try is 0.75. The probability that an individual who fails on the first test will pass on the second try is 0.80, and the probability that an individual who fails the first and second tests will pass the third time is 0.70. Find the probabilities that an individual will do the following.

   (a) Fail both the first and second tests

   (b) Fail three times in a row

   (c) Require at least two tries

83. Ballooning A pair of mathematicians in a hot air balloon were told that there are four independent burners, any one of which is sufficient to keep the balloon aloft. If the probability of any one burner failing during a flight is 0.001, what is the probability that the balloon will crash due to all four burners failing?

84. Speeding Tickets A smooth-talking young man has a 1/3 probability of talking a policeman out of giving him a speeding ticket. The probability that he is stopped for speeding during a given weekend is 1/2. Find the probabilities of the events in parts (a) and (b).

   (a) He will receive no speeding tickets on a given weekend.

   (b) He will receive no speeding tickets on 3 consecutive weekends.

   (c) We have assumed that what happens on the second or third weekend is the same as what happened on the first weekend. Is this realistic? Will driving habits remain the same after getting a ticket?

	Children		Women		Men		Totals	
	On	Survived	On	Survived	On	Survived	On	Survived
First Class	6	6	144	140	175	57	325	203
Second Class	24	24	93	80	168	14	285	118
Third Class	79	27	165	76	462	75	706	178
Totals	109	57	402	296	805	146	1316	499

85. Luxury Cars   In one area, 4% of the population drive luxury cars. However, 17% of the CPAs drive luxury cars. Are the events "person drives a luxury car" and "person is a CPA" independent?

86. Studying   A teacher has found that the probability that a student studies for a test is 0.60, the probability that a student gets a good grade on a test is 0.70, and the probability that both occur is 0.52.

(a) Are these events independent?

(b) Given that a student studies, find the probability that the student gets a good grade.

(c) Given that a student gets a good grade, find the probability that the student studied.

87. Basketball   A basketball player is fouled and now faces a one-and-one free throw situation. She shoots the first free throw. If she misses it, she scores 0 points. If she makes the first free throw, she gets to shoot a second free throw. If she misses the second free throw, she scores only one point for the first shot. If she makes the second free throw, she scores two points (one for each made shot). *Source: The Mathematics Teacher.*

(a) If her free-throwing percentage for this season is 60%, calculate the probability that she scores 0 points, 1 point, or 2 points.

(b) Determine the free-throwing percentage necessary for the probability of scoring 0 points to be the same as the probability of scoring 2 points.* (*Hint:* Let p be the free-throwing percentage, and then solve $p^2 = 1 - p$ for p. Use only the positive value of p.)

88. Basketball   The same player from Exercise 87 is now shooting two free throws (that is, she gets to shoot a second free throw whether she makes or misses the first shot.) Assume her free-throwing percentage is still 60%. Find the probability she scores 0 points, 1 point, or 2 points. *Source: The Mathematics Teacher.*

89. Football   A football coach whose team is 14 points behind needs two touchdowns to win. Each touchdown is worth 6 points. After a touchdown, the coach can choose either a 1-point kick, which is almost certain to succeed, or a 2-point conversion, which is roughly half as likely to succeed. After the first touchdown, the coach must decide whether to go for 1 or 2 points. If the 2-point conversion is successful, the almost certain 1-point kick after the second touchdown will win the game. If the 2-point conversion fails, the team can try another 2-point conversion after the second touchdown to tie. Some coaches, however, prefer to go for the almost certain 1-point kick after the first touchdown, hoping that the momentum will help them get a 2-point conversion after the second touchdown and win the game. They fear that an unsuccessful 2-point conversion after the first touchdown will discourage the team, which can then at best tie. *Source: The Mathematics Teacher.*

(a) Draw a tree diagram for the 1-point kick after the first touchdown and the 2-point conversion after the second touchdown. Letting the probability of success for the 1-point kick and the 2-point conversion be k and r, respectively, show that

$$P(\text{win}) = kr,$$
$$P(\text{tie}) = r(1 - k), \quad \text{and}$$
$$P(\text{lose}) = 1 - r.$$

(b) Consider the case of trying for a 2-point conversion after the first touchdown. If it succeeds, try a 1-point kick after the second touchdown. If the 2-point conversion fails, try another one after the second touchdown. Draw a tree diagram and use it to show that

$$P(\text{win}) = kr,$$
$$P(\text{tie}) = r(2 - k - r), \quad \text{and}$$
$$P(\text{lose}) = (1 - r)^2.$$

(c) What can you say about the probability of winning under each strategy?

(d) Given that $r < 1$, which strategy has a smaller probability of losing? What does this tell you about the value of the two strategies?

90. NCAA   Large money prizes are offered each year to anyone who can correctly pick the outcome of all 63 games in the NCAA's men's college basketball tournament. The probability of correctly doing so has been estimated as between one in 150 million and one in nine million trillion. *Source: The Numbers Guy.*

(a) Suppose you choose the winner of each game by flipping a fair coin. What is the probability of getting all 63 games correct?

(b) Explain why someone who knows something about basketball should have a higher probability of getting all 63 games correct than the answer to part (a).

(c) What probability of predicting the outcome of a game would be necessary to predict all 63 games correctly with a probability of one in 150 million? Assume that the probability of getting each game correct is constant.

---

* The solution is the reciprocal of the number $\frac{1 + \sqrt{5}}{2}$, known as the golden ratio or the divine proportion. This number has great significance in architecture, science, and mathematics.

YOUR TURN ANSWERS

1. $30/55 = 6/11$ **2.** 0.625

3. 2/3   **4.** 1/5

5. 1/6   **6.** 1/5

7. 1/36   **8.** No

7.6 Bayes' Theorem

APPLY IT What is the probability that a particular defective item was produced by a new machine operator?

This question will be answered in Example 2 using Bayes' theorem, discussed in this section.

Suppose the probability that an applicant is hired, *given the applicant is qualified*, is known. The manager might also be interested in the probability that the applicant is qualified, *given the applicant was hired*. More generally, if $P(E|F)$ is known for two events E and F, then $P(F|E)$ can be found using a tree diagram. Since $P(E|F)$ is known, the first outcome is either F or F'. Then for each of these outcomes, either E or E' occurs, as shown in Figure 27.

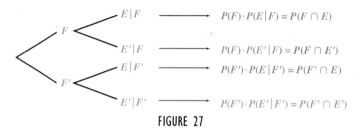

FIGURE 27

The four cases have the probabilities shown on the right. Notice $P(E \cap F)$ is the first case and $P(E)$ is the sum of the first and third cases in the tree diagram. By the definition of conditional probability,

$$P(F|E) = \frac{P(F \cap E)}{P(E)} = \frac{P(F) \cdot P(E|F)}{P(F) \cdot P(E|F) + P(F') \cdot P(E|F')}.$$

This result is a special case of Bayes' theorem, which is generalized later in this section.

Bayes' Theorem (Special Case)

$$P(F|E) = \frac{P(F) \cdot P(E|F)}{P(F) \cdot P(E|F) + P(F') \cdot P(E|F')}$$

EXAMPLE 1   Worker Errors

For a fixed length of time, the probability of a worker error on a certain production line is 0.1, the probability that an accident will occur when there is a worker error is 0.3, and the probability that an accident will occur when there is no worker error is 0.2. Find the probability of a worker error if there is an accident.

SOLUTION   Let E represent the event of an accident, and let F represent the event of worker error. From the information given,

$$P(F) = 0.1, \qquad P(E|F) = 0.3, \qquad \text{and} \qquad P(E|F') = 0.2.$$

These probabilities are shown on the tree diagram in Figure 28 on the next page.

Find $P(F|E)$ by dividing the probability that both E and F occur, given by branch 1, by the probability that E occurs, given by the sum of branches 1 and 3.

$$P(F|E) = \frac{P(F) \cdot P(E|F)}{P(F) \cdot P(E|F) + P(F') \cdot P(E|F')}$$

$$= \frac{(0.1)(0.3)}{(0.1)(0.3) + (0.9)(0.2)} = \frac{0.03}{0.21} = \frac{1}{7} \approx 0.1429$$

TRY YOUR TURN 1

YOUR TURN 1 The probability that a student will pass a math exam is 0.8 if he or she attends the review session and 0.65 if he or she does not attend the review session. Sixty percent of the students attend the review session. What is the probability that, given a student passed, the student attended the review session?

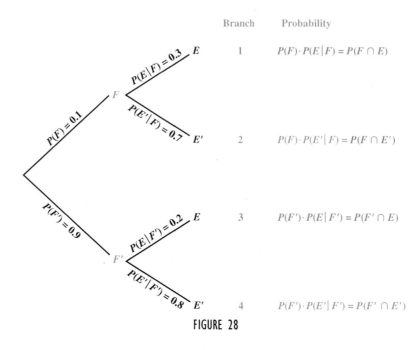

FIGURE 28

The special case of Bayes' theorem can be generalized to more than two events with the tree diagram in Figure 29. This diagram shows the paths that can produce an event E. We assume that the events $F_1, F_2, \ldots, F_n$ are mutually exclusive events (that is, disjoint events) whose union is the sample space, and that E is an event that has occurred. See Figure 30.

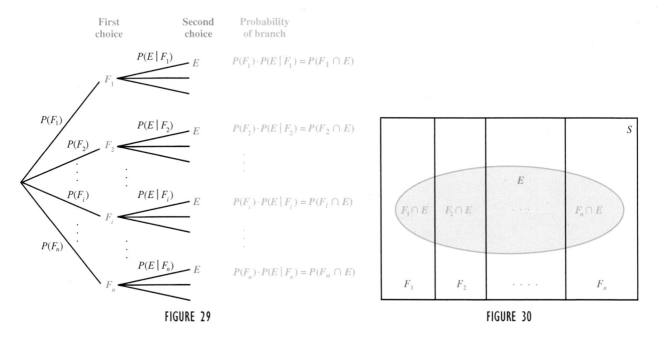

FIGURE 29   FIGURE 30

The probability $P(F_i | E)$, where $1 \leq i \leq n$, can be found by dividing the probability for the branch containing $P(E | F_i)$ by the sum of the probabilities of all the branches producing event E.

Bayes' Theorem

$$P(F_i | E) = \frac{P(F_i) \cdot P(E | F_i)}{P(F_1) \cdot P(E | F_1) + P(F_2) \cdot P(E | F_2) + \cdots + P(F_n) \cdot P(E | F_n)}$$

This result is known as **Bayes' theorem**, after the Reverend Thomas Bayes (1702–1761), whose paper on probability was published about three years after his death.

The statement of Bayes' theorem can be daunting. Actually, it is easier to remember the formula by thinking of the tree diagram that produced it. Use the following steps.

Using Bayes' Theorem

1. Start a tree diagram with branches representing $F_1, F_2, \ldots, F_n$. Label each branch with its corresponding probability.

2. From the end of each of these branches, draw a branch for event E. Label this branch with the probability of reaching it, $P(E|F_i)$.

3. You now have n different paths that result in event E. Next to each path, put its probability—the product of the probabilities that the first branch occurs, $P(F_i)$, and that the second branch occurs, $P(E|F_i)$; that is, the product $P(F_i) \cdot P(E|F_i)$, which equals $P(F_i \cap E)$.

4. $P(F_i|E)$ is found by dividing the probability of the branch for F_i by the sum of the probabilities of all the branches producing event E.

EXAMPLE 2 Machine Operators

Based on past experience, a company knows that an experienced machine operator (one or more years of experience) will produce a defective item 1% of the time. Operators with some experience (up to one year) have a 2.5% defect rate, and new operators have a 6% defect rate. At any one time, the company has 60% experienced operators, 30% with some experience, and 10% new operators. Find the probability that a particular defective item was produced by a new operator.

APPLY IT **SOLUTION** Let E represent the event "item is defective," F_1 represent "item was made by an experienced operator," F_2 represent "item was made by an operator with some experience," and F_3 represent "item was made by a new operator." Then

$$P(F_1) = 0.60 \qquad P(E|F_1) = 0.01$$
$$P(F_2) = 0.30 \qquad P(E|F_2) = 0.025$$
$$P(F_3) = 0.10 \qquad P(E|F_3) = 0.06.$$

We need to find $P(F_3|E)$, the probability that an item was produced by a new operator, given that it is defective. First, draw a tree diagram using the given information, as in Figure 31. The steps leading to event E are shown in red.

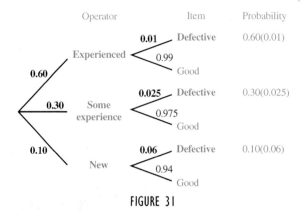

FIGURE 31

YOUR TURN 2 The English department at a small college has found that 12% of freshmen test into English I, 68% test into English II, and 20% test into English III. Eighty percent of students in English I will seek help from the writing center, 40% of those in English II, and 11% of those in English III. Given that a student received help from the writing center, find the probability that the student is in English I.

Find $P(F_3 | E)$ with the bottom branch of the tree in Figure 31: Divide the probability for this branch by the sum of the probabilities of all the branches leading to E, or

$$P(F_3 | E) = \frac{0.10(0.06)}{0.60(0.01) + 0.30(0.025) + 0.10(0.06)} = \frac{0.006}{0.0195} = \frac{4}{13} \approx 0.3077.$$

In a similar way, the probability that the defective item was produced by an operator with some experience is

$$P(F_2 | E) = \frac{0.30(0.025)}{0.60(0.01) + 0.30(0.025) + 0.10(0.06)} = \frac{0.0075}{0.0195} = \frac{5}{13} \approx 0.3846.$$

Finally, the probability that the defective item was produced by an experienced operator is $P(F_1 | E) = 4/13 \approx 0.3077$. Check that $P(F_1 | E) + P(F_2 | E) + P(F_3 | E) = 1$ (that is, the defective item was made by *someone*). **TRY YOUR TURN 2**

EXAMPLE 3 Manufacturing

A manufacturer buys items from six different suppliers. The fraction of the total number of items obtained from each supplier, along with the probability that an item purchased from that supplier is defective, is shown in the following table.

Manufacturing Supplies		
Supplier	Fraction of Total Supplied	Probability of Defect
1	0.05	0.04
2	0.12	0.02
3	0.16	0.07
4	0.23	0.01
5	0.35	0.03
6	0.09	0.05

Find the probability that a defective item came from supplier 5.

SOLUTION Let F_1 be the event that an item came from supplier 1, with F_2, F_3, F_4, F_5, and F_6 defined in a similar manner. Let E be the event that an item is defective. We want to find $P(F_5 | E)$. Use the probabilities in the table above to prepare a tree diagram, or work with the rows of the table to get

$$P(F_5 | E) = \frac{(0.35)(0.03)}{(0.05)(0.04) + (0.12)(0.02) + (0.16)(0.07) + (0.23)(0.01) + (0.35)(0.03) + (0.09)(0.05)}$$

$$= \frac{0.0105}{0.0329} \approx 0.319.$$

There is about a 32% chance that a defective item came from supplier 5. Even though supplier 5 has only 3% defectives, his probability of being "guilty" is relatively high, about 32%, because of the large fraction supplied by 5.

CAUTION Notice that the 0.04 in the upper right of the previous table represents the probability of a defective item *given* that the item came from supplier 1. In contrast, the probability of 0.035 in the table for Exercises 54–61 of the previous section represents the probability that a person is color-blind *and* male. The tables in this section represent probability in a different way than those of the previous section. Tables that you encounter outside of this course might represent probability in either way. You can usually tell what is intended by the context, but be careful!

⊞ TECHNOLOGY NOTE
The calculations in the previous example can be easily performed using Excel. Put the fraction of total supplied in column A and the probability of defect in column B. In cell C1, put "=A1*B1". Copy this formula and paste it into cells C2 through C6. In cell C7, put "=SUM(C1:C6)". Finally, in any cell, put "=C5/C7".

7.6 WARM-UP EXERCISES

Suppose 1/3 of the marbles in jar A are red, and the rest are yellow. Of the marbles in jar B, 1/5 are red and the rest are yellow. Jar A is selected with probability 3/4 and jar B with probability 1/4. A jar is selected, and a marble is then picked from that jar. Find the probabilities of the following.

W1. The marble is from jar A and is yellow. *(Sec. 7.5)*　　　**W2.** The marble is red. *(Sec. 7.5)*

7.6 EXERCISES

For two events M and N, $P(M) = 0.4$, $P(N|M) = 0.3$, and $P(N|M') = 0.4$. Find the following.

1. $P(M|N)$　　　　　　**2.** $P(M'|N)$

For mutually exclusive events R_1, R_2, and R_3, we have $P(R_1) = 0.15$, $P(R_2) = 0.55$, and $P(R_3) = 0.30$. Also, $P(Q|R_1) = 0.40$, $P(Q|R_2) = 0.20$, and $P(Q|R_3) = 0.70$. Find the following.

3. $P(R_1|Q)$　　　　　　**4.** $P(R_2|Q)$

5. $P(R_3|Q)$　　　　　　**6.** $P(R_1'|Q)$

Suppose you have three jars with the following contents: 2 black balls and 1 white ball in the first, 1 black ball and 2 white balls in the second, and 1 black ball and 1 white ball in the third. One jar is to be selected, and then 1 ball is to be drawn from the selected jar. If the probabilities of selecting the first, second, or third jar are 1/2, 1/3, and 1/6, respectively, find the probabilities that if a white ball is drawn, it came from the following jars.

7. The second jar　　　　　**8.** The third jar

APPLICATIONS

Business and Economics

9. Employment Test A manufacturing firm finds that 70% of its new hires turn out to be good workers and 30% become poor workers. All current workers are given a reasoning test. Of the good workers, 85% pass it; 35% of the poor workers pass it. Assume that these figures will hold true in the future. If the company makes the test part of its hiring procedure and only hires people who meet the previous requirements and pass the test, what percent of the new hires will turn out to be good workers?

Job Qualifications Of all the people applying for a certain job, 75% are qualified and 25% are not. The personnel manager claims that she approves qualified people 85% of the time; she approves an unqualified person 20% of the time. Find each probability.

10. A person is qualified if he or she was approved by the manager.

11. A person is unqualified if he or she was approved by the manager.

Quality Control A building contractor buys 70% of his cement from supplier A and 30% from supplier B. A total of 90% of the bags from A arrive undamaged, while 95% of the bags from B arrive undamaged. Give the probabilities that a damaged bag is from the following sources.

12. Supplier A　　　　　　**13.** Supplier B

Appliance Reliability Companies A, B, and C produce 15%, 40%, and 45%, respectively, of the major appliances sold in a certain area. In that area, 1% of the company A appliances, $1\frac{1}{2}$% of the company B appliances, and 2% of the company C appliances need service within the first year. Suppose a defective appliance is chosen at random; find the probabilities that it was manufactured by the following companies.

14. Company A　　　　　　**15.** Company B

Television Advertising On a given weekend in the fall, a tire company can buy television advertising time for a college football game, a baseball game, or a professional football game. If the company sponsors the college football game, there is a 70% chance of a high rating, a 50% chance if they sponsor a baseball game, and a 60% chance if they sponsor a professional football game. The probabilities of the company sponsoring these various games are 0.5, 0.2, and 0.3, respectively. Suppose the company does get a high rating; find the probabilities that it sponsored the following.

16. A college football game

17. A professional football game

18. Auto Insurance An auto insurance company insures drivers of all ages. An actuary compiled the following statistics on the company's insured drivers:

Age of Driver	Probability Of Accident	Portion of Company's Insured Drivers
16–20	0.06	0.08
21–30	0.03	0.15
31–65	0.02	0.49
66–99	0.04	0.28

A randomly selected driver that the company insures has an accident. Calculate the probability that the driver was age 16–20. Choose one of the following. *Source: Society of Actuaries.*

(a) 0.13   (b) 0.16   (c) 0.19   (d) 0.23   (e) 0.40

19. Life Insurance   An insurance company issues life insurance policies in three separate categories: standard, preferred, and ultra-preferred. Of the company's policyholders, 50% are standard, 40% are preferred, and 10% are ultra-preferred. Each standard policyholder has probability 0.010 of dying in the next year, each preferred policyholder has probability 0.005 of dying in the next year, and each ultra-preferred policyholder has probability 0.001 of dying in the next year. A policyholder dies in the next year. What is the probability that the deceased policyholder was ultra-preferred? Choose one of the following. *Source: Society of Actuaries.*

(a) 0.0001   (b) 0.0010   (c) 0.0071   (d) 0.0141   (e) 0.2817

20. Automobile Collisions   An actuary studied the likelihood that different types of drivers would be involved in at least one collision during any one-year period. The results of the study are presented below.

Type of Driver	Percentage of All Drivers	Probability of at Least One Collision
Teen	8%	0.15
Young Adult	16%	0.08
Midlife	45%	0.04
Senior	31%	0.05
Total	100%	

Given that a driver has been involved in at least one collision in the past year, what is the probability that the driver is a young adult driver? Choose one of the following. *Source: Society of Actuaries.*

(a) 0.06   (b) 0.16   (c) 0.19   (d) 0.22   (e) 0.25

21. Shipping Errors   The following information pertains to three shipping terminals operated by Krag Corp. *Source: CPA Examination.*

Terminal	Percentage of Cargo Handled	Percentage of Error
Land	50	2
Air	40	4
Sea	10	14

Krag's internal auditor randomly selects one set of shipping documents, ascertaining that the set selected contains an error. Which of the following gives the probability that the error occurred in the Land Terminal?

(a) 0.02   (b) 0.10   (c) 0.25   (d) 0.50

22. Mortgage Defaults   A bank finds that the relationship between mortgage defaults and the size of the down payment is given by the following table.

Down Payment	Number of Mortgages with This Down Payment	Probability of Default
5%	1260	0.06
10%	700	0.04
20%	560	0.02
25%	280	0.01

(a) If a default occurs, what is the probability that it is on a mortgage with a 5% down payment?

(b) What is the probability that a mortgage that is paid to maturity has a 10% down payment?

Life Sciences

23. Colorectal Cancer   Researchers found that only one out of 24 physicians could give the correct answer to the following problem: "The probability of colorectal cancer can be given as 0.3%. If a person has colorectal cancer, the probability that the hemoccult test is positive is 50%. If a person does not have colorectal cancer, the probability that he still tests positive is 3%. What is the probability that a person who tests positive actually has colorectal cancer?" What is the correct answer? *Source: Science.*

24. Hepatitis Blood Test   The probability that a person with certain symptoms has hepatitis is 0.8. The blood test used to confirm this diagnosis gives positive results for 90% of people with the disease and 5% of those without the disease. What is the probability that an individual who has the symptoms and who reacts positively to the test actually has hepatitis?

25. Sensitivity and Specificity   The **sensitivity** of a medical test is defined as the probability that a test will be positive given that a person has a disease, written $P(T^+ \mid D^+)$. The **specificity** of a test is defined as the probability that a test will be negative given that the person does not have the disease, written $P(T^- \mid D^-)$. For example, the sensitivity and specificity for breast cancer during a mammography exam are approximately 79.6% and 90.2%, respectively. *Source: National Cancer Institute.*

(a) It is estimated that 0.5% of U.S. women under the age 40 have breast cancer. Find the probability that a woman under 40 who tests positive during a mammography exam actually has breast cancer.

(b) Given that a woman under 40 tests negative during a mammography exam, find the probability that she does not have breast cancer.

(c) According to the National Cancer Institute, failure to diagnose breast cancer is the most common cause of medical malpractice litigation. Given a woman under 40 tests negative for breast cancer, find the probability that she does have breast cancer.

(d) It is estimated that 1.5% of U.S. women over the age of 50 have breast cancer. Find the probability that a woman over 50 who tests positive actually has breast cancer.

26. Test for HIV Clinical studies have demonstrated that rapid HIV tests have a sensitivity (probability that a test will be positive given that a person has the disease) of approximately 99.9% and a specificity (probability that a test will be negative given that the person does not have the disease) of approximately 99.8%. *Source: Centers for Disease Control and Prevention*

(a) In some HIV clinics, the prevalence of HIV was high, about 5%. Find the probability a person actually has HIV, given that the test came back positive from one of these clinics.

(b) In other clinics, like a family planning clinic, the prevalence of HIV was low, about 0.1%. Find the probability that a person actually has HIV, given that the test came back positive from one of these clinics.

(c) The answers in parts (a) and (b) are significantly different. Explain why.

27. Smokers A health study tracked a group of persons for five years. At the beginning of the study, 20% were classified as heavy smokers, 30% as light smokers, and 50% as non-smokers. Results of the study showed that light smokers were twice as likely as nonsmokers to die during the five-year study but only half as likely as heavy smokers. A randomly selected participant from the study died over the five-year period. Calculate the probability that the participant was a heavy smoker. Choose one of the following. (*Hint:* Let $x = P$(a nonsmoker dies).) *Source: Society of Actuaries.*

(a) 0.20 **(b)** 0.25 **(c)** 0.35 **(d)** 0.42 **(e)** 0.57

28. Emergency Room Upon arrival at a hospital's emergency room, patients are categorized according to their condition as critical, serious, or stable. In the past year:

(i) 10% of the emergency room patients were critical;

(ii) 30% of the emergency room patients were serious;

(iii) the rest of the emergency room patients were stable;

(iv) 40% of the critical patients died;

(v) 10% of the serious patients died; and

(vi) 1% of the stable patients died.

Given that a patient survived, what is the probability that the patient was categorized as serious upon arrival? Choose one of the following. *Source: Society of Actuaries.*

(a) 0.06 **(b)** 0.29 **(c)** 0.30 **(d)** 0.39 **(e)** 0.64

29. Blood Test A blood test indicates the presence of a particular disease 95% of the time when the disease is actually present. The same test indicates the presence of the disease 0.5% of the time when the disease is not present. One percent of the population actually has the disease. Calculate the probability that a person has the disease, given that the test indicates the presence of the disease. Choose one of the following. *Source: Society of Actuaries.*

(a) 0.324 **(b)** 0.657 **(c)** 0.945 **(d)** 0.950 **(e)** 0.995

30. Circulation The probability that a randomly chosen male has a circulation problem is 0.25. Males who have a circulation problem are twice as likely to be smokers as those who do not have a circulation problem. What is the conditional probability that a male has a circulation problem, given that he is a smoker? Choose one of the following. *Source: Society of Actuaries.*

(a) 1/4 **(b)** 1/3 **(c)** 2/5 **(d)** 1/2 **(e)** 2/3

Social Sciences

31. Alcohol Abstinence The Harvard School of Public Health completed a study on alcohol consumption on college campuses. They concluded that 20.7% of women attending all-women colleges abstained from alcohol, compared to 18.6% of women attending coeducational colleges. Approximately 4.7% of women college students attend all-women schools. *Source: Harvard School of Public Health.*

(a) What is the probability that a randomly selected female student abstains from alcohol?

(b) If a randomly selected female student abstains from alcohol, what is the probability she attends a coeducational college?

32. Murder During the murder trial of O. J. Simpson, Alan Dershowitz, an advisor to the defense team, stated on television that only about 0.1% of men who batter their wives actually murder them. Statistician I. J. Good observed that even if, given that a husband is a batterer, the probability he is guilty of murdering his wife is 0.001, what we really want to know is the probability that the husband is guilty, given that the wife was murdered. Good estimates the probability of a battered wife being murdered, given that her husband is not guilty, as 0.001. The probability that she is murdered if her husband is guilty is 1, of course. Using these numbers and Dershowitz's 0.001 probability of the husband being guilty, find the probability that the husband is guilty, given that the wife was murdered. *Source: Nature.*

Children's Economic Situation The following table gives the proportion of children in the United States in 2012 who are living in a family in each income group, as well as the proportion who are living with two married parents in each income group. *Source: U.S. Census Bureau.*

Family Income	Proportion of Population	Proportion with two Married Parents
Under $15,000	0.132	0.187
$15,000–$29,999	0.147	0.385
$30,000–$49,999	0.177	0.576
$50,000–$74,999	0.171	0.727
$75,000–$99,999	0.124	0.854
$100,000 and over	0.249	0.916

33. Find the probability that a child living with two married parents lives in a family with an income of $100,000 or over.

34. Find the probability that a child not living with two married parents lives in a family with an income of $100,000 or over.

35. Find the probability that a child living with two married parents lives in a family with an income under $15,000.

36. Seat Belt Effectiveness A federal study showed that 63.8% of occupants involved in a fatal car crash wore seat belts. Of those in a fatal crash who wore seat belts, 2% were ejected from the vehicle. For those not wearing seat belts, 36% were ejected from the vehicle. *Source: National Highway Traffic Safety Administration.*

(a) Find the probability that a randomly selected person in a fatal car crash who was ejected from the vehicle was wearing a seat belt.

(b) Find the probability that a randomly selected person in a fatal car crash who was not ejected from the vehicle was not wearing a seat belt.

Smokers by Age Group **The following table gives the proportion of U.S. adults in each age group in 2012, as well as the proportion in each group who smoke.** *Source: Centers for Disease Control and Prevention.*

Age	Proportion of Population	Proportion that Smoke
18–24 years	0.131	0.173
25–44 years	0.345	0.216
45–64 years	0.345	0.195
65 years and over	0.180	0.089

37. Find the probability that a randomly selected adult who smokes is between 18 and 24 years of age (inclusive).

38. Find the probability that a randomly selected adult who does not smoke is between 45 and 64 years of age (inclusive).

General Interest

39. Terrorists John Allen Paulos has pointed out a problem with massive, untargeted wiretaps. To illustrate the problem, he supposes that one out of every million Americans has terrorist ties.

Furthermore, he supposes that the terrorist profile is 99% accurate, so that if a person has terrorist ties, the profile will pick them up 99% of the time, and if the person does not have terrorist ties, the profile will accidentally pick them up only 1% of the time. Given that the profile has picked up a person, what is the probability that the person actually has terrorist ties? Discuss how your answer affects your opinion on domestic wiretapping. *Source: Who's Counting.*

40. Three Prisoners The famous "problem of three prisoners" is as follows.

Three men, A, B, and C, were in jail. A knew that one of them was to be set free and the other two were to be executed. But he didn't know who was the one to be spared. To the jailer who did know, A said, "Since two out of the three will be executed, it is certain that either B or C will be, at least. You will give me no information about my own chances if you give me the name of one man, B or C, who is going to be executed." Accepting this argument after some thinking, the jailer said "B will be executed." Thereupon A felt happier because now either he or C would go free, so his chance had increased from 1/3 to 1/2. *Source: Cognition.*

(a) Assume that initially each of the prisoners is equally likely to be set free. Assume also that if both B and C are to be executed, the jailer is equally likely to name either B or C. Show that A is wrong, and that his probability of being freed, given that the jailer says B will be executed, is still 1/3.

(b) Now assume that initially the probabilities of A, B, and C being freed are 1/4, 1/4, and 1/2, respectively. As in part (a), assume also that if both B and C are to be executed, the jailer is equally likely to name either B or C. Now show that A's probability of being freed, given that the jailer says B will be executed, actually drops to 1/5. Discuss the reasonableness of this answer, and why this result might violate someone's intuition.

YOUR TURN ANSWERS ▬▬
1. 0.6486
2. 0.2462

---

7 CHAPTER REVIEW

SUMMARY

We began this chapter by introducing sets, which are collections of objects. We introduced the following set operations:

- complement (A' is the set of elements not in A),
- intersection ($A \cap B$ is the set of elements belonging to both set A and set B), and
- union ($A \cup B$ is the set of elements belonging to either set A or set B or both).

We used tree diagrams and Venn diagrams to define and study concepts in set operations as well as in probability. We introduced the following terms:

- experiment (an activity or occurrence with an observable result),
- trial (a repetition of an experiment),
- outcome (a result of a trial),

- sample space (the set of all possible outcomes for an experiment), and
- event (a subset of a sample space).

We investigated how to compute various probabilities and we explored some of the properties of probability. In particular, we studied the following concepts:

- empirical probability (based on how frequently an event actually occurred),
- conditional probability (in which some other event is assumed to have occurred),
- odds (an alternative way of expressing probability),
- independent events (in which the occurrence of one event does not affect the probability of another), and
- Bayes' theorem (used to calculate certain types of conditional probability).

Throughout the chapter, many applications of probability were introduced and analyzed. In the next two chapters, we will employ these techniques to further our study into the fields of probability and statistics.

Sets Summary

Number of Subsets
A set of k distinct elements has 2^k subsets.

Disjoint Sets
If sets A and B are disjoint, then

$$A \cap B = \varnothing \quad \text{and} \quad n(A \cap B) = 0.$$

Union Rule for Sets
For any sets A and B,

$$n(A \cup B) = n(A) + n(B) - n(A \cap B).$$

Probability Summary

Basic Probability Principle
Let S be a sample space of equally likely outcomes, and let event E be a subset of S. Then the probability that event E occurs is

$$P(E) = \frac{n(E)}{n(S)}.$$

Mutually Exclusive Events
If E and F are mutually exclusive events,

$$E \cap F = \varnothing \quad \text{and} \quad P(E \cap F) = 0.$$

Union Rule
For any events E and F from a sample space S,

$$P(E \cup F) = P(E) + P(F) - P(E \cap F).$$

Complement Rule
$P(E) = 1 - P(E') \quad \text{and} \quad P(E') = 1 - P(E)$

Odds
The odds in favor of event E are $\dfrac{P(E)}{P(E')}$, where $P(E') \neq 0$.

If the odds favoring event E are m to n, then

$$P(E) = \frac{m}{m + n} \quad \text{and} \quad P(E') = \frac{n}{m + n}.$$

Properties of Probability
1. For any event E in sample space S, $0 \leq P(E) \leq 1$.
2. The sum of the probabilities of all possible distinct outcomes is 1.

Conditional Probability
The conditional probability of event E, given that event F has occurred, is

$$P(E|F) = \frac{P(E \cap F)}{P(F)}, \quad \text{where } P(F) \neq 0.$$

For equally likely outcomes, conditional probability is found by reducing the sample space to event F; then

$$P(E|F) = \frac{n(E \cap F)}{n(F)}.$$

Product Rule of Probability   If E and F are events, then $P(E \cap F)$ may be found by either of these formulas.

$$P(E \cap F) = P(F) \cdot P(E|F) \quad \text{or} \quad P(E \cap F) = P(E) \cdot P(F|E)$$

Independent Events   If E and F are independent events,

$$P(E|F) = P(E), \quad P(F|E) = P(F), \quad \text{and} \quad P(E \cap F) = P(E) \cdot P(F).$$

Bayes' Theorem $P(F_i|E) = \dfrac{P(F_i) \cdot P(E|F_i)}{P(F_1) \cdot P(E|F_1) + P(F_2) \cdot P(E|F_2) + \cdots + P(F_n) \cdot P(E|F_n)}$

KEY TERMS

7.1
set
element (member)
empty set (or null set)
set-builder notation
universal set
subset
tree diagram
Venn diagram
complement
intersection

disjoint sets
union
7.2
union rule for sets
7.3
experiment
trial
outcome
sample space
event

simple event
certain event
impossible event
mutually exclusive events
probability
empirical probability
7.4
union rule for probability
odds
probability distribution

7.5
conditional probability
product rule
independent events
dependent events
7.6
Bayes' theorem
sensitivity
specificity

REVIEW EXERCISES

CONCEPT CHECK

Determine whether each of the following statements is true or false, and explain why.

1. A set is a subset of itself.

2. A set has more subsets than it has elements.

3. The union of two sets always has more elements than either set.

4. The intersection of two sets always has fewer elements than either set.

5. The number of elements in the union of two sets can be found by adding the number of elements in each set.

6. The probability of an event is always at least 0 and no larger than 1.

7. The probability of the union of two events can be found by adding the probability of each event.

8. The probability of drawing the Queen of Hearts from a deck of cards is an example of empirical probability.

9. If two events are mutually exclusive, then they are independent.

10. The probability of two independent events can be found by multiplying the probabilities of each event.

11. The probability of an event E given an event F is the same as the probability of F given E.

12. Bayes' theorem can be useful for calculating conditional probability.

PRACTICE AND EXPLORATIONS

Write true or false for each statement.

13. $9 \in \{8, 4, -3, -9, 6\}$

14. $4 \notin \{3, 9, 7\}$

15. $2 \notin \{0, 1, 2, 3, 4\}$

16. $0 \in \{0, 1, 2, 3, 4\}$

17. $\{3, 4, 5\} \subseteq \{2, 3, 4, 5, 6\}$

18. $\{1, 2, 5, 8\} \subseteq \{1, 2, 5, 10, 11\}$

19. $\{3, 6, 9, 10\} \subseteq \{3, 9, 11, 13\}$

20. $\varnothing \subseteq \{1\}$

21. $\{2, 8\} \nsubseteq \{2, 4, 6, 8\}$

22. $0 \subseteq \varnothing$

In Exercises 23–32, let $U = \{a, b, c, d, e, f, g, h\}$, $K = \{c, d, e, f, h\}$, and $R = \{a, c, d, g\}$. Find the following.

23. The number of subsets of K

24. The number of subsets of R

25. K' 26. R'

27. $K \cap R$ 28. $K \cup R$

29. $(K \cap R)'$ 30. $(K \cup R)'$

31. $\varnothing'$ 32. U'

In Exercises 33–38, let

U = {all employees of the K. O. Brown Company};

A = {employees in the accounting department};

B = {employees in the sales department};

C = {female employees};

D = {employees with an MBA degree}.

Describe each set in words.

33. $A \cap C$ **34.** $B \cap D$ **35.** $A \cup D$

36. $A' \cap D$ **37.** $B' \cap C'$ **38.** $(B \cup C)'$

Draw a Venn diagram and shade each set.

39. $A \cup B'$ **40.** $A' \cap B$

41. $(A \cap B) \cup C$ **42.** $(A \cup B)' \cap C$

Write the sample space S for each experiment, choosing an S with equally likely outcomes, if possible.

43. Rolling a die

44. Drawing a card from a deck containing only the 13 spades

45. Measuring the weight of a person to the nearest half pound (the scale will not measure more than 300 lb)

46. Tossing a coin 4 times

A jar contains 5 balls labeled 3, 5, 7, 9, and 11, respectively, while a second jar contains 4 red and 2 green balls. An experiment consists of pulling 1 ball from each jar, in turn. In Exercises 47–50, write each set using set notation.

47. The sample space

48. The number on the first ball is greater than 5.

49. The second ball is green.

50. Are the outcomes in the sample space in Exercise 47 equally likely?

In Exercises 51–58, find the probability of each event when a single card is drawn from an ordinary deck.

51. A heart **52.** A red queen

53. A face card or a heart

54. Black or a face card

55. Red, given that it is a queen

56. A jack, given that it is a face card

57. A face card, given that it is a king

58. A king, given that it is not a face card

59. Describe what is meant by disjoint sets.

60. Describe what is meant by mutually exclusive events.

61. How are disjoint sets and mutually exclusive events related?

62. Define independent events.

63. Are independent events always mutually exclusive? Are they ever mutually exclusive?

64. An uproar has raged since September 1990 over the answer to a puzzle published in *Parade* magazine, a supplement of the Sunday newspaper. In the "Ask Marilyn" column, Marilyn vos Savant answered the following question:

"Suppose you're on a game show, and you're given the choice of three doors. Behind one door is a car; behind the others, goats. You pick a door, say number 1, and the host, who knows what's behind the other doors, opens another door, say number 3, which has a goat. He then says to you, 'Do you want to pick door number 2?' Is it to your advantage to take the switch?"

Ms. vos Savant estimates that she has since received some 10,000 letters; most of them, including many from mathematicians and statisticians, disagreed with her answer. Her answer has been debated by both professionals and amateurs and tested in classes at all levels from grade school to graduate school. But by performing the experiment repeatedly, it can be shown that vos Savant's answer was correct. Find the probabilities of getting the car if you switch or do not switch, and then answer the question yourself. (*Hint:* Consider the sample space.) *Source: Parade magazine.*

Find the odds in favor of a card drawn from an ordinary deck being the following.

65. A club **66.** A black jack

67. A red face card or a queen

68. An ace or a club

Find the probabilities of getting the following sums when two fair dice are rolled.

69. 8 **70.** 0

71. At least 10 **72.** No more than 5

73. An odd number greater than 8

74. 12, given that the sum is greater than 10

75. 7, given that at least one die shows a 4

76. At least 9, given that at least one die shows a 5

77. Suppose $P(E) = 0.51$, $P(F) = 0.37$, and $P(E \cap F) = 0.22$. Find the following.

(a) $P(E \cup F)$ (b) $P(E \cap F')$

(c) $P(E' \cup F)$ (d) $P(E' \cap F')$

78. An urn contains 10 balls: 4 red and 6 blue. A second urn contains 16 red balls and an unknown number of blue balls. A single ball is drawn from each urn. The probability that both balls are the same color is 0.44. Calculate the number of blue balls in the second urn. Choose one of the following. *Source: Society of Actuaries.*

(a) 4 (b) 20 (c) 24 (d) 44 (e) 64

79. Box A contains 5 red balls and 1 black ball; box B contains 2 red balls and 3 black balls. A box is chosen, and a ball is selected from it. The probability of choosing box A is 3/8. If the selected ball is black, what is the probability that it came from box A?

80. Find the probability that the ball in Exercise 79 came from box B, given that it is red.

Let E and F be two events with $P(E) = 0.2$, $P(F) = 0.3$, and $P(E \cap F) = 0.05$. Calculate each of the following. *Source: Mike Cohen.*

81. $P(E \cup F)$ **82.** $P(E' \cap F')$ **83.** $P(E' \cap F)$

84. $P(E' \cup F')$ **85.** $P(E \cap F')$ **86.** $P(E \mid F)$

87. $P(F \mid E)$ **88.** $P(E' \mid F')$ **89.** $P(F' \mid E)$

90. $P(E' \mid E)$ **91.** $P(E \mid E \cap F)$ **92.** $P(E \mid E \cup F)$

93. Are events E and F independent? Explain.

94. Explain why the answer to Exercise 90 must be 0.

95. Explain why the answer to Exercise 91 must be 1.

APPLICATIONS

Business and Economics

96. Workplace Drug Testing In the "Ask Marilyn" column of *Parade* magazine, a reader wrote:

> "I manage a drug-testing program for an organization with 400 employees. Every three months, a random-number generator selects 100 names for testing. Afterward, these names go back into the selection pool. Obviously, the probability of an employee being chosen in one quarter is 25 percent. But what's the likelihood of being chosen over the course of a year?" *Source: Parade magazine.*

(a) Marilyn originally interpreted the question as, "What is the probability of being selected in any specific quarter in the year?" What is the answer to that question?

(b) Another reader wrote to point out that Marilyn answered a different question. What is the correct answer to the question that the reader asked?

Appliance Repairs Of the appliance repair shops listed in the phone book, 80% are competent and 20% are not. A competent shop can repair an appliance correctly 95% of the time; an incompetent shop can repair an appliance correctly 55% of the time. Suppose an appliance was repaired correctly. Find the probabilities that it was repaired by the following.

97. A competent shop   **98.** An incompetent shop

Suppose an appliance was repaired incorrectly. Find the probabilities that it was repaired by the following.

99. A competent shop   **100.** An incompetent shop

101. Find the probability that an appliance brought to a shop chosen at random is repaired correctly.

102. Are the events that a repair shop is competent and that the repair is done correctly independent? Explain.

103. Sales A company sells printers and copiers. Let E be the event "a customer buys a printer," and let F be the event "a customer buys a copier." Write the following using $\cap, \cup,$ or $'$ as necessary.

(a) A customer buys neither machine.

(b) A customer buys at least one of the machines.

104. Defective Items A sample shipment of five hair dryers is chosen at random. The probability of exactly 0, 1, 2, 3, 4, or 5 hair dryers being defective is given in the following table.

Number Defective	0	1	2	3	4	5
Probability	0.34	0.26	0.18	0.12	0.07	0.03

Find the probabilities that the following numbers of hair dryers are defective.

(a) No more than 3   (b) At least 3

105. Defective Items A manufacturer buys items from four different suppliers. The fraction of the total number of items that is obtained from each supplier, along with the probability that an item purchased from that supplier is defective, is shown in the table.

Supplier	Fraction of Total Supplied	Probability of Defective
1	0.17	0.01
2	0.39	0.02
3	0.35	0.05
4	0.09	0.03

(a) Find the probability that a randomly selected item is defective.

(b) Find the probability that a defective item came from supplier 4.

(c) Find the probability that a defective item came from supplier 2.

(d) Are the events that an item came from supplier 4 and that the item is defective independent? Explain.

106. Car Buyers The table shows the results of a survey of buyers of a certain model of car.

Car Type	Satisfied	Not Satisfied	Totals
New	300	100	
Used	450		600
Totals		250	

(a) Complete the table.

(b) How many buyers were surveyed?

(c) How many bought a new car and were satisfied?

(d) How many were not satisfied?

(e) How many bought used cars?

(f) How many of those who were not satisfied had purchased a used car?

(g) Rewrite the event stated in part (f) using the expression "given that."

(h) Find the probability of the outcome in parts (f) and (g).

(i) Find the probability that a used-car buyer is not satisfied.

(j) You should have different answers in parts (h) and (i). Explain why.

(k) Are the events that a car is new and that the customer is satisfied independent? Explain.

107. Auto Insurance An insurance company examines its pool of auto insurance customers and gathers the following information:

    (i) All customers insure at least one car.

    (ii) 70% of the customers insure more than one car.

    (iii) 20% of the customers insure a sports car.

    (iv) Of those customers who insure more than one car, 15% insure a sports car.

Calculate the probability that a randomly selected customer insures exactly one car and that car is not a sports car. Choose one of the following. (*Hint:* Draw a tree diagram, and let x be the probability that a customer who insures exactly one car insures a sports car.) *Source: Society of Actuaries.*

    (a) 0.13   **(b)** 0.21   **(c)** 0.24   **(d)** 0.25   **(e)** 0.30

108. Auto Insurance An auto insurance company has 10,000 policyholders. Each policyholder is classified as:

    (i) young or old;

    (ii) male or female; and

    (iii) married or single.

Of these policyholders, 3000 are young, 4600 are male, and 7000 are married. The policyholders can also be classified as 1320 young males, 3010 married males, and 1400 young married persons. Finally, 600 of the policyholders are young married males. How many of the company's policyholders are young, female, and single? Choose one of the following. *Source: Society of Actuaries.*

    (a) 280   **(b)** 423   **(c)** 486   **(d)** 880   **(e)** 896

109. Auto Insurance An actuary studying the insurance preferences of automobile owners makes the following conclusions:

    (i) An automobile owner is twice as likely to purchase collision coverage as disability coverage.

    (ii) The event that an automobile owner purchases collision coverage is independent of the event that he or she purchases disability coverage.

    (iii) The probability that an automobile owner purchases both collision and disability coverages is 0.15.

What is the probability that an automobile owner purchases neither collision nor disability coverage? Choose one of the following. *Source: Society of Actuaries.*

    (a) 0.18   **(b)** 0.33   **(c)** 0.48   **(d)** 0.67   **(e)** 0.82

110. Insurance An insurance company estimates that 40% of policyholders who have only an auto policy will renew next year and 60% of policyholders who have only a homeowners policy will renew next year. The company estimates that 80% of policyholders who have both an auto and a homeowners policy will renew at least one of these policies next year. Company records show that 65% of policyholders have an auto policy, 50% of policyholders have a homeowners policy, and 15% of policyholders have both an auto and a homeowners policy. Using the company's estimates, calculate the percentage of policyholders that will renew at least one policy next year. Choose one of the following. *Source: Society of Actuaries.*

    (a) 20   **(b)** 29   **(c)** 41   **(d)** 53   **(e)** 70

Life Sciences

111. Sickle Cell Anemia The table shows the four possible (equally likely) combinations when both parents are carriers of the sickle cell anemia trait. Each carrier parent has normal cells (N) and trait cells (T).

		Second Parent	
		N_2	T_2
First Parent	N_1		N_1T_2
	T_1		

    (a) Complete the table.

    (b) If the disease occurs only when two trait cells combine, find the probability that a child born to these parents will have sickle cell anemia.

    (c) The child will carry the trait but not have the disease if a normal cell combines with a trait cell. Find this probability.

    (d) Find the probability that the child is neither a carrier nor has the disease.

112. Blood Antigens In Exercise 46 of Section 7.2, we described the eight types of human blood. The percentage of the population having each type is as follows:

    O^+: 38%; O^-: 8%; A^+: 32%; A^-: 7%;
    B^+: 9%; B^-: 2%; AB^+: 3%; AB^-: 1%.

When a person receives a blood transfusion, it is important that the blood be compatible, which means that it introduces no new antigens into the recipient's blood. The following diagram helps illustrate what blood types are compatible.

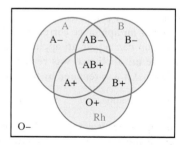

The universal blood type is O^-, since it has none of the additional antigens. The circles labeled A, B, and Rh contain blood types with the A antigen, B antigen, and Rh antigen, respectively. A person with O^- blood can be transfused only with O^- blood, because any other type would introduce a new antigen. Thus the probability that blood from a random donor is compatible is just 8%. A person with AB^+ blood already has all antigens, so the probability that blood from a random donor is compatible is 100%. Find the probability that blood from a random donor is compatible with a person with each blood type. *Source: The Mathematics Teacher.*

    (a) O^+ **(b)** A^+ **(c)** B^+

    (d) A^- **(e)** B^- **(f)** AB^-

113. Risk Factors An actuary is studying the prevalence of three health risk factors, denoted by A, B, and C, within a population of women. For each of the three factors, the probability is 0.1 that a woman in the population has only this risk factor (and no others). For any two of the three factors, the probability is 0.12 that she has exactly these two risk factors (but not the other). The probability that a woman has all three risk factors, given that she has A and B, is 1/3. What is the probability that a woman has none of the three risk factors, given that she does not have risk factor A? Choose one of the following. *Source: Society of Actuaries.*

   (a) 0.280   (b) 0.311   (c) 0.467   (d) 0.484   (e) 0.700

Social Sciences

114. Elections In the 2012 presidential election, over 126 million people voted, of which 46% were male and 54% were female. Of the male voters, 45% voted for Barack Obama and 52% voted for Mitt Romney. Of the female voters, 55% voted for Obama and 44% voted for Romney. *Source: Huffington Post.*

   (a) Find the percentage of voters who voted for Obama.

   (b) Find the probability that a randomly selected voter for Obama was male.

   (c) Find the probability that a randomly selected voter for Obama was female.

115. Television Viewing Habits A telephone survey of television viewers revealed the following information:

   20 watch situation comedies;
   19 watch reality shows;
   27 watch movies;
   19 watch movies but not reality shows;
   15 watch situation comedies but not reality shows;
   10 watch both situation comedies and movies;
    3 watch all three;
    7 watch none of these.

   (a) How many viewers were interviewed?

   (b) How many viewers watch comedies and movies but not reality shows?

   (c) How many viewers watch only movies?

   (d) How many viewers do not watch movies?

116. Randomized Response Method for Getting Honest Answers to Sensitive Questions There are many personal questions that most people would rather not answer. In fact, when a person is asked such a question, a common response is to provide a false answer. In 1965, Stanley Warner developed a method to ensure that the identity of an individual who answers a question remains anonymous, thus ensuring an honest answer to the question. For this method, instead of one sensitive question being asked to a person, there are two questions, one sensitive and one non-sensitive, and which question the person answers depends on a randomized procedure. The interviewer, who doesn't know which question a person is answering, simply records the answer given as either "Yes" or "No." In this way, there is no way of knowing to which question the person answered "Yes" or "No." Then, using conditional probability, we can estimate the percentage of people who answer "Yes" to the sensitive question. For example, suppose that the two questions are

   A: Does your birth year end in an odd digit? (Nonsensitive)
   B: Have you ever intentionally cheated on an examination? (Sensitive)

We already know that $P(\text{"Yes"} \mid \text{Question } A) = 1/2$, since half the years are even and half are odd. The answer we seek is $P(\text{"Yes"} \mid \text{Question } B)$. In this experiment, a student is asked to flip a coin and answer question A if the coin comes up heads and otherwise answer question B. Note that the interviewer does not know the outcome of the coin flip or which question is being answered. The percentage of students answering "Yes" is used to approximate $P(\text{"Yes"})$, which is then used to estimate the percentage of students who have cheated on an examination. *Source: Journal of the American Statistical Association.*

   (a) Use the fact that the event "Yes" is the union of the event "Yes and Question A" with the event "Yes and Question B" to prove that

   $$P(\text{"Yes"} \mid \text{Question } B)$$
   $$= \frac{P(\text{"Yes"}) - P(\text{"Yes"} \mid \text{Question } A) \cdot P(\text{Question } A)}{P(\text{Question } B)}.$$

   (b) If this technique is tried on 100 subjects and 60 answered "Yes," what is the approximated probability that a person randomly selected from the group has intentionally cheated on an examination?

117. Police Lineup To illustrate the difficulties with eyewitness identifications from police lineups, John Allen Paulos considers a "lineup" of three pennies, in which we know that two are fair (innocent) and the third (the culprit) has a 75% probability of landing heads. The probability of picking the culprit by chance is, of course, 1/3. Suppose we observe three heads in a row on one of the pennies. If we then guess that this penny is the culprit, what is the probability that we're right? *Source: Who's Counting.*

118. SIDS On July 15, 2005, a panel in England ruled that Roy Meadow, a renowned expert on child abuse and co-founder of London's Royal College of Paediatrics and Child Health, should be erased from the register of physicians in Britain for his faulty statistics at the trial of Sally Clark, who was convicted of murdering her first two babies. Meadow testified at the trial that the probability of a baby dying of sudden death syndrome (SIDS) is 1/8543. He then calculated that the probability of two babies in a family dying of SIDS is $(1/8543)^2 \approx 1/73,000,000$. With such a small probability of both babies dying of SIDS, he concluded that the babies were instead murdered. What assumption did Meadow make in doing this calculation? Discuss reasons why this assumption may be invalid. (*Note:* Clark spent three years in prison before her conviction was reversed.) *Source: Science.*

Physical Sciences

119. Earthquake It has been reported that government scientists have predicted that the odds for a major earthquake occurring in the San Francisco Bay area during the next 30 years are 9 to 1. What is the probability that a major earthquake will occur during the next 30 years in San Francisco? *Source: The San Francisco Chronicle.*

General Interest

120. Making a First Down A first down is desirable in football—it guarantees four more plays by the team making it, assuming no score or turnover occurs in the plays. After getting a first down, a team can get another by advancing the ball at least 10 yards. During the four plays given by a first down, a team's position will be indicated by a phrase such as "third and 4," which means that the team has already had two of its four plays, and that 4 more yards are needed to get 10 yards necessary for another first down. An article in a management journal offers the following results for 189 games for a particular National Football League season. "Trials" represents the number of times a team tried to make a first down, given that it was currently playing either a third or a fourth down. Here, n represents the number of yards still needed for a first down. *Source: Management Science.*

n	Trials	Successes	Probability of Making First Down with n Yards to Go
1	543	388	
2	327	186	
3	356	146	
4	302	97	
5	336	91	

(a) Complete the table.

(b) Why is the sum of the answers in the table not equal to 1?

121. States Of the 50 United States, the following is true:

24 are west of the Mississippi River (western states);*

22 had populations less than 3.6 million in the 2010 census (small states);

26 begin with the letters A through M (early states);

9 are large late (beginning with the letters N through Z) eastern states;

14 are small western states;

11 are small early states;

7 are small early western states.

(a) How many western states had populations more than 3.6 million in the 2010 census and begin with the letters N through Z?

(b) How many states east of the Mississippi had populations more than 3.6 million in the 2010 census?

122. Music Country-western songs often emphasize three basic themes: love, prison, and trucks. A survey of the local country-western radio station produced the following data:

12 songs were about a truckdriver who was in love while in prison;

13 were about a prisoner in love;

28 were about a person in love;

18 were about a truckdriver in love;

33 were about people not in prison;

18 were about prisoners;

15 were about truckdrivers who were in prison;

16 were about truckdrivers who were not in prison.

*We count here states such as Minnesota, which has more than half of its area to the west of the Mississippi.

(a) How many songs were surveyed?

Find the number of songs about

(b) truckdrivers;

(c) prisoners who are neither truckdrivers nor in love;

(d) prisoners who are in love but are not truckdrivers;

(e) prisoners who are not truckdrivers;

(f) people not in love.

123. Gambling The following puzzle was featured on the Puzzler part of the radio program *Car Talk* on February 23, 2002. A con man puts three cards in a bag; one card is green on both sides, one is red on both sides, and the third is green on one side and red on the other. He lets you pick one card out of the bag and put it on a table, so you can see that a red side is face up, but neither of you can see the other side. He offers to bet you even money that the other side is also red. In other words, if you bet $1, you lose if the other side is red but get back $2 if the other side is green. Is this a good bet? What is the probability that the other side is red? *Source: Car Talk.*

124. Missiles In his novel *Debt of Honor*, Tom Clancy writes the following:

"There were ten target points—missile silos, the intelligence data said, and it pleased the Colonel [Zacharias] to be eliminating the hateful things, even though the price of that was the lives of other men. There were only three of them [bombers], and his bomber, like the others, carried only eight weapons [smart bombs]. The total number of weapons carried for the mission was only twenty-four, with two designated for each silo, and Zacharias's last four for the last target. Two bombs each. Every bomb had a 95% probability of hitting within four meters of the aim point, pretty good numbers really, except that this sort of mission had precisely no margin for error. Even the paper probability was less than half a percent chance of a double miss, but that number times ten targets meant a 5% chance that [at least] one missile would survive, and that could not be tolerated." *Source: Debt of Honor.*

Determine whether the calculations in this quote are correct by the following steps.

(a) Given that each bomb had a 95% probability of hitting the missile silo on which it was dropped, and that two bombs were dropped on each silo, what is the probability of a double miss?

(b) What is the probability that a specific silo was destroyed (that is, that at least one bomb of the two bombs struck the silo)?

(c) What is the probability that all ten silos were destroyed?

(d) What is the probability that at least one silo survived? Does this agree with the quote?

(e) What assumptions need to be made for the calculations in parts (a) through (d) to be valid? Discuss whether these assumptions seem reasonable.

125. Viewing Habits A survey of a group's viewing habits over the last year revealed the following information:

(i) 28% watched gymnastics;

(ii) 29% watched baseball;

(iii) 19% watched soccer;

(iv) 14% watched gymnastics and baseball;

(v) 12% watched baseball and soccer;

(vi) 10% watched gymnastics and soccer;

(vii) 8% watched all three sports.

Calculate the percentage of the group that watched none of the three sports during the last year. Choose one of the following. *Source: Society of Actuaries.*

(a) 24   (b) 36   (c) 41

(d) 52   (e) 60

EXTENDED APPLICATION

MEDICAL DIAGNOSIS

When a patient exhibits symptoms that may, or may not, indicate one of many possible diseases, an understanding of probability can be useful. Data giving the probability that someone with a particular disease will exhibit certain symptoms are readily available. What the medical team wants to know, however, is the probability that the patient has the disease, given the presence of these specific symptoms. This is a classic situation for Bayes' Theorem: We know $P(A|B)$, but what we really want to know is $P(B|A)$.

People suffering from hypothyroidism (underactive thyroid) can experience tiredness, inability to tolerate cold, and weight gain. By contrast, hyperthyroidism, or overactive thyroid, can speed up virtually every function of the body.

The table at the bottom of the page contains data from a study of 879 people. These included 314 with normal thyroids, 268 with some thyroid abnormality but who were otherwise euthyroid (normal thyroid), 123 who were hypothyroid, and 174 who were hyperthyroid. The original data listed 21 symptoms, but for simplicity we have listed only the first five, with the proportion of patients in each group exhibiting each symptom.

These numbers tell us, for example, that a hypothyroid person has a 0.06 probability of exhibiting a recent onset of nervousness. The figures for a euthyroid or a hyperthyroid person are 0.37 and 0.92, respectively. If we denote

T_1 = patient is hypothyroid,

T_2 = patient is euthyroid, and

T_3 = patient is hyperthyroid,

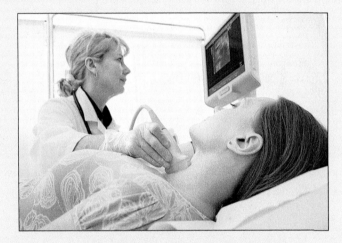

then we could write this information as $P(N|T_1) = 0.06$, $P(N|T_2) = 0.37$, and $P(N|T_3) = 0.92$. It is known that for the general population, $P(T_1) = 0.15$, $P(T_2) = 0.65$, and $P(T_3) = 0.20$.

The study's authors assumed the symptoms to be independent. For example, if a patient is euthyroid, they calculated the probability that the patient had a recent onset of both nervousness and heat sensitivity as

$$P(N \cap H|T_2) = P(N|T_2)P(H|T_2) = (0.37)(0.17) = 0.06,$$

or 6%. (Following the researchers' practice in most of their calculations, we will round all probabilities to the hundredth place. Higher precision is not justified because some of the original probabilities were known only to the hundredth place.)

Symptom	Hypothyroid	Euthyroid	Hyperthyroid
Recent onset of nervousness (N)	0.06	0.37	0.92
Recent onset of heat sensitivity (H)	0.00	0.17	0.74
Recent onset of increased sweating (S)	0.13	0.25	0.68
Recent onset of increased appetite (A)	0.03	0.10	0.61
Recent onset of weight loss (W)	0.13	0.45	0.84

Suppose a patient has a recent onset of nervousness, and the medical team wants to know the probability of hyperthyroidism. We know that $P(N|T_3) = 0.92$, but the medical team wants to know $P(T_3|N)$. For the general population, $P(T_3) = 0.20$, but we would expect the probability to be higher for someone with a symptom. The question is how much higher. Using Bayes' Theorem,

$$P(T_3|N) = \frac{P(N|T_3)P(T_3)}{P(N|T_1)P(T_1) + P(N|T_2)P(T_2) + P(N|T_3)P(T_3)}$$

$$= \frac{(0.92)(0.20)}{(0.06)(0.15) + (0.37)(0.65) + (0.92)(0.20)}$$

$$\approx 0.42.$$

There is a 42% chance that a patient with a recent onset of nervousness is hyperthyroid. *Source: JAMA.*

EXERCISES

1. Find the probability that a randomly selected patient has a recent onset of nervousness and is euthyroid.

2. Find the probability that a randomly selected patient has a recent onset of heat sensitivity.

3. Find the probability that a patient with a recent onset of heat sensitivity is hyperthyroid.

4. Find the probability that a patient with a recent onset of weight loss is hypothyroid.

 5. Put the probabilities in the table into a spreadsheet. Then create additional cells in the spreadsheet that will calculate the probability of hypothyroid, euthyroid, or hyperthyroid given any of the five symptoms. (*Hint:* To copy and paste the formula from one cell into another, you may want to use notation such as A$1, which allows the column to change but keeps the row fixed at row 1, or A1, which keeps the row and column fixed.)

DIRECTIONS FOR GROUP PROJECT

Find an article on medical decision making from a medical journal and develop a doctor-patient scenario for that particular decision. Then create a role-playing activity in which the physician and medical team present the various options and the mathematics associated with making such a decision to a patient. Make sure to present the mathematics in a manner that the average patient might understand. (Hint: Many leading medical journals include articles on decision making in medical settings; one such journal is Medical Decision Making.*)*

8 Counting Principles; Further Probability Topics

If you have 31 ice cream flavors available, how many different three-scoop cones can you make? The answer, which is surprisingly large, involves counting permutations or combinations, the subject of the first two sections in this chapter. The counting formulas we will develop have important applications in probability theory.

f we flip two coins and record heads or tails for each coin, we can list the four possible outcomes in the sample space as $S = \{hh, ht, th, tt\}$. But what if we flip 10 coins? As we shall see, there are over 1000 possible outcomes, which makes a list of the sample space impractical. Fortunately, there are methods for counting the outcomes in a set without actually listing them. We introduce these methods in the first two sections, and then we use this approach in the third section to find probabilities. In the fourth section, we introduce binomial experiments, which consist of repeated independent trials with only two possible outcomes, and develop a formula for binomial probabilities. The final section continues the discussion of probability distributions that we began in Chapter 7.

8.1 The Multiplication Principle; Permutations

APPLY IT **In how many ways can seven panelists be seated in a row of seven chairs?** *Before we answer this question in Example 8, we will begin with a simpler example.*

Suppose a breakfast consists of one pastry, for which you can choose a bagel, a muffin, or a donut, and one beverage, for which you can choose coffee or juice. How many different breakfasts can you have? For each of the 3 pastries there are 2 different beverages, or a total of $3 \cdot 2 = 6$ different breakfasts, as shown in Figure 1. This example illustrates a general principle of counting, called the **multiplication principle**.

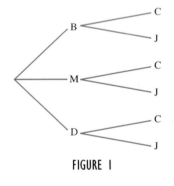

FIGURE 1

Multiplication Principle

Suppose n choices must be made, with

$$m_1 \text{ ways to make choice 1,}$$
$$m_2 \text{ ways to make choice 2,}$$

and so on, with

$$m_n \text{ ways to make choice } n.$$

Then there are

$$m_1 \cdot m_2 \cdot \cdots \cdot m_n$$

different ways to make the entire sequence of choices.

EXAMPLE 1 Combination Lock

A certain combination lock can be set to open to any 3-letter sequence.

(a) How many sequences are possible?

SOLUTION Since there are 26 letters in the alphabet, there are 26 choices for each of the 3 letters. By the multiplication principle, there are $26 \cdot 26 \cdot 26 = 17{,}576$ different sequences.

(b) How many sequences are possible if no letter is repeated?

SOLUTION There are 26 choices for the first letter. It cannot be used again, so there are 25 choices for the second letter and then 24 choices for the third letter. Consequently, the number of such sequences is $26 \cdot 25 \cdot 24 = 15{,}600$. **TRY YOUR TURN 1**

YOUR TURN 1 A combination lock can be set to open to any 4-digit sequence. How many sequences are possible? How many sequences are possible if no digit is repeated?

EXAMPLE 2   Morse Code

Morse code uses a sequence of dots and dashes to represent letters and words. How many sequences are possible with at most 3 symbols?

SOLUTION   "At most 3" means "1 or 2 or 3" here. Each symbol may be either a dot or a dash. Thus the following number of sequences are possible in each case.

Morse Code	
Number of Symbols	Number of Sequences
1	2
2	$2 \cdot 2 = 4$
3	$2 \cdot 2 \cdot 2 = 8$

Altogether, $2 + 4 + 8 = 14$ different sequences are possible.

EXAMPLE 3   I Ching

yin   yang

FIGURE 2

An ancient Chinese philosophical work known as the *I Ching (Book of Changes)* is often used as an oracle from which people can seek and obtain advice. The philosophy describes the duality of the universe in terms of two primary forces: *yin* (passive, dark, receptive) and *yang* (active, light, creative). Figure 2 shows the traditional symbol for yin and yang. The yin energy can also be represented by a broken line (– –) and the yang by a solid line (—). These lines are written on top of one another in groups of three, known as *trigrams*. For example, the trigram ☱ is called *Tui,* the Joyous, and has the image of a lake.

(a) How many trigrams are there altogether?

   SOLUTION   Think of choosing between the 2 types of lines for each of the 3 positions in the trigram. There will be 2 choices for each position, so there are $2 \cdot 2 \cdot 2 = 8$ different trigrams.

(b) The trigrams are grouped together, one on top of the other, in pairs known as *hexagrams.* Each hexagram represents one aspect of the *I Ching* philosophy. How many hexagrams are there?

   SOLUTION   For each position in the hexagram there are 8 possible trigrams, giving $8 \cdot 8 = 64$ hexagrams.

EXAMPLE 4   Books

YOUR TURN 2   A teacher is lining up 8 students for a spelling bee. How many different line-ups are possible?

A teacher has 5 different books that he wishes to arrange side by side. How many different arrangements are possible?

SOLUTION   Five choices will be made, one for each space that will hold a book. Any of the 5 books could be chosen for the first space. There are 4 choices for the second space, since 1 book has already been placed in the first space; there are 3 choices for the third space, and so on. By the multiplication principle, the number of different possible arrangements is $5 \cdot 4 \cdot 3 \cdot 2 \cdot 1 = 120$.   **TRY YOUR TURN 2**

FOR REVIEW

The natural numbers, also referred to as the positive integers, are the numbers 1, 2, 3, 4, etc.

   The use of the multiplication principle often leads to products such as $5 \cdot 4 \cdot 3 \cdot 2 \cdot 1$, the product of all the natural numbers from 5 down to 1. If n is a natural number, the symbol $n!$ (read "n *factorial*") denotes the product of all the natural numbers from n down to 1. If $n = 1$, this formula is understood to give $1! = 1$.

Factorial Notation

For any natural number n,

$$n! = n(n - 1)(n - 2) \cdots (3)(2)(1).$$

Also, by definition,

$$0! = 1.$$

With this symbol, the product $5 \cdot 4 \cdot 3 \cdot 2 \cdot 1$ can be written as 5!. Also, $3! = 3 \cdot 2 \cdot 1 = 6$. The definition of $n!$ could be used to show that $n[(n - 1)]! = n!$ for all natural numbers $n \geq 2$. It is helpful if this result also holds for $n = 1$. This can happen only if 0! equals 1, as defined above.

As n gets large, $n!$ grows very quickly. For example, $5! = 120$, while $10! = 3,628,800$. Most calculators can be used to determine $n!$ for small values of n. A calculator with a 10-digit display and scientific notation capability will usually give the exact value of $n!$ for $n \leq 13$, and approximate values of $n!$ for $14 \leq n \leq 69$. The value of 70! is approximately 1.198×10^{100}, which is too large for most calculators. To get a sense of how large 70! is, suppose a computer counted the numbers from 1 to 70! at a rate of 1 billion numbers per second. If the computer started when the universe began, by now it would have calculated only a tiny fraction of the total.

TECHNOLOGY NOTE

On many graphing calculators, the factorial of a number is accessible through a menu. On the TI-84 Plus C, for example, this menu is found by pressing the MATH key, selecting PROB (for probability), and then selecting the !.

YOUR TURN 3 A teacher wishes to place 5 out of 8 different books on her shelf. How many arrangements of 5 books are possible?

EXAMPLE 5 Books

Suppose the teacher in Example 4 wishes to place only 3 of the 5 books on his desk. How many arrangements of 3 books are possible?

SOLUTION The teacher again has 5 ways to fill the first space, 4 ways to fill the second space, and 3 ways to fill the third. Since he wants to use only 3 books, only 3 spaces can be filled (3 events) instead of 5, for $5 \cdot 4 \cdot 3 = 60$ arrangements. **TRY YOUR TURN 3**

Permutations The answer 60 in Example 5 is called the number of *permutations* of 5 things taken 3 at a time. A **permutation** of r (where $r \geq 1$) elements from a set of n elements is any specific ordering or arrangement, *without repetition*, of the r elements. Each rearrangement of the r elements is a different permutation. The number of permutations of n things taken r at a time (with $r \leq n$) is written $P(n, r)$.* Based on the work in Example 5,

$$P(5, 3) = 5 \cdot 4 \cdot 3 = 60.$$

Factorial notation can be used to express this product as follows.

$$5 \cdot 4 \cdot 3 = 5 \cdot 4 \cdot 3 \cdot \frac{2 \cdot 1}{2 \cdot 1} = \frac{5 \cdot 4 \cdot 3 \cdot 2 \cdot 1}{2 \cdot 1} = \frac{5!}{2!} = \frac{5!}{(5 - 3)!}$$

This example illustrates the general rule of permutations, which can be stated as follows.

Permutations

If $P(n, r)$ (where $r \leq n$) is the number of permutations of n elements taken r at a time, then

$$P(n, r) = \frac{n!}{(n - r)!}.$$

*An alternate notation for $P(n, r)$ is $_nP_r$.

| CAUTION | The letter P here represents *permutations*, not *probability*. In probability notation, the quantity in parentheses describes an *event*. In permutations notation, the quantity in parentheses always comprises *two numbers*. |

The proof of the permutations rule follows the discussion in Example 5. There are n ways to choose the first of the r elements, $n - 1$ ways to choose the second, and $n - r + 1$ ways to choose the rth element, so that

$$P(n, r) = n(n - 1)(n - 2) \cdots (n - r + 1).$$

Now multiply on the right by $(n - r)!/(n - r)!$.

$$P(n, r) = n(n - 1)(n - 2) \cdots (n - r + 1) \cdot \frac{(n - r)!}{(n - r)!}$$

$$= \frac{n(n - 1)(n - 2) \cdots (n - r + 1)(n - r)!}{(n - r)!}$$

$$= \frac{n!}{(n - r)!}$$

Because we defined 0! equal to 1, the formula for permutations gives the special case

$$P(n, n) = \frac{n!}{(n - n)!} = \frac{n!}{0!} = \frac{n!}{1} = n!.$$

This result also follows from the multiplication principle, because $P(n, n)$ gives the number of permutations of n objects, and there are n choices for the first object, $n - 1$ for the second, and so on, down to just 1 choice for the last object. Example 4 illustrated this idea.

> $P(n, n)$
> The number of permutations of a set with n elements is $n!$; that is $P(n, n) = n!$.

EXAMPLE 6   Permutations of Letters

Find the following.

(a) The number of permutations of the letters A, B, and C.

SOLUTION   By the formula $P(n, n) = n!$, with $n = 3$,

$$P(3, 3) = 3! = 3 \cdot 2 \cdot 1 = 6.$$

The 6 *permutations* (or *arrangements*) are ABC, ACB, BAC, BCA, CAB, CBA.

(b) The number of permutations if just 2 of the letters A, B, and C are to be used

SOLUTION   Find $P(3, 2)$.

$$P(3, 2) = \frac{3!}{(3 - 2)!} = \frac{3!}{1!} = 3! = 6$$

This result is exactly the same answer as in part (a). This is because, in the case of $P(3, 3)$, after the first 2 choices are made, the third is already determined, as shown in the table below.

YOUR TURN 4   Find the number of permutations of the letters L, M, N, O, P, and Q, if just three of the letters are to be used.

Permutations of Three Letters					
First Two Letters	AB	AC	BA	BC	CA	CB
Third Letter	C	B	C	A	B	A

TRY YOUR TURN 4

To find $P(n, r)$, we can use either the permutations formula or direct application of the multiplication principle, as the following example shows.

EXAMPLE 7 Politics

In a recent election, eight candidates sought the Republican nomination for president. In how many ways could voters rank their first, second, and third choices?

SOLUTION

Method 1
Calculating by Hand

This is the same as finding the number of permutations of 8 elements taken 3 at a time. Since there are 3 choices to be made, the multiplication principle gives $P(8, 3) = 8 \cdot 7 \cdot 6 = 336$. Alternatively, use the permutations formula to get

$$P(8, 3) = \frac{8!}{(8 - 3)!} = \frac{8!}{5!} = \frac{8 \cdot 7 \cdot 6 \cdot 5 \cdot 4 \cdot 3 \cdot 2 \cdot 1}{5 \cdot 4 \cdot 3 \cdot 2 \cdot 1} = 8 \cdot 7 \cdot 6 = 336.$$

Method 2
Graphing Calculator

Graphing calculators have the capacity to compute permutations. For example, on a TI-84 Plus C, $P(8, 3)$ can be calculated by inputting 8 followed by nPr (found in the MATH-PROB menu), and a 3 yielding 336, as shown in Figure 3.

FIGURE 3

Method 3
Spreadsheet

Spreadsheets can also compute permutations. For example, in Microsoft Excel, $P(8, 3)$ can be calculated by inputting 8 and 3 in cells, say, A1 and B1, and then typing "=FACT(A1)/FACT(A1-B1)" in cell C1 or, for that matter, any other cell.

CAUTION When calculating the number of permutations with the formula, do not try to cancel unlike factorials. For example,

$$\frac{8!}{4!} \neq 2! = 2 \cdot 1 = 2.$$

$$\frac{8!}{4!} = \frac{8 \cdot 7 \cdot 6 \cdot 5 \cdot 4 \cdot 3 \cdot 2 \cdot 1}{4 \cdot 3 \cdot 2 \cdot 1} = 8 \cdot 7 \cdot 6 \cdot 5 = 1680.$$

Always write out the factors first, then cancel where appropriate.

EXAMPLE 8 Television Panel

A televised talk show will include 4 women and 3 men as panelists.

(a) In how many ways can the panelists be seated in a row of 7 chairs?

 APPLY IT

SOLUTION Find $P(7, 7)$, the total number of ways to seat 7 panelists in 7 chairs.

$$P(7, 7) = 7! = 7 \cdot 6 \cdot 5 \cdot 4 \cdot 3 \cdot 2 \cdot 1 = 5040$$

There are 5040 ways to seat the 7 panelists.

(b) In how many ways can the panelists be seated if the men and women are to be alternated?

SOLUTION Use the multiplication principle. In order to alternate men and women, a woman must be seated in the first chair (since there are 4 women and only 3 men), any of the men next, and so on. Thus there are 4 ways to fill the first seat, 3 ways to fill the second seat, 3 ways to fill the third seat (with any of the 3 remaining women), and so on. This gives

$$\underset{W_1}{4} \cdot \underset{M_1}{3} \cdot \underset{W_2}{3} \cdot \underset{M_2}{2} \cdot \underset{W_3}{2} \cdot \underset{M_3}{1} \cdot \underset{W_4}{1} = 144$$

ways to seat the panelists.

(c) In how many ways can the panelists be seated if the men must sit together, and the women must also sit together?

SOLUTION Use the multiplication principle. We first must decide how to arrange the two groups (men and women). There are 2! ways of doing this. Next, there are 4! ways of arranging the women and 3! ways of arranging the men, for a total of

$$2! \, 4! \, 3! = 2 \cdot 24 \cdot 6 = 288$$

ways.

YOUR TURN 5 Two freshmen, 2 sophomores, 2 juniors, and 3 seniors are on a panel. In how many ways can the panelists be seated if each class must sit together?

(d) In how many ways can one woman and one man from the panel be selected?

SOLUTION There are 4 ways to pick the woman and 3 ways to pick the man, for a total of

$$4 \cdot 3 = 12$$

ways.

TRY YOUR TURN 5

If the n objects in a permutation are not all distinguishable—that is, if there are n_1 of type 1, n_2 of type 2, and so on for r different types, then the number of **distinguishable permutations** is

$$\frac{n!}{n_1! \, n_2! \cdots n_r!}.$$

For example, suppose we want to find the number of permutations of the numbers 1, 1, 4, 4, 4. We cannot distinguish between the two 1's or among the three 4's, so using 5! would give too many distinguishable arrangements. Since the two 1's are indistinguishable and account for 2! of the permutations, we divide 5! by 2!. Similarly, we also divide by 3! to account for the three indistinguishable 4's. This gives

$$\frac{5!}{2! \, 3!} = 10$$

permutations.

EXAMPLE 9 Mississippi

In how many ways can the letters in the word *Mississippi* be arranged?

SOLUTION This word contains 1 m, 4 i's, 4 s's, and 2 p's. To use the formula, let $n = 11$, $n_1 = 1$, $n_2 = 4$, $n_3 = 4$, and $n_4 = 2$ to get

$$\frac{11!}{1! \, 4! \, 4! \, 2!} = 34{,}650$$

YOUR TURN 6 In how many ways can the letters in the word *Tennessee* be arranged?

arrangements.

TRY YOUR TURN 6

EXAMPLE 10 Yogurt

NOTE
If Example 9 had asked for the number of ways that the letters in a word with 11 *different* letters could be arranged, the answer would be 11! = 39,916,800.

A student buys 3 cherry yogurts, 2 raspberry yogurts, and 2 blueberry yogurts. She puts them in her dormitory refrigerator to eat one a day for the next week. Assuming yogurts of the same flavor are indistinguishable, in how many ways can she select yogurts to eat for the next week?

YOUR TURN 7 A student has 4 pairs of identical blue socks, 5 pairs of identical brown socks, 3 pairs of identical black socks, and 2 pairs of identical white socks. In how many ways can he select socks to wear for the next two weeks?

SOLUTION This problem is again one of distinguishable permutations. The 7 yogurts can be selected in 7! ways, but since the 3 cherry, 2 raspberry, and 2 blueberry yogurts are indistinguishable, the total number of distinguishable orders in which the yogurts can be selected is

$$\frac{7!}{3!\,2!\,2!} = 210.$$

TRY YOUR TURN 7

8.1 EXERCISES

In Exercises 1–12, evaluate the factorial or permutation.

1. 6!
2. 7!
3. 15!
4. 16!
5. $P(13, 2)$
6. $P(12, 3)$
7. $P(38, 17)$
8. $P(33, 19)$
9. $P(n, 0)$
10. $P(n, n)$
11. $P(n, 1)$
12. $P(n, n - 1)$

13. How many different types of homes are available if a builder offers a choice of 6 basic plans, 3 roof styles, and 2 exterior finishes?

14. A menu offers a choice of 3 salads, 8 main dishes, and 7 desserts. How many different meals consisting of one salad, one main dish, and one dessert are possible?

15. A couple has narrowed down the choice of a name for their new baby to 4 first names and 5 middle names. How many different first- and middle-name arrangements are possible?

16. In a club with 16 members, how many ways can a slate of 3 officers consisting of president, vice-president, and secretary/treasurer be chosen?

17. Define *permutation* in your own words.

18. Explain the difference between *distinguishable* and *indistinguishable* permutations.

19. In Example 6, there are six 3-letter permutations of the letters A, B, and C. How many 3-letter subsets (unordered groups of letters) are there?

20. In Example 6, how many unordered 2-letter subsets of the letters A, B, and C are there?

21. Find the number of distinguishable permutations of the letters in each word.

   (a) initial   (b) little   (c) decreed

22. A printer has 5 A's, 4 B's, 2 C's, and 2 D's. How many different "words" are possible that use all these letters? (A "word" does not have to have any meaning here.)

23. Kelly Clark has different books to arrange on a shelf: 4 blue, 3 green, and 2 red.

   (a) In how many ways can the books be arranged on a shelf?

   (b) If books of the same color are to be grouped together, how many arrangements are possible?

   (c) In how many distinguishable ways can the books be arranged if books of the same color are identical but need not be grouped together?

   (d) In how many ways can you select 3 books, one of each color, if the order in which the books are selected does not matter?

   (e) In how many ways can you select 3 books, one of each color, if the order in which the books are selected matters?

24. A child has a set of differently shaped plastic objects. There are 3 pyramids, 4 cubes, and 7 spheres.

   (a) In how many ways can she arrange the objects in a row if each is a different color?

   (b) How many arrangements are possible if objects of the same shape must be grouped together and each object is a different color?

   (c) In how many distinguishable ways can the objects be arranged in a row if objects of the same shape are also the same color (and thus indistinguishable) but need not be grouped together?

   (d) In how many ways can you select 3 objects, one of each shape, if the order in which the objects are selected does not matter and each object is a different color?

   (e) In how many ways can you select 3 objects, one of each shape, if the order in which the objects are selected matters and each object is a different color?

25. If you already knew the value of 9!, how could you find the value of 10! quickly?

26. Given that 450! is approximately equal to $1.7333687 \times 10^{1000}$ (to 8 digits of accuracy), find 451! to 7 digits of accuracy.

27. When calculating $n!$, the number of ending zeros in the answer can be determined prior to calculating the actual number by finding the number of times 5 can be factored from $n!$. For example, 7! has only one 5 occurring in its calculation, and so there is only one ending zero in 5040. The number 10! has two 5's (one from the 5 and one from the 10) and so there must be two ending zeros in the answer 3,628,800. Use this idea to determine the number of zeros that occur in the following factorials, and then explain why this works.

   (a) 13!   (b) 27!   (c) 75!

28. Because of the view screen, calculators show only a fixed number of digits, often 10 digits. Thus, an approximation of a number will be shown by including only the 10 largest place values of the number. Using the ideas from the previous exercise, determine if the following numbers are correct or if they are incorrect by checking if they have the correct number of ending zeros. (*Note:* Just because a number has the correct number of zeros does not imply that it is correct.)

  (a) $12! = 479{,}001{,}610$

  (b) $23! = 25{,}852{,}016{,}740{,}000{,}000{,}000{,}000{,}000$

  (c) $15! = 1{,}307{,}643{,}680{,}000$

  (d) $14! = 87{,}178{,}291{,}200$

29. Some students find it puzzling that $0! = 1$, and think that $0!$ should equal 0. If this were true, what would be the value of $P(4, 4)$ using the permutations formula?

APPLICATIONS

Business and Economics

30. **Messenger Bags** Timbuk2 sells custom messenger bags in 4 sizes. For each size, there are 53 color/fabric combinations. Any of these 53 can be chosen for the left, center, and right panel. In addition, there are 18 choices of binding color, 27 choices of logo color, 12 choices of liner color, and 48 choices of strap pad color. There are 3 choices for the interior style. The bag can be right- or left-handed. It can be ordered with or without a grab strap, a chiller insert, a camera insert, and a water-bottle pocket. How many different Timbuk2 bags are possible? *Source: Timbuk2.com.*

31. **Marketing** In a recent marketing campaign, Olive Garden Italian Restaurant® offered a "Never-Ending Pasta Bowl." The customer could order an array of pasta dishes, selecting from 7 types of pasta and 6 types of sauce, including 2 with meat.

  (a) If the customer selects one pasta type and one sauce type, how many different "pasta bowls" can a customer order?

  (b) How many different "pasta bowls" can a customer order without meat?

32. **Investments** Kristen Elmore's financial advisor has given her a list of 9 potential investments and has asked her to select and rank her favorite five. In how many different ways can she do this?

33. **Scheduling** A local television station has eleven slots for commercials during a special broadcast. Six restaurants and 5 stores have bought slots for the broadcast.

  (a) In how many ways can the commercials be arranged?

  (b) In how many ways can the commercials be arranged so that the restaurants are grouped together and the stores are grouped together?

  (c) In how many ways can the commercials be arranged so that the restaurant and store commercials are alternating?

Life Sciences

34. **Drug Sequencing** Twelve drugs have been found to be effective in the treatment of a disease. It is believed that the sequence in which the drugs are administered is important in the effectiveness of the treatment. In how many different sequences can 5 of the 12 drugs be administered?

35. **Insect Classification** A biologist is attempting to classify 52,000 species of insects by assigning 3 initials to each species. Is it possible to classify all the species in this way? If not, how many initials should be used?

36. **Science Conference** At an annual college science conference, student presentations are scheduled one after another in the afternoon session. This year, 5 students are presenting in biology, 5 students are presenting in chemistry, and 2 students are presenting in physics.

  (a) In how many ways can the presentations be scheduled?

  (b) In how many ways can the presentations be scheduled so that each subject is grouped together?

  (c) In how many ways can the presentations be scheduled if the conference must begin and end with a physics presentation?

Social Sciences

37. **Social Science Experiment** In an experiment on social interaction, 6 people will sit in 6 seats in a row. In how many ways can this be done?

38. **Election Ballots** In an election with 3 candidates for one office and 6 candidates for another office, how many different ballots may be printed?

General Interest

39. **Baseball Teams** A baseball team has 19 players. How many 9-player batting orders are possible?

40. **Union Elections** A chapter of union Local 715 has 35 members. In how many different ways can the chapter select a president, a vice-president, a treasurer, and a secretary?

41. **Programming Music** A concert to raise money for an economics prize is to consist of 5 works: 2 overtures, 2 sonatas, and a piano concerto.

  (a) In how many ways can the program be arranged?

  (b) In how many ways can the program be arranged if an overture must come first?

42. **Programming Music** A zydeco band from Louisiana will play 5 traditional and 3 original Cajun compositions at a concert. In how many ways can they arrange the program if

  (a) they begin with a traditional piece?

  (b) an original piece will be played last?

43. **Radio Station Call Letters** How many different 4-letter radio station call letters can be made if

  (a) the first letter must be K or W and no letter may be repeated?

  (b) repeats are allowed, but the first letter is K or W?

  (c) the first letter is K or W, there are no repeats, and the last letter is R?

44. **Telephone Numbers** How many 7-digit telephone numbers are possible if the first digit cannot be zero and

  (a) only odd digits may be used?

  (b) the telephone number must be a multiple of 10 (that is, it must end in zero)?

  (c) the telephone number must be a multiple of 100?

  (d) the first 3 digits are 481?

  (e) no repetitions are allowed?

Several years ago, the United States began running out of telephone numbers. Telephone companies introduced new area codes as numbers were used up, and eventually almost all area codes were used up.

45. **(a)** Until recently, all area codes had a 0 or 1 as the middle digit, and the first digit could not be 0 or 1. How many area codes are there with this arrangement? How many telephone numbers does the current 7-digit sequence permit per area code? (The 3-digit sequence that follows the area code cannot start with 0 or 1. Assume there are no other restrictions.)

(b) The actual number of area codes under the previous system was 152. Explain the discrepancy between this number and your answer to part (a).

(c) The shortage of area codes was avoided by removing the restriction on the second digit. (This resulted in problems for some older equipment, which used the second digit to determine that a long-distance call was being made.) How many area codes are available under the new system?

46. IP Addresses   Every computer or other device connected to the Internet has an IP address, which until recently consisted of 32 binary digits, known as bits, each of which can be 0 or 1. As all the available IP addresses were becoming used up, a new system was devised with 128 bits. How many IP addresses were available under the older system, and how many are available with the new system? *Source: The New York Times.*

47. License Plates   For many years, the state of California used 3 letters followed by 3 digits on its automobile license plates.

(a) How many different license plates are possible with this arrangement?

(b) When the state ran out of new numbers, the order was reversed to 3 digits followed by 3 letters. How many new license plate numbers were then possible?

(c) By 1980, the numbers described in part (b) were also used up. The state then issued plates with 1 digit followed by 3 letters and then 3 digits. How many new license plate numbers will this provide?

48. Social Security Numbers   A social security number has 9 digits. How many social security numbers are there? The U.S. population in 2014 was about 318 million. Is it possible for every U.S. resident to have a unique social security number? (Assume no restrictions.)

49. Postal Zip Codes   The U.S. Postal Service currently uses 5-digit zip codes in most areas. How many zip codes are possible if there are no restrictions on the digits used? How many would be possible if the first number could not be 0?

50. Postal Zip Codes   The U.S. Postal Service is encouraging the use of 9-digit zip codes in some areas, adding 4 digits after the usual 5-digit code. How many such zip codes are possible with no restrictions?

51. Games   The game of Sets uses a special deck of cards. Each card has either one, two, or three identical shapes, all of the same color and style. There are three possible shapes: squiggle, diamond, and oval. There are three possible colors: green, purple, and red. There are three possible styles: solid, shaded, or outline. The deck consists of all possible combinations of shape, color, style, and number of shapes. How many cards are in the deck? *Source: Sets.*

52. Games   In the game of Scattergories, the players take 12 turns. In each turn, a 20-sided die is rolled; each side has a letter. The players must then fill in 12 categories (e.g., vegetable, city, etc.) with a word beginning with the letter rolled. Considering that a game consists of 12 rolls of the 20-sided die, and that rolling the same side more than once is allowed, how many possible games are there? *Source: Milton Bradley.*

53. Games   The game of Twenty Questions consists of asking 20 questions to determine a person, place, or thing that the other person is thinking of. The first question, which is always "Is it an animal, vegetable, or mineral?" has three possible answers. All the other questions must be answered "Yes" or "No." How many possible objects can be distinguished in this game, assuming that all 20 questions are asked? Are 20 questions enough?

54. Traveling Salesman   In the famous Traveling Salesman Problem, a salesman starts in any one of a set of cities, visits every city in the set once, and returns to the starting city. He would like to complete this circuit with the shortest possible distance.

(a) Suppose the salesman has 10 cities to visit. Given that it does not matter what city he starts in, how many different circuits can he take?

(b) The salesman decides to check all the different paths in part (a) to see which is shortest, but realizes that a circuit has the same distance whichever direction it is traveled. How many different circuits must he check?

(c) Suppose the salesman has 70 cities to visit. Would it be feasible to have a computer check all the different circuits? Explain your reasoning.

55. Circular Permutations   Circular permutations arise in applications involving arrangements around a closed loop, as in the previous exercise. Here are two examples.

(a) A ferris wheel has 20 seats. How many ways can 20 students arrange themselves on the ferris wheel if each student takes a different seat? We consider two arrangements to be identical if they differ only by rotations of the wheel.

(b) A necklace is to be strung with 15 beads, each of a different color. In how many ways can the beads be arranged? We consider two arrangements to be identical if they differ only by rotations of the necklace or by flipping the necklace over. (*Hint:* If every arrangement is counted twice, the correct number of arrangements can be found by dividing by 2.)

YOUR TURN ANSWERS
1. 10,000; 5040   **2.** 40,320   **3.** 6720   **4.** 120
5. 1152   **6.** 3780   **7.** 2,522,520

8.2 Combinations

In how many ways can a manager select 4 employees for promotion from 12 eligible employees?

As we shall see in Example 5, permutations alone cannot be used to answer this question, but combinations will provide the answer.

In the previous section, we saw that there are 60 ways that a teacher can arrange 3 of 5 different books on his desk. That is, there are 60 permutations of 5 books taken 3 at a time. Suppose now that the teacher does not wish to arrange the books on his desk but rather wishes to choose, without regard to order, any 3 of the 5 books for a book sale to raise money for his school. In how many ways can this be done?

At first glance, we might say 60 again, but this is incorrect. The number 60 counts all possible *arrangements* of 3 books chosen from 5. The following 6 arrangements, however, would all lead to the same set of 3 books being given to the book sale.

mystery-biography-textbook	biography-textbook-mystery
mystery-textbook-biography	textbook-biography-mystery
biography-mystery-textbook	textbook-mystery-biography

The list shows 6 different *arrangements* of 3 books, but only one *subset* of 3 books. A subset of items listed *without regard to order* is called a **combination**. The number of combinations of 5 things taken 3 at a time is written $C(5, 3)$.* Since they are subsets, combinations are *not ordered*.

To evaluate $C(5, 3)$, start with the $5 \cdot 4 \cdot 3$ *permutations* of 5 things taken 3 at a time. Since combinations are not ordered, find the number of combinations by dividing the number of permutations by the number of ways each group of 3 can be ordered; that is, divide by 3!.

$$C(5, 3) = \frac{5 \cdot 4 \cdot 3}{3!} = \frac{5 \cdot 4 \cdot 3}{3 \cdot 2 \cdot 1} = 10$$

There are 10 ways that the teacher can choose 3 books for the book sale.

Generalizing this discussion gives the following formula for the number of combinations of n elements taken r at a time:

$$C(n, r) = \frac{P(n, r)}{r!}.$$

Another version of this formula is found as follows.

$$C(n, r) = \frac{P(n, r)}{r!}$$
$$= \frac{n!}{(n - r)!} \cdot \frac{1}{r!} \qquad P(n, r) = \frac{n!}{(n - r)!}.$$
$$= \frac{n!}{(n - r)! \, r!}$$

*Other common notations for $C(n, r)$ are $_nC_r$, C_r^n, and $\binom{n}{r}$.

The previous steps lead to the following result.

> ### Combinations
>
> If $C(n, r)$, denotes the number of combinations of n elements taken r at a time, where $r \leq n$, then
>
> $$C(n, r) = \frac{n!}{(n - r)! \, r!}.$$

EXAMPLE 1 Committees

How many committees of 3 people can be formed from a group of 8 people?

SOLUTION

Method 1
Calculating by Hand

A committee is an unordered group, so use the combinations formula for $C(8, 3)$.

$$C(8, 3) = \frac{8!}{5!3!} = \frac{8 \cdot 7 \cdot 6 \cdot 5 \cdot 4 \cdot 3 \cdot 2 \cdot 1}{5 \cdot 4 \cdot 3 \cdot 2 \cdot 1 \cdot 3 \cdot 2 \cdot 1} = \frac{8 \cdot 7 \cdot 6}{3 \cdot 2 \cdot 1} = 56$$

Method 2
Graphing Calculator

Graphing calculators have the capacity to compute combinations. For example, on a TI-84 Plus C, $C(8, 3)$ can be calculated by inputting 8 followed by nCr (found in the MATH-PROB menu) and a 3 yielding 56, as shown in Figure 4.

FIGURE 4

Method 3
Spreadsheet

Spreadsheets can also compute combinations. For example, in Microsoft Excel, $C(8, 3)$ can be calculated by inputting 8 and 3 in cells, say, A1 and B1, and then typing "=FACT(A1)/(FACT(A1-B1)*FACT(B1))" in cell C1 or, for that matter, any other cell. The command "=MULTINOMIAL(5,3)" also gives this answer.

YOUR TURN 1 How many committees of 4 people can be formed from a group of 10 people?

TRY YOUR TURN 1

Example 1 shows an alternative way to compute $C(n, r)$. Take r or $n - r$, whichever is smaller. Write the factorial of this number in the denominator. In the numerator, write out a sufficient number of factors of $n!$ so there is one factor in the numerator for each factor in the denominator. For example, to calculate $C(8, 3)$ or $C(8, 5)$ write

$$\frac{8 \cdot 7 \cdot 6}{3 \cdot 2 \cdot 1} = 56.$$

The factors that are omitted (written in color in Example 1) cancel out of the numerator and denominator, so need not be included.

Notice from the previous discussion that $C(8, 3) = C(8, 5)$. (See Exercise 25 for a generalization of this idea.) One interpretation of this fact is that the number of ways to form a committee of 3 people chosen from a group of 8 is the same as the number of ways to choose the 5 people who are not on the committee.

Notice that this is *not* true with permutations: $P(8, 3) \neq P(8, 5)$.

EXAMPLE 2 Lawyers

Three lawyers are to be selected from a group of 30 to work on a special project.

(a) In how many different ways can the lawyers be selected?

SOLUTION Here we wish to know the number of 3-element combinations that can be formed from a set of 30 elements. (We want combinations, not permutations, since order within the group of 3 doesn't matter.)

$$C(30, 3) = \frac{30!}{27!3!} = \frac{30 \cdot 29 \cdot 28 \cdot 27!}{27! \cdot 3 \cdot 2 \cdot 1} \qquad 30! = 30 \cdot 29 \cdot 28 \cdot 27!$$
$$= \frac{30 \cdot 29 \cdot 28}{3 \cdot 2 \cdot 1}$$
$$= 4060$$

There are 4060 ways to select the project group.

(b) In how many ways can the group of 3 be selected if a certain lawyer must work on the project?

SOLUTION Since 1 lawyer already has been selected for the project, the problem is reduced to selecting 2 more from the remaining 29 lawyers.

$$C(29, 2) = \frac{29!}{27! \, 2!} = \frac{29 \cdot 28 \cdot 27!}{27! \cdot 2 \cdot 1} = \frac{29 \cdot 28}{2 \cdot 1} = 29 \cdot 14 = 406$$

In this case, the project group can be selected in 406 ways.

(c) In how many ways can a nonempty group of at most 3 lawyers be selected from these 30 lawyers?

SOLUTION Here, by "at most 3" we mean "1 or 2 or 3." (The number 0 is excluded because the group is nonempty.) Find the number of ways for each case.

Case	Number of Ways
1	$C(30, 1) = \dfrac{30!}{29! \, 1!} = \dfrac{30 \cdot 29!}{29! \, (1)} = 30$
2	$C(30, 2) = \dfrac{30!}{28! \, 2!} = \dfrac{30 \cdot 29 \cdot 28!}{28! \cdot 2 \cdot 1} = 435$
3	$C(30, 3) = \dfrac{30!}{27! \, 3!} = \dfrac{30 \cdot 29 \cdot 28 \cdot 27!}{27! \cdot 3 \cdot 2 \cdot 1} = 4060$

YOUR TURN 2 From a class of 15 students, a group of 3 or 4 students will be selected to work on a special project. In how many ways can a group of 3 or 4 students be selected?

The total number of ways to select at most 3 lawyers will be the sum

$$30 + 435 + 4060 = 4525. \qquad \textbf{TRY YOUR TURN 2}$$

EXAMPLE 3 Sales

A salesman has 10 accounts in a certain city.

(a) In how many ways can he select 3 accounts to call on?

SOLUTION Within a selection of 3 accounts, the arrangement of the calls is not important, so there are

$$C(10, 3) = \frac{10!}{7! \, 3!} = \frac{10 \cdot 9 \cdot 8}{3 \cdot 2 \cdot 1} = 120$$

ways he can make a selection of 3 accounts.

FOR REVIEW
Notice in Example 3 that to calculate the number of ways to select 8 or 9 or 10 accounts, we added the three numbers found. The union rule for sets from Chapter 7 says that when A and B are disjoint sets, the number of elements in A or B is the number of elements in A plus the number in B.

(b) In how many ways can he select at least 8 of the 10 accounts to use in preparing a report?

SOLUTION "At least 8" means "8 or more," which is "8 or 9 or 10." First find the number of ways to choose in each case.

Case	Number of Ways
8	$C(10, 8) = \dfrac{10!}{2!\, 8!} = \dfrac{10 \cdot 9}{2 \cdot 1} = 45$
9	$C(10, 9) = \dfrac{10!}{1!\, 9!} = \dfrac{10}{1} = 10$
10	$C(10, 10) = \dfrac{10!}{0!\, 10!} = 1$

He can select at least 8 of the 10 accounts in $45 + 10 + 1 = 56$ ways.

CAUTION When we are making a first decision *and* a second decision, we *multiply* to find the total number of ways. When we are making a decision in which the first choice *or* the second choice are valid choices, we *add* to find the total number of ways.

The formulas for permutations and combinations given in this section and in the previous section will be very useful in solving probability problems in the next section. Any difficulty in using these formulas usually comes from being unable to differentiate between them. Both permutations and combinations give the number of ways to choose r objects from a set of n objects. The differences between permutations and combinations are outlined in the following table.

Permutations	Combinations
Different orderings or arrangements of the r objects are different permutations.	Each choice or subset of r objects gives one combination. Order within the group of r objects does not matter.
$P(n, r) = \dfrac{n!}{(n - r)!}$	$C(n, r) = \dfrac{n!}{(n - r)!\, r!}$
Clue words: arrangement, schedule, order	Clue words: group, committee, set, sample
Order matters!	Order does not matter!

In the next examples, concentrate on recognizing which formula should be applied.

EXAMPLE 4 Permutations and Combinations

For each problem, tell whether permutations or combinations should be used to solve the problem.

(a) How many 4-digit code numbers are possible if no digits are repeated?

SOLUTION Since changing the order of the 4 digits results in a different code, use permutations.

(b) A sample of 3 light bulbs is randomly selected from a batch of 15. How many different samples are possible?

SOLUTION The order in which the 3 light bulbs are selected is not important. The sample is unchanged if the items are rearranged, so combinations should be used.

(c) In a baseball conference with 8 teams, how many games must be played so that each team plays every other team exactly once?

SOLUTION   Selection of 2 teams for a game is an *unordered* subset of 2 from the set of 8 teams. Use combinations again.

(d) In how many ways can 4 patients be assigned to 6 different hospital rooms so that each patient has a private room?

SOLUTION   The room assignments are an *ordered* selection of 4 rooms from the 6 rooms. Exchanging the rooms of any 2 patients within a selection of 4 rooms gives a different assignment, so permutations should be used.   **TRY YOUR TURN 3**

YOUR TURN 3 Solve the problems in Example 4.

EXAMPLE 5   **Promotions**

A manager must select 4 employees for promotion; 12 employees are eligible.

APPLY IT

(a) In how many ways can the 4 be chosen?

SOLUTION   Since there is no reason to differentiate among the 4 who are selected, use combinations.

$$C(12, 4) = \frac{12!}{8!\, 4!} = 495$$

YOUR TURN 4 In how many ways can a committee of 3 be chosen from a group of 20 students? In how many ways can three officers (president, treasurer, and secretary) be selected from a group of 20 students?

(b) In how many ways can 4 employees be chosen (from 12) to be placed in 4 different jobs?

SOLUTION   In this case, once a group of 4 is selected, they can be assigned in many different ways (or arrangements) to the 4 jobs. Therefore, this problem requires permutations.

$$P(12, 4) = \frac{12!}{8!} = 11{,}880$$ **TRY YOUR TURN 4**

FOR REVIEW

Example 6 involves a standard deck of 52 playing cards, as shown in Figure 17 in Chapter 7. Recall the discussion that accompanies the photograph.

EXAMPLE 6   **Playing Cards**

Five cards are dealt from a standard 52-card deck.

(a) How many such hands have only face cards?

SOLUTION   The face cards are the king, queen, and jack of each suit. Since there are 4 suits, there are 12 face cards. The arrangement of the 5 cards is not important, so use combinations to get

$$C(12, 5) = \frac{12!}{7!\, 5!} = 792.$$

(b) How many such hands have a full house of aces and eights (3 aces and 2 eights)?

SOLUTION   The arrangement of the 3 aces or the 2 eights does not matter, so we use combinations. There are $C(4, 3)$ ways to get 3 aces from the four aces in the deck, and $C(4, 2)$ ways to get 2 eights. By the multiplication principle we get

$$C(4, 3) \cdot C(4, 2) = 4 \cdot 6 = 24.$$

(c) How many such hands have exactly 2 hearts?

SOLUTION   There are 13 hearts in the deck, so the 2 hearts will be selected from those 13 cards. The other 3 cards must come from the remaining 39 cards that are not hearts. Use combinations and the multiplication principle to get

$$C(13, 2) \cdot C(39, 3) = 78 \cdot 9139 = 712{,}842.$$

Notice that the two numbers in red in the combinations add up to 52, the total number of cards, and the two numbers in blue add up to 5, the number of cards in a hand.

(d) How many such hands have cards of a single suit?

SOLUTION Since the arrangement of the 5 cards is not important, use combinations. The total number of ways that 5 cards of a particular suit of 13 cards can occur is $C(13, 5)$. There are four different suits, so the multiplication principle gives

$$4 \cdot C(13, 5) = 4 \cdot 1287 = 5148$$

YOUR TURN 5 How many five card hands have exactly 2 aces?

ways to deal 5 cards of the same suit.   **TRY YOUR TURN 5**

As Example 6 shows, often both combinations and the multiplication principle must be used in the same problem.

EXAMPLE 7   Soup

To illustrate the differences between permutations and combinations in another way, suppose 2 cans of soup are to be selected from 4 cans on a shelf: noodle (N), bean (B), mushroom (M), and tomato (T). As shown in Figure 5(a), there are 12 ways to select 2 cans from the 4 cans if the order matters (if noodle first and bean second is considered different from bean, then noodle, for example). On the other hand, if order is unimportant, then there are 6 ways to choose 2 cans of soup from the 4, as illustrated in Figure 5(b).

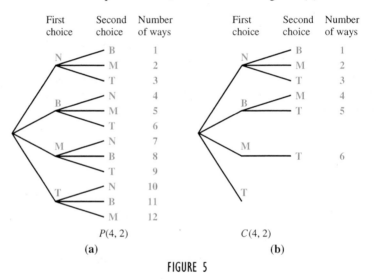

FIGURE 5

CAUTION | It should be stressed that not all counting problems lend themselves to either permutations or combinations. When a tree diagram or the multiplication principle can be used directly, it's often best to use it.

8.2 WARM-UP EXERCISES

W1. How many three-digit numbers can be formed using only odd digits if no repetitions are allowed? *(Sec. 8.1)*

W2. How many distinguishable permutations of the letters in the word "bananas" are there? *(Sec. 8.1)*

8.2   EXERCISES

 1. Define combinations in your own words.

 2. Explain the difference between a permutation and a combination.

Evaluate each combination.

3. $C(8, 3)$

4. $C(12, 5)$

5. $C(44, 20)$

6. $C(40, 18)$

7. $C(n, 0)$

8. $C(n, n)$

9. $C(n, 1)$

10. $C(n, n - 1)$

11. In how many ways can a hand of 6 clubs be chosen from an ordinary deck?

12. In how many ways can a hand of 6 red cards be chosen from an ordinary deck?

13. Five cards are marked with the numbers 1, 2, 3, 4, and 5, then shuffled, and 2 cards are drawn.

    (a) How many different 2-card combinations are possible?

    (b) How many 2-card hands contain a number less than 3?

14. An economics club has 31 members.

    (a) If a committee of 4 is to be selected, in how many ways can the selection be made?

    (b) In how many ways can a committee of at least 1 and at most 3 be selected?

15. Use a tree diagram for the following.

    (a) Find the number of ways 2 letters can be chosen from the set {L, M, N} if order is important and repetition is allowed.

    (b) Reconsider part (a) if no repeats are allowed.

    (c) Find the number of combinations of 3 elements taken 2 at a time. Does this answer differ from part (a) or (b)?

16. Repeat Exercise 15 using the set {L, M, N, P}.

In Exercises 17–24, decide whether each exercise involves permutations or combinations, and then solve the problem.

17. In a club with 9 male and 11 female members, how many 5-member committees can be chosen that have

    (a) all men?   (b) all women?

    (c) 3 men and 2 women?

18. In Exercise 17, how many committees can be selected that have

    (a) at least 4 women?   (b) no more than 2 men?

19. In a game of musical chairs, 12 children will sit in 11 chairs arranged in a row (one will be left out). In how many ways can this happen, if we count rearrangements of the children in the chairs as different outcomes?

20. A group of 3 students is to be selected from a group of 14 students to take part in a class in cell biology.

    (a) In how many ways can this be done?

    (b) In how many ways can the group who will not take part be chosen?

21. Marbles are being drawn without replacement from a bag containing 16 marbles.

    (a) How many samples of 2 marbles can be drawn?

    (b) How many samples of 4 marbles can be drawn?

    (c) If the bag contains 3 yellow, 4 white, and 9 blue marbles, how many samples of 2 marbles can be drawn in which both marbles are blue?

22. There are 7 rotten apples in a crate of 26 apples.

    (a) How many samples of 3 apples can be drawn from the crate?

    (b) How many samples of 3 could be drawn in which all 3 are rotten?

    (c) How many samples of 3 could be drawn in which there are two good apples and one rotten one?

23. A bag contains 5 black, 1 red, and 3 yellow jelly beans; you take 3 at random. How many samples are possible in which the jelly beans are

    (a) all black?   (b) all red?

    (c) all yellow?   (d) 2 black and 1 red?

    (e) 2 black and 1 yellow?   (f) 2 yellow and 1 black?

    (g) 2 red and 1 yellow?

24. In how many ways can 5 out of 9 plants be arranged in a row on a windowsill?

25. Show that $C(n, r) = C(n, n - r)$.

26. (a) Calculate how many numbers between 100 and 999 contain exactly one 5 by subtracting the number that contain no 5's, two 5's, or three 5's from the total.

    (b) Calculate the answer to part (a) directly by creating a tree diagram and considering whether the first digit is a 5 or not, then the second digit, and then the third.

27. The following problem was posed on National Public Radio's *Weekend Edition*: In how many points can 6 circles intersect? *Source: National Public Radio.*

    (a) Find the answer for 6 circles.

    (b) Find the general answer for *n* circles.

28. How many different dominoes can be formed from the numbers 0 . . . 6? (*Hint:* A domino may have the same number of dots on both halves of it, or it may have a different number of dots on each half.)

APPLICATIONS

Business and Economics

29. Work Assignments   From a group of 8 newly hired office assistants, 3 are selected. Each of these 3 assistants will be assigned to a different manager. In how many ways can they be selected and assigned?

30. Assembly Line Sampling   Five items are to be randomly selected from the first 50 items on an assembly line to determine the defect rate. How many different samples of 5 items can be chosen?

31. Sales Schedules   A salesperson has the names of 6 prospects.

    (a) In how many ways can she arrange her schedule if she calls on all 6?

    (b) In how many ways can she arrange her schedule if she can call on only 4 of the 6?

32. Worker Grievances   A group of 9 workers decides to send a delegation of 3 to their supervisor to discuss their grievances.

    (a) How many delegations are possible?

    (b) If it is decided that a particular worker must be in the delegation, how many different delegations are possible?

    (c) If there are 4 women and 5 men in the group, how many delegations would include at least 1 woman?

33. Hamburger Variety Hamburger Hut sells regular hamburgers as well as a larger burger. Either type can include cheese, relish, lettuce, tomato, mustard, or catsup.

(a) How many different hamburgers can be ordered with exactly three extras?

(b) How many different regular hamburgers can be ordered with exactly three extras?

(c) How many different regular hamburgers can be ordered with at least five extras?

34. Ice Cream Flavors Baskin-Robbins advertises that it has 31 flavors of ice cream.

(a) How many different double-scoop cones can be made? Assume that the order of the scoops matters.

(b) How many different triple-scoop cones can be made?

(c) How many different double-scoop cones can be made if order doesn't matter?

(d) How many different triple-scoop cones can be made if order doesn't matter?

Life Sciences

35. Research Participants From a group of 16 smokers and 22 nonsmokers, a researcher wants to randomly select 8 smokers and 8 nonsmokers for a study. In how many ways can the study group be selected?

36. Plant Hardiness In an experiment on plant hardiness, a researcher gathers 6 wheat plants, 3 barley plants, and 2 rye plants. She wishes to select 4 plants at random.

(a) In how many ways can this be done?

(b) In how many ways can this be done if exactly 2 wheat plants must be included?

Social Sciences

37. Legislative Committee A legislative committee consists of 5 Democrats and 4 Republicans. A delegation of 3 is to be selected to visit a small Pacific island republic.

(a) How many different delegations are possible?

(b) How many delegations would have all Democrats?

(c) How many delegations would have 2 Democrats and 1 Republican?

(d) How many delegations would include at least 1 Republican?

38. Political Committee From 10 names on a ballot, 4 will be elected to a political party committee. In how many ways can the committee of 4 be formed if each person will have a different responsibility, and different assignments of responsibility are considered different committees?

39. Judges When Paul Martinek, publisher of *Lawyers Weekly USA*, was a guest on the television news program *The O'Reilly Factor*, he discussed a decision by a three-judge panel, chosen at random from judges in the Ninth Circuit in California. The judges had ruled that the mandatory recitation of the Pledge of Allegiance is unconstitutional because of the phrase "under God." According to Martinek, "Because there are 45 judges in the Ninth Circuit, there are 3000 different combinations of three-judge panels." Is this true? If not, what is the correct number? *Source: The Mathematics Teacher.*

General Interest

40. Bridge How many different 13-card bridge hands can be selected from an ordinary deck?

41. Poker Five cards are chosen from an ordinary deck to form a hand in poker. In how many ways is it possible to get the following results?

(a) 4 queens   (b) No face card

(c) Exactly 2 face cards   (d) At least 2 face cards

(e) 1 heart, 2 diamonds, and 2 clubs

42. Poker In poker, a flush consists of 5 cards with the same suit, such as 5 diamonds.

(a) Find the number of ways of getting a flush consisting of cards with values from 5 to 10 by listing all the possibilities.

(b) Find the number of ways of getting a flush consisting of cards with values from 5 to 10 by using combinations.

43. Baseball If a baseball coach has 5 good hitters and 4 poor hitters on the bench and chooses 3 players at random, in how many ways can he choose at least 2 good hitters?

44. Softball The coach of the Morton Valley Softball Team has 6 good hitters and 8 poor hitters. He chooses 3 hitters at random.

(a) In how many ways can he choose 2 good hitters and 1 poor hitter?

(b) In how many ways can he choose 3 good hitters?

(c) In how many ways can he choose at least 2 good hitters?

45. Flower Selection Five orchids from a collection of 20 are to be selected for a flower show.

(a) In how many ways can this be done?

(b) In how many ways can the 5 be selected if 2 special plants from the 20 must be included?

46. Lottery A state lottery game requires that you pick 6 different numbers from 1 to 99. If you pick all 6 winning numbers, you win the jackpot.

(a) How many ways are there to choose 6 numbers if order is not important?

(b) How many ways are there to choose 6 numbers if order matters?

47. Lottery In Exercise 46, if you pick 5 of the 6 numbers correctly, you win $250,000. In how many ways can you pick exactly 5 of the 6 winning numbers without regard to order?

48. Committees Suppose that out of 19 members of a club, two committees are to be formed. A nominating committee is to consist of 7 members, and a public relations committee is to consist of 5 members. No one can be on both committees.

(a) Calculate the number of ways that the two committees can be formed, assuming that the nominating committee is formed first.

(b) Calculate the number of ways that the two committees can be formed, assuming that the public relations committee is formed first. Verify that this answer is the same as that of part (a).

(c) Suppose the 7 members of the nominating committee wear red T-shirts, the 5 members of the public relations committee wear yellow T-shirts, and the remaining members of the club wear white T-shirts. A photographer lines up the members of the club to take a picture, but the picture is so blurry that people wearing the same color T-shirt are indistinguishable. In how many distinguishable ways can the club members line up? Explain why this answer is the same as the answers to parts (a) and (b).

49. Committee A small department of 5 people decides to form a hiring committee. The only restriction on the size of the committee is that it must have at least 2 members.

(a) Calculate the number of different committees possible by adding up the number of committees of different sizes.

(b) Calculate the number of different committees possible by taking the total number of subsets of the 5 members and subtracting the number of committees that are invalid because they have too few members.

50. License Plates Officials from a particular state are considering a new type of license plate consisting of three letters followed by three numbers. If the letters cannot be repeated and must be in alphabetical order, calculate the number of possible distinct license plates.

51. Passwords A certain website requires users to log on using a security password.

(a) If passwords must consist of six letters, followed by a single digit, determine the total number of possible distinct passwords.

(b) If passwords must consist of six non-repetitive letters, followed by a single digit, determine the total number of possible distinct passwords.

52. Pizza Varieties A television commercial for Little Caesars pizza announced that with the purchase of two pizzas, one could receive free any combination of up to five toppings on each pizza. The commercial shows a young child waiting in line at Little Caesars who calculates that there are 1,048,576 possibilities for the toppings on the two pizzas. *Source: The Mathematics Teacher.*

(a) Verify the child's calculation. Use the fact that Little Caesars has 11 toppings to choose from. Assume that the order of the two pizzas matters; that is, if the first pizza has combination 1 and the second pizza has combination 2, that is different from combination 2 on the first pizza and combination 1 on the second.

(b) In a letter to *The Mathematics Teacher*, Joseph F. Heiser argued that the two combinations described in part (a) should be counted as the same, so the child has actually overcounted. Give the number of possibilities if the order of the two pizzas doesn't matter.

53. Pizza In an ad for Pizza Hut, Jessica Simpson explains to the Muppets that there are more than 6 million possibilities for their 4forAll Pizza. Griffin Weber and Glenn Weber wrote an article explaining that the number of possibilities is far more than 6 million. *Source: The College Mathematics Journal.*

(a) Each pizza can have up to 3 toppings, out of 17 possible choices, or can be one of four specialty pizzas. Calculate the number of different pizzas possible.

(b) Out of the total possible pizzas calculated in part (a), a 4forAll Pizza consists of four pizzas in a box. Keeping in mind that the four pizzas could all be different, or there could be two or three different pizzas in the box, or all four pizzas could be the same, calculate the total number of 4forAll Pizzas possible.

(c) The article considers another way of counting the number in part (b). Suppose that only 8 pizzas were available, and they were listed in a row with lines separating each type, as in the following diagram:

$$A\,|\,B\,|\,C\,|\,D\,|\,E\,|\,F\,|\,G\,|\,H.$$

A person orders 4 pizzas by placing 4 X's in the desired places on the diagram, after which the letters can be ignored. For example, an order for 2 of A, 1 of C, and 1 of G would look like the following diagram:

$$XX\,|\,|\,X\,|\,|\,|\,|\,X\,|$$

The number of ways this can be done is then the number of ways of arranging 11 objects, 4 of which are X and the other 7 of which are vertical lines, or

$$C(11, 4) = 330.$$

Use similar reasoning to verify the answer to part (b).

54. Cereal The Post Corporation once introduced the cereal, *Create a Crunch*™, in which the consumers could combine ingredients to create their own unique cereal. Each box contained 8 packets of food goods. There were four types of cereal: Frosted Alpha Bits®, Cocoa Pebbles®, Fruity Pebbles®, and Honey Comb®. Also included in the box were four "Add-Ins": granola, blue rice cereal, marshmallows, and sprinkles.

(a) What is the total number of breakfasts that could be made if a breakfast is defined as any one or more cereals or add-ins?

(b) If Sarah Taylor chose to mix one type of cereal with one add-in, how many different breakfasts could she make?

(c) If Kristen Schmitt chose to mix two types of cereal with three add-ins, how many different breakfasts could she make?

(d) If Matthew Piscicuto chose to mix at least one type of cereal with at least one type of add-in, how many breakfasts could he make?

(e) If Heather Murray's favorite cereal is Fruity Pebbles®, how many different cereals could she make if each of her mixtures must include this cereal?

55. Appetizers Applebee's restaurant recently advertised "Ultimate Trios," where the customer was able to pick any three trio-sized appetizers from a list of nine options. The ad claimed that there were over 200 combinations.

(a) If each customer's selection must be a different item, how many meal combinations are possible?

(b) If each customer can select the same item two or even three times in each trio, how many different trios are possible?

(c) Using the answers to parts (a) and (b), discuss that restaurant's claim.

(d) Two of the trio items, the Buffalo chicken wings and the boneless Buffalo wings, each have five different sauce options. This implies that there are actually 17 different trio choices that are available to a customer. In this scenario, how many different trio meal combinations are possible? (Assume that each of the three selected items is different.)

(e) How many different trios are possible if 2 of the items are different flavored boneless Buffalo wings? (Assume that the third item is not a boneless Buffalo wing.)

56. Football Writer Gregg Easterbrook, discussing ESPN's unsuccessful attempt to predict the winners for the six National Football League (NFL) divisions and the six wild-card slots, claimed that there were 180 different ways to make this forecast. Reader Milton Eisner wrote in to tell him that the actual number is much larger. To make the calculation, note that at the time the NFL consisted of two conferences, each of which consisted of three divisions. Five of the divisions had five teams, while the other had six. There was one winner from each of the six divisions, plus three wild-card slots from each of the two conferences. How many ways could the six division winners and six wild-card slots have been chosen? *Source: Slate Magazine.*

57. Music In the opera *Amahl and the Night Visitors*, the shepherds sing a chorus involving 18 different names, a challenge for singers trying to remember the names in the correct order. (Two of the three authors of this textbook have sung this chorus in public.)

(a) In how many ways can the names be arranged?

(b) Not all the arrangements of names in part (a) could be sung, because 10 of the names have 3 syllables, 4 have 2 syllables, and 4 have 4 syllables. Of the 6 lines in the chorus, 4 lines consist of a 3-syllable name repeated, followed by a 2-syllable and then a 4-syllable name (e.g., Emily, Emily, Michael, Bartholomew), and 2 lines consist of a 3-syllable name repeated, followed by two more 3-syllable names (e.g., Josephine, Josephine, Angela, Jeremy). No names are repeated except where we've indicated. (If you think this is confusing, you should try memorizing the chorus.) How many arrangements of the names could fit this pattern?

58. Olympics In a recent Winter Olympics, there were 12 judges for each part of the women's figure skating program, but the scores of only 9 of the judges were randomly selected for the final results. *Source: The New York Times.*

(a) In how many ways can the 9 judges whose scores are counted be selected?

(b) Women's figure skating consists of a short program and a long program, with different judges for each part. How many different sets of judges' scores are possible for the entire event?

YOUR TURN ANSWERS ▬▬▬
1. 210　　**2.** 1820　**3. (a)** 5040 **(b)** 455 **(c)** 28 **(d)** 360
4. 1140; 6840　**5.** 103,776

8.3 Probability Applications of Counting Principles

APPLY IT If 3 engines are tested from a shipping container packed with 12 diesel engines, 2 of which are defective, what is the probability that at least 1 of the defective engines will be found (in which case the container will not be shipped)?

This problem, which is solved in Example 3, could theoretically be solved with a tree diagram, but it would require a tree with a large number of branches. Many of the probability problems involving *dependent* events that were solved earlier by using tree diagrams can also be solved by using permutations or combinations. Permutations and combinations are especially helpful when the numbers involved are large.

To compare the method of using permutations or combinations with the method of tree diagrams used in Section 7.5, the first example repeats Example 7 from that section.

EXAMPLE 1　Environmental Inspections

The Environmental Protection Agency is considering inspecting 6 plants for environmental compliance: 3 in Chicago, 2 in Los Angeles, and 1 in New York. Due to a lack of inspectors, they decide to inspect 2 plants selected at random, 1 this month and 1 next month, with each plant equally likely to be selected, but no plant is selected twice. What is the probability that 1 Chicago plant and 1 Los Angeles plant are selected?

SOLUTION

Method 1
Multiplication Principle

To find the probability, we use the probability fraction, $P(E) = n(E)/n(S)$, where E is the event that 1 Chicago plant and 1 Los Angeles plant is selected and S is the sample space. We will use the multiplication principle, since the plants are selected one at a time, and the first is inspected this month while the second is inspected next month.

To calculate the numerator, we find the number of elements in E. There are two ways to select a Chicago plant and a Los Angeles plant: Chicago first and Los Angeles second, or Los Angeles first and Chicago second. The Chicago plant can be selected from the 3 Chicago plants in $C(3, 1)$ ways, and the Los Angeles plant can be selected from the 2 Los Angeles plants in $C(2, 1)$ ways. Using the multiplication principle, we can select a Chicago plant then a Los Angeles plant in $C(3, 1) \cdot C(2, 1)$ ways, and a Los Angeles plant then a Chicago plant in $C(2, 1) \cdot C(3, 1)$ ways. By the union rule, we can select one Chicago plant and one Los Angeles plant in

$$C(3, 1) \cdot C(2, 1) + C(2, 1) \cdot C(3, 1) \text{ ways,}$$

giving the numerator of the probability fraction.

For the denominator, we calculate the number of elements in the sample space. There are 6 ways to select the first plant and 5 ways to select the second, for a total of $6 \cdot 5$ ways. The required probability is

$$P(1 \text{ C and } 1 \text{ LA}) = \frac{C(3, 1) \cdot C(2, 1) + C(2, 1) \cdot C(3, 1)}{6 \cdot 5}$$

$$= \frac{3 \cdot 2 + 2 \cdot 3}{6 \cdot 5} = \frac{12}{30} = \frac{2}{5}.$$

This agrees with the answer found in Example 7 of Section 7.5.

FOR REVIEW

The use of combinations to solve probability problems depends on the basic probability principle introduced in Section 7.3 and repeated here:
Let S be a sample space with equally likely outcomes, and let event E be a subset of S. Then the probability that event E occurs, written $P(E)$, is

$$P(E) = \frac{n(E)}{n(S)},$$

where $n(E)$ and $n(S)$ represent the number of elements in sets E and S.

Method 2
Combinations

This example can be solved more simply by observing that the probability that 1 Chicago plant and 1 Los Angeles plant are selected should not depend upon the order in which the plants are selected, so we may use combinations. The numerator is simply the number of ways of selecting 1 Chicago plant out of 3 Chicago plants and 1 Los Angeles plant out of 2 Los Angeles plants. The denominator is just the number of ways of selecting 2 plants out of 6. Then

$$P(1 \text{ C and } 1 \text{ LA}) = \frac{C(3, 1) \cdot C(2, 1)}{C(6, 2)} = \frac{6}{15} = \frac{2}{5}.$$

This helps explain why combinations tend to be used more often than permutations in probability. Even if order matters in the original problem, it is sometimes possible to ignore order and use combinations. Be careful to do this only when the final result does not depend on the order of events. Order often does matter. (If you don't believe this, try getting dressed tomorrow morning and then taking your shower.)

Method 3
Tree Diagram

In Section 7.5, we found this probability using the tree diagram shown in Figure 6 on the next page. Two of the branches correspond to drawing 1 Chicago plant and 1 Los Angeles plant. The probability for each branch is calculated by multiplying the probabilities along the branch, as we did in the previous chapter. The resulting probabilities for the two branches are then added, giving the result

$$P(1 \text{ C and } 1 \text{ LA}) = \frac{3}{6} \cdot \frac{2}{5} + \frac{2}{6} \cdot \frac{3}{5} = \frac{2}{5}.$$

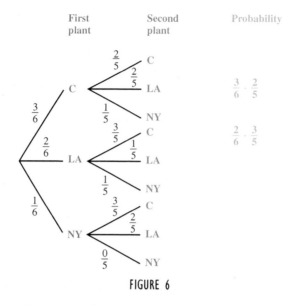

First plant   Second plant   Probability

FIGURE 6

YOUR TURN 1 In Example 1, what is the probability that 1 New York plant and 1 Chicago plant are selected?

TRY YOUR TURN 1

CAUTION The problems in the first two sections of this chapter asked how many ways a certain operation can be done. The problems in this section ask what is the probability that a certain event occurs; the solution involves answering questions about how many ways the event and the operation can be done.

- If a problem asks how many ways something can be done, the answer must be a nonnegative integer.
- If a problem asks for a probability, the answer must be a number between 0 and 1.

EXAMPLE 2 Nursing

From a group of 22 nurses, 4 are to be selected to present a list of grievances to management.

(a) In how many ways can this be done?

SOLUTION Four nurses from a group of 22 can be selected in $C(22, 4)$ ways. (Use combinations, since the group of 4 is an unordered set.)

$$C(22, 4) = \frac{22!}{18!\, 4!} = \frac{(22)(21)(20)(19)}{(4)(3)(2)(1)} = 7315$$

There are 7315 ways to choose 4 people from 22.

(b) One of the nurses is Erica Eastep. Find the probability that Erica will be among the 4 selected.

SOLUTION The probability that Erica will be selected is given by $n(E)/n(S)$, where E is the event that the chosen group includes Erica, and S is the sample space for the experiment of choosing a group of 4. There is only $C(1, 1) = 1$ way to choose Erica. The number of ways that the other 3 nurses can be chosen from the remaining 21 nurses is

$$C(21, 3) = \frac{21!}{18!\, 3!} = 1330.$$

The probability that Erica will be one of the 4 chosen is

$$P(\text{Erica is chosen}) = \frac{n(E)}{n(S)} = \frac{C(1, 1) \cdot C(21, 3)}{C(22, 4)} = \frac{1330}{7315} \approx 0.1818.$$

YOUR TURN 2 If 8 of the 22 nurses are men in Example 2, what is the probability that exactly 2 men are among the 4 nurses selected?

Notice that the two numbers in red in the numerator, 1 and 21, add up to the number in red in the denominator, 22. This indicates that the 22 nurses have been split into two groups, one of size 1 (Erica) and the other of size 21 (the other nurses). Similarly, the green numbers indicate that the 4 nurses chosen consist of two groups of size 1 (Erica) and size 3 (the other nurses chosen).

(c) Find the probability that Erica will not be selected.

   SOLUTION   The probability that Erica will not be chosen is $1 - 0.1818 = 0.8182$.

                                                                 TRY YOUR TURN 2

EXAMPLE 3   Diesel Engines

When shipping diesel engines abroad, it is common to pack 12 engines in one container. Suppose that a company has received complaints from its customers that many of the engines arrive in nonworking condition. To help solve this problem, the company decides to make a spot check of containers after loading. The company will test 3 engines from a container at random; if any of the 3 are nonworking, the container will not be shipped until each engine in it is checked. Suppose a given container has 2 nonworking engines. Find the probability that the container will not be shipped.

APPLY IT   **SOLUTION**   The container will not be shipped if the sample of 3 engines contains 1 or 2 defective engines. If $P(1 \text{ defective})$ represents the probability of exactly 1 defective engine in the sample, then

$$P(\text{not shipping}) = P(1 \text{ defective}) + P(2 \text{ defective}).$$

There are $C(12, 3)$ ways to choose the 3 engines for testing:

$$C(12, 3) = \frac{12!}{9! \, 3!} = 220.$$

There are $C(2, 1)$ ways of choosing 1 defective engine from the 2 in the container, and for each of these ways, there are $C(10, 2)$ ways of choosing 2 good engines from among the 10 in the container. By the multiplication principle, there are

$$C(2, 1) \cdot C(10, 2) = \frac{2!}{1! \, 1!} \cdot \frac{10!}{8! \, 2!} = 2 \cdot 45 = 90$$

ways of choosing a sample of 3 engines containing 1 defective engine with

$$P(1 \text{ defective}) = \frac{90}{220} = \frac{9}{22}.$$

There are $C(2, 2)$ ways of choosing 2 defective engines from the 2 defective engines in the container, and $C(10, 1)$ ways of choosing 1 good engine from among the 10 good engines, for

$$C(2, 2) \cdot C(10, 1) = 1 \cdot 10 = 10$$

ways of choosing a sample of 3 engines containing 2 defective engines. Finally,

$$P(2 \text{ defective}) = \frac{10}{220} = \frac{1}{22}$$

and

$$P(\text{not shipping}) = P(1 \text{ defective}) + P(2 \text{ defective})$$

$$= \frac{9}{22} + \frac{1}{22} = \frac{10}{22} \approx 0.4545.$$

YOUR TURN 3 Suppose the container in Example 3 has 4 nonworking engines. Find the probability that the container will not be shipped.

Notice that the probability is $1 - 0.4545 = 0.5455$ that the container will be shipped, even though it has 2 defective engines. The management must decide whether this probability is acceptable; if not, it may be necessary to test more than 3 engines from a container.

                                                                 TRY YOUR TURN 3

Observe that in Example 3, the complement of finding 1 or 2 defective engines is finding 0 defective engines. Then instead of finding the sum $P(1 \text{ defective}) + P(2 \text{ defective})$, the result in Example 3 could be found as $1 - P(0 \text{ defective})$.

$$P(\text{not shipping}) = 1 - P(0 \text{ defective in sample})$$

$$= 1 - \frac{C(2, 0) \cdot C(10, 3)}{C(12, 3)}$$

$$= 1 - \frac{1(120)}{220}$$

$$= 1 - \frac{120}{220} = \frac{100}{220} \approx 0.4545$$

EXAMPLE 4 Poker

In a common form of the card game *poker*, a hand of 5 cards is dealt to each player from a deck of 52 cards. There are a total of

$$C(52, 5) = \frac{52!}{47! \, 5!} = 2{,}598{,}960$$

such hands possible. Find the probability of getting each of the following hands.

(a) A hand containing only hearts, called a *heart flush*

SOLUTION There are 13 hearts in a deck, with

$$C(13, 5) = \frac{13!}{8! \, 5!} = \frac{(13)(12)(11)(10)(9)}{(5)(4)(3)(2)(1)} = 1287$$

different hands containing only hearts. The probability of a heart flush is

$$P(\text{heart flush}) = \frac{C(13, 5) \cdot C(39, 0)}{C(52, 5)} = \frac{1287}{2{,}598{,}960} \approx 0.0004952.$$

You don't really need the $C(39, 0)$, since this just equals 1, but it might help to remind you that you are choosing none of the 39 cards that remain after the hearts are removed.

(b) A flush of any suit (5 cards of the same suit)

SOLUTION There are 4 suits in a deck, so

$$P(\text{flush}) = 4 \cdot P(\text{heart flush}) = 4 \cdot 0.0004952 \approx 0.001981.$$

(c) A full house of aces and eights (3 aces and 2 eights)

SOLUTION There are $C(4, 3)$ ways to choose 3 aces from among the 4 in the deck, and $C(4, 2)$ ways to choose 2 eights.

$$P(3 \text{ aces}, 2 \text{ eights}) = \frac{C(4, 3) \cdot C(4, 2) \cdot C(44, 0)}{C(52, 5)} = \frac{4 \cdot 6 \cdot 1}{2{,}598{,}960} \approx 0.000009234$$

(d) Any full house (3 cards of one value, 2 of another)

SOLUTION

Method 1
Standard Procedure

The 13 values in a deck give 13 choices for the first value. As in part (c), there are $C(4, 3)$ ways to choose the 3 cards from among the 4 cards that have that value. This leaves 12 choices for the second value (order *is* important here, since a full house of 3 aces and 2 eights is not the same as a full house of 3 eights and 2 aces). From the 4 cards that have the second value, there are $C(4, 2)$ ways to choose 2. The probability of any full house is then

$$P(\text{full house}) = \frac{13 \cdot C(4, 3) \cdot 12 \cdot C(4, 2)}{2{,}598{,}960} \approx 0.001441.$$

Method 2
Alternative Procedure

YOUR TURN 4 In Example 4, what is the probability of a hand containing two pairs, one of aces and the other of kings? (This hand contains 2 aces, 2 kings, and a fifth card that is neither an ace nor a king.)

As an alternative way of counting the numerator, first count the number of different values in the hand.* Since there are 13 values from which to choose, and we need 2 different values (one for the set of 3 cards and one for the set of 2), there are $C(13, 2)$ ways to choose the values. Next, of the two values chosen, select the value for which there are 3 cards, which can be done $C(2, 1)$ ways. This automatically determines that the other value is the one for which there are 2 cards. Next, choose the suits for each value. For the value with 3 cards, there are $C(4, 3)$ values of the suits, and for the value with 2 cards, there are $C(4, 2)$ values. Putting this all together,

$$P(\text{full house}) = \frac{C(13, 2) \cdot C(2, 1) \cdot C(4, 3) \cdot C(4, 2)}{2{,}598{,}960} \approx 0.001441.$$

TRY YOUR TURN 4 ▮▮▮

EXAMPLE 5   Letters

Each of the letters w, y, o, m, i, n, and g is placed on a separate slip of paper. A slip is pulled out, and its letter is recorded in the order in which the slip was drawn. This is done four times.

(a) If the slip is not replaced after the letter is recorded, find the probability that the word "wing" is formed.

SOLUTION   The sample space contains all possible arrangements of the seven letters, taken four at a time. Since order matters, use *permutations* to find the number of arrangements in the sample space.

$$P(7, 4) = \frac{7!}{3!} = 7 \cdot 6 \cdot 5 \cdot 4 = 840$$

YOUR TURN 5 Find the probability that the word "now" is formed if 3 slips are chosen without replacement in Example 5. Find the probability that the word "now" is formed if 3 slips are chosen with replacement.

Since there is only one way that the word "wing" can be formed, the required probability is $1/840 \approx 0.001190$.

(b) If the slip is replaced after the letter is recorded, find the probability that the word "wing" is formed.

SOLUTION   Since the letters can be repeated, there are 7 possible outcomes for each draw of the slip. To calculate the number of arrangements in the sample space, use the *multiplication principle*. The number of arrangements in the sample space is $7^4 = 2401$, and the required probability is $1/2401 \approx 0.0004165$.   TRY YOUR TURN 5 ▮▮▮

EXAMPLE 6   Birthdays

Suppose a group of n people is in a room. Find the probability that at least 2 of the people have the same birthday.

SOLUTION   "Same birthday" refers to the month and the day, not necessarily the same year. Also, ignore leap years, and assume that each day in the year is equally likely as a birthday. To see how to proceed, we first look at the case in which $n = 5$ and find the probability that *no 2 people* from among 5 people have the same birthday. There are 365 different birthdays possible for the first of the 5 people, 364 for the second (so that the people have different birthdays), 363 for the third, and so on. The number of ways the 5 people can have different birthdays is thus the number of permutations of 365 days taken 5 at a time or

$$P(365, 5) = 365 \cdot 364 \cdot 363 \cdot 362 \cdot 361.$$

The number of ways that 5 people can have the same birthday or different birthdays is

$$365 \cdot 365 \cdot 365 \cdot 365 \cdot 365 = (365)^5.$$

*We learned this approach from Professor Peter Grassi of Hofstra University.

Finally, the *probability* that none of the 5 people have the same birthday is

$$\frac{P(365, 5)}{365^5} = \frac{365 \cdot 364 \cdot 363 \cdot 362 \cdot 361}{365 \cdot 365 \cdot 365 \cdot 365 \cdot 365} \approx 0.9729.$$

The probability that at least 2 of the 5 people *do* have the same birthday is $1 - 0.9729 = 0.0271$.

Now this result can be extended to more than 5 people. Generalizing, the probability that no 2 people among n people have the same birthday is

$$\frac{P(365, n)}{365^n}.$$

The probability that at least 2 of the n people *do* have the same birthday is

$$1 - \frac{P(365, n)}{365^n}.$$

The following table shows this probability for various values of n.

Number of People, n	Probability That Two Have the Same Birthday
5	0.0271
10	0.1169
15	0.2529
20	0.4114
22	0.4757
23	0.5073
25	0.5687
30	0.7063
35	0.8144
40	0.8912
50	0.9704
366	1

The probability that 2 people among 23 have the same birthday is 0.5073, a little more than half. Many people are surprised at this result; it seems that a larger number of people should be required. ▬

TECHNOLOGY NOTE

Using a graphing calculator, we can graph the probability formula in the previous example as a function of n, but care must be taken that the graphing calculator evaluates the function at integer points. Figure 7 was produced on a TI-84 Plus C by letting $Y_1 = 1 - (365 \ nPr \ X)/365 \wedge X$ on $0 \leq x \leq 44$. (This domain ensures integer values for x.) Notice that the graph does not extend past $x = 39$. This is because $P(365, n)$ and 365^n are too large for the calculator when $n \geq 40$.

An alternative way of doing the calculations that does not run into such large numbers is based on the concept of conditional probability. The probability that the first person's birthday does not match any so far is 365/365. The probability that the second person's birthday does not match the first's is 364/365. The probability that the third person's birthday does not match the first's or the second's is 363/365. By the product rule of probability, the probability that none of the first 3 people have matching birthdays is

$$\frac{365}{365} \cdot \frac{364}{365} \cdot \frac{363}{365}.$$

FIGURE 7

Similarly, the probability that no two people in a group of 40 have the same birthday is

$$\frac{365}{365} \cdot \frac{364}{365} \cdot \frac{363}{365} \cdot \ldots \cdot \frac{326}{365}.$$

This probability can be calculated (and then subtracted from 1 to get the probability we seek) without overflowing the calculator by multiplying each fraction times the next, rather then trying to compute the entire numerator and the entire denominator. The calculations are somewhat tedious to do by hand but can be programmed on a graphing calculator or computer.

As we saw in Examples 1 and 4(d), probability can sometimes be calculated in more than one way. We now look at one more example of this.

EXAMPLE 7   Fruit

Ray and Nate are arranging a row of fruit at random on a table. They have 5 apples, 6 oranges, and 7 lemons. What is the probability that all fruit of the same kind are together?

SOLUTION

Method 1
Distinguishable Permutations

Ray can't tell individual pieces of fruit of the same kind apart. All apples look the same to him, as do all oranges and all lemons. So in the denominator of the probability, he calculates the number of distinguishable ways to arrange the 18 pieces of fruit, given that all apples are indistinguishable, as are all oranges and all lemons.

$$\frac{18!}{5! \, 6! \, 7!} = 14{,}702{,}688$$

As for the numerator, the only choice is how to arrange the 3 kinds of fruit, for which there are $3! = 6$ ways. Thus

$$P(\text{all fruit of the same kind are together}) = \frac{6}{14{,}702{,}688} \approx 4.081 \times 10^{-7}.$$

Method 2
Permutations

Nate has better eyesight than Ray and can tell the individual pieces of fruit apart. So in the denominator of the probability, he calculates the number of ways to arrange the 18 pieces of fruit, which is

$$18! \approx 6.4024 \times 10^{15}.$$

For the numerator, he first must choose how to arrange the 3 kinds of fruit, for which there are $3!$ ways. Then there are $5!$ ways to arrange the apples, $6!$ ways to arrange the oranges, and $7!$ ways to arrange the lemons, for a total number of possibilities of

$$3! \, 5! \, 6! \, 7! = 2{,}612{,}736{,}000.$$

Therefore,

YOUR TURN 6 If Ray and Nate arrange 2 kiwis, 3 apricots, 4 pineapples, and 5 coconuts in a row at random, what is the probability that all fruit of the same kind are together?

$$P(\text{all fruit of the same kind are together}) = \frac{2{,}612{,}736{,}000}{6.4024 \times 10^{15}} \approx 4.081 \times 10^{-7}.$$

The results for Method 1 and Method 2 are the same. The probability does not depend on whether a person can distinguish individual pieces of the same kind of fruit.

TRY YOUR TURN 6

W1. How many ways is it possible to select 6 cards from an ordinary deck if all cards must be from the same suit? (*Sec. 8.2*)

W2. If the Senate has 59 Democrats and 41 Republicans, how many ways can a committee be chosen with 3 of each? (*Sec. 8.2*)

8.3 EXERCISES

A basket contains 7 red apples and 4 yellow apples. A sample of 3 apples is drawn. Find the probabilities that the sample contains the following.

1. All red apples

2. All yellow apples

3. 2 yellow and 1 red apple

4. More red than yellow apples

In a club with 9 male and 11 female members, a 5-member committee will be randomly chosen. Find the probability that the committee contains the following.

5. All men

6. All women

7. 3 men and 2 women

8. 2 men and 3 women

9. At least 4 women

10. No more than 2 men

Two cards are drawn at random from an ordinary deck of 52 cards.

11. How many 2-card hands are possible?

Find the probability that the 2-card hand described above contains the following.

12. 2 aces

13. At least 1 ace

14. All spades

15. 2 cards of the same suit

16. Only face cards

17. No face cards

18. No card higher than 8 (count ace as 1)

Twenty-six slips of paper are each marked with a different letter of the alphabet and placed in a basket. A slip is pulled out, its letter recorded (in the order in which the slip was drawn), and the slip is replaced. This is done 5 times. Find the probabilities that the following "words" are formed.

19. Chuck

20. A word that starts with "p"

21. A word with no repetition of letters

22. A word that contains no "x," "y," or "z"

23. Discuss the relative merits of using tree diagrams versus combinations to solve probability problems. When would each approach be most appropriate?

24. Several examples in this section used the rule $P(E') = 1 - P(E)$. Explain the advantage (especially in Example 6) of using this rule.

For Exercises 25–28, refer to Example 6 in this section.

25. A total of 43 men have served as president through 2010.* Set up the probability that, if 43 men were selected at random, at least 2 have the same birthday.[†]

26. Set up the probability that at least 2 of the 100 U.S. senators have the same birthday.

27. What is the probability that at least 2 of the 435 members of the House of Representatives have the same birthday?

28. Argue that the probability that in a group of n people *exactly one pair* have the same birthday is

$$C(n, 2) \cdot \frac{P(365, n - 1)}{365^n}.$$

29. After studying all night for a final exam, a bleary-eyed student randomly grabs 2 socks from a drawer containing 9 black, 6 brown, and 2 blue socks, all mixed together. What is the probability that she grabs a matched pair?

30. Three crows, 4 blue jays, and 5 starlings sit in a random order on a section of telephone wire. Find the probability that birds of a feather flock together, that is, that all birds of the same type are sitting together.

31. If the letters l, i, t, t, l, and e are chosen at random, what is the probability that they spell the word "little"?

32. If the letters M, i, s, s, i, s, s, i, p, p, and i are chosen at random, what is the probability that they spell the word "Mississippi"?

33. An elevator has 4 passengers and stops at 7 floors. It is equally likely that a person will get off at any one of the 7 floors. Find the probability that at least 2 passengers leave at the same floor. (*Hint:* Compare this with the birthday problem.)

34. On National Public Radio, the *Weekend Edition* program posed the following probability problem: Given a certain number of balls, of which some are blue, pick 5 at random. The probability that all 5 are blue is 1/2. Determine the original number of balls and decide how many were blue. *Source: Weekend Edition.*

*Although Obama is the 44th president, the 22nd and 24th presidents were the same man: Grover Cleveland.

[†]In fact, James Polk and Warren Harding were both born on November 2.

35. A reader wrote to the "Ask Marilyn" column in *Parade* magazine, "You have six envelopes to pick from. Two-thirds (that is, four) are empty. One-third (that is, two) contain a $100 bill. You're told to choose 2 envelopes at random. Which is more likely: (1) that you'll get at least one $100 bill, or (2) that you'll get no $100 bill at all?"

Find the two probabilities. *Source: Parade magazine.*

APPLICATIONS

Business and Economics

Quality Control   A shipment of 11 printers contains 2 that are defective. Find the probability that a sample of the following sizes, drawn from the 11, will not contain a defective printer.

36. 1   **37.** 2   **38.** 3   **39.** 4

Refer to Example 3. The managers feel that the probability of 0.5455 that a container will be shipped even though it contains 2 defective engines is too high. They decide to increase the sample size chosen. Find the probabilities that a container will be shipped even though it contains 2 defective engines, if the sample size is increased to the following.

40. 4   **41.** 5

42. Sales Presentations   Melanie Banfield and Boyd Shepherd are among 9 representatives making presentations at the annual sales meeting. The presentations are randomly ordered. Find the probability that Melanie is the first presenter and Boyd is the last presenter.

43. Sales Schedule   Dan LaChapelle has the name of 6 prospects, including a customer in Scottsdale. He randomly arranges his schedule to call on only 4 of the 6 prospects. Find the probability that the customer from Scottsdale is not called upon.

Social Sciences

44. Election Ballots   Five names are put on a ballot in a randomly selected order. What is the probability that they are not in alphabetical order?

45. Native American Council   At the first meeting of a committee to plan a Northern California pow-wow, there were 3 women and 3 men from the Miwok tribe, 3 women and 2 men from the Hoopa tribe, and 4 women and 5 men from the Pomo tribe. If the ceremony subcouncil consists of 5 people and is randomly selected, find the probabilities that the subcouncil contains the following:

(a) 3 men and 2 women;

(b) exactly 3 Miwoks and 2 Pomos;

(c) 2 Miwoks, 2 Hoopas, and a Pomo;

(d) 2 Miwoks, 2 Hoopas, and 2 Pomos;

(e) more women than men;

(f) exactly 3 Hoopas;

(g) at least 2 Pomos.

46. Education   A school in Bangkok requires that students take an entrance examination. After the examination, there is a drawing in which 5 students are randomly selected from each group of 40 for automatic acceptance into the school, regardless of their performance on the examination. The drawing consists of placing 35 red and 5 green pieces of paper into a box. Each student picks a piece of paper from the box and then does not return the piece of paper to the box. The 5 lucky students who pick the green pieces are automatically accepted into the school. *Source: The Mathematics Teacher.*

(a) What is the probability that the first person wins automatic acceptance?

(b) What is the probability that the last person wins automatic acceptance?

(c) If the students are chosen by the order of their seating, does this give the student who goes first a better chance of winning than the second, third, . . . person? (*Hint:* Imagine that the 40 pieces of paper have been mixed up and laid in a row so that the first student picks the first piece of paper, the second student picks the second piece of paper, and so on.)

47. Education   At a conference promoting excellence in education for African Americans in Detroit, special-edition books were selected to be given away in contests. There were 9 books written by Langston Hughes, 5 books by James Baldwin, and 7 books by Toni Morrison. The judge of one contest selected 6 books at random for prizes. Find the probabilities that the selection consisted of the following.

(a) 3 Hughes and 3 Morrison books

(b) Exactly 4 Baldwin books

(c) 2 Hughes, 3 Baldwin, and 1 Morrison book

(d) At least 4 Hughes books

(e) Exactly 4 books written by males (Morrison is female)

(f) No more than 2 books written by Baldwin

General Interest

Poker   Find the probabilities of the following hands at poker. Assume aces are either high or low.

48. Royal flush (5 highest cards of a single suit)

49. Straight flush (5 in a row in a single suit, but not a royal flush)

50. Four of a kind (4 cards of the same value)

51. Straight (5 cards in a row, not all of the same suit), with ace either high or low

52. Three of a kind (3 cards of one value, with the other cards of two different values)

53. Two pairs (2 cards of one value, 2 of another value, and 1 of a third value)

54. One pair (2 cards of one value, with the other cards of three different values)

Bridge   A bridge hand is made up of 13 cards from a deck of 52. Find the probabilities that a hand chosen at random contains the following.

55. Only hearts

56. At least 3 aces

57. Exactly 2 aces and exactly 2 kings

58. 6 of one suit, 4 of another, and 3 of another

Texas Hold'Em In a version of poker called Texas Hold'Em, each player has 2 cards, and by the end of the round an additional 5 cards are on the table, shared by all the players. (For more about poker hands, see Example 4 and Exercises 48–54.) Each player's hand consists of the best 5 cards out of the 7 cards available to that player. For example, if a player holds 2 kings, and on the table there is one king and 4 cards with 4 other values, then the player has three of a kind. It's possible that the player has an even better hand. Perhaps five of the seven cards are of the same suit, making a flush, or the other 4 cards are queen, jack, 10, and 9, so the player has a straight. For Exercises 59–64, calculate the probability of each hand in Texas Hold'Em, but for simplicity, ignore the possibility that the cards might form an even better hand.

59. One pair (2 cards of one value, with the other cards of five different values)

60. Two pairs (2 cards of one value, 2 of another, with the other cards of three different values)

61. Three of a kind (3 cards of one value, with the other cards of four different values)

62. Four of a kind (4 cards of one value, with the other cards of three different values)

63. Flush (at least 5 cards of the same suit)

64. Full house (3 cards of one value and two of another. Careful: The two unused cards could be a pair of another value or two different cards of other values. Also, the 7 cards could consist of 3 cards of one value, 3 of second value, and one card of a third value. We won't consider the case of 3 cards of one value and 4 of another, because even though this forms a full house, it also forms four of a kind, which is better.)

65. Suppose you are playing Texas Hold'Em and you've just received your two cards. You observe that they are both hearts. You get excited, because if at least 3 of the 5 cards that are on the table are hearts, you'll have a flush, which means that you'll likely win the round. Given that your two cards are hearts, and you know nothing of any other cards, what is the probability that you'll have a flush by the time all 5 cards are on the table?

66. *Lottery* In the previous section, we found the number of ways to pick 6 different numbers from 1 to 99 in a state lottery. Assuming order is unimportant, what is the probability of picking all 6 numbers correctly to win the big prize?

67. *Lottery* In Exercise 66, what is the probability of picking exactly 5 of the 6 numbers correctly?

68. *Lottery* An article in *The New York Times* discussing the odds of winning the lottery stated,

"And who cares if a game-theory professor once calculated the odds of winning as equal to a poker player's chance of drawing four royal flushes in a row, all in spades—then getting up from the card table and meeting four strangers, all with the same birthday?"

Calculate this probability. Does this probability seem comparable to the odds of winning the lottery? (Ignore February 29 as a birthday, and assume that all four strangers have the same birthday as each other, not necessarily the same as the poker player.) *Source: The New York Times Magazine.*

69. *Lottery* A reader wrote to the "Ask Marilyn" column in *Parade* magazine, "A dozen glazed doughnuts are riding on the answer to this question: Are the odds of winning in a lotto drawing higher when picking 6 numbers out of 49 or when picking 5 numbers out of 52?" Calculate each probability to answer the question. *Source: Parade magazine.*

70. *Lottery* On May 18, 2013, the Powerball Lottery had a jackpot of $590.5 million, which was a record at the time. To enter the lottery, 5 numbers are picked between 1 and 55, plus a bonus number between 1 and 42. All 6 numbers must be correct to win the jackpot.

(a) What is the probability of winning the jackpot with a single ticket?

(b) In an article for the *Minneapolis Star Tribune*, mathematician Douglas Arnold was quoted as saying, "If you were to select a group of Powerball numbers every minute for 138 years, you would have about a 50 percent chance of picking the winning Powerball ticket." Calculate the actual probability, using an estimate of 365.25 for the number of days in the year. (Arnold later told *Chance News* that this was an "off-the-top-of-my-head calculation" made when a reporter called.) *Sources: Minneapolis Star Tribune and Chance News.*

71. *Canadian Lottery* In June 2004, Canada introduced a change in its lottery that violated the usual convention that the smaller the probability of an event, the bigger the prize. In this lottery, participants have to guess six numbers from 1 to 49. Six numbers between 1 and 49 are then drawn at random, plus a seventh "bonus number." *Source: Chance.*

(a) A fifth prize of $10 goes to those who correctly guess exactly three of the six numbers, but do not guess the bonus number. Find the probability of winning fifth prize.

(b) A sixth prize of $5 goes to those who correctly guess exactly two of the six numbers plus the bonus number. Find the probability of winning sixth prize, and compare this with the probability of winning fifth prize.

72. *Barbie* A controversy arose in 1992 over the Teen Talk Barbie doll, each of which was programmed with four sayings randomly picked from a set of 270 sayings. The controversy was over the saying, "Math class is tough," which some felt gave a negative message toward girls doing well in math. In an interview with *Science*, a spokeswoman for Mattel, the makers of Barbie, said that "There's a less than 1% chance you're going to get a doll that says math class is tough." Is this figure correct? If not, give the correct figure. *Source: Science.*

73. *Football* During the 1988 college football season, the Big Eight Conference ended the season in a "perfect progression," as shown in the following table. *Source: The American Statistician.*

Won	Lost	Team
7	0	Nebraska (NU)
6	1	Oklahoma (OU)
5	2	Oklahoma State (OSU)
4	3	Colorado (CU)
3	4	Iowa State (ISU)
2	5	Missouri (MU)
1	6	Kansas (KU)
0	7	Kansas State (KSU)

Someone wondered what the probability of such an outcome might be.

(a) How many games do the 8 teams play?

(b) Assuming no ties, how many different outcomes are there for all the games together?

(c) In how many ways could the 8 teams end in a perfect progression?

(d) Assuming that each team had an equally likely probability of winning each game, find the probability of a perfect progression with 8 teams.

(e) Find a general expression for the probability of a perfect progression in an *n*-team league with the same assumptions.

74. Unluckiest Fan During the 2009 season, the Washington Nationals baseball team won 59 games and lost 103 games. Season ticket holder Stephen Krupin reported in an interview that he watched the team lose all 19 games that he attended that season. The interviewer speculated that this must be a record for bad luck. *Source:* **NPR**.

(a) Based on the full 2009 season record, calculate the probability that a person would attend 19 Washington Nationals games and the Nationals would lose all 19 games.

(b) However, Mr. Krupin only attended home games. The Nationals had 33 wins and 48 losses at home in 2009. Calculate the probability that a person would attend 19 Washington Nationals home games and the Nationals would lose all 19 games.

75. Bingo Bingo has become popular in the United States, and it is an efficient way for many organizations to raise money. The bingo card has 5 rows and 5 columns of numbers from 1 to 75, with the center given as a free cell. Balls showing one of the 75 numbers are picked at random from a container. If the drawn number appears on a player's card, then the player covers the number. In general, the winner is the person who first has a card with an entire row, column, or diagonal covered. *Source: Mathematics Teacher*.

(a) Find the probability that a person will win bingo after just four numbers are called.

(b) An L occurs when the first column and the bottom row are both covered. Find the probability that an L will occur in the fewest number of calls.

(c) An X-out occurs when both diagonals are covered. Find the probability that an X-out occurs in the fewest number of calls.

(d) If bingo cards are constructed so that column one has 5 of the numbers from 1 to 15, column two has 5 of the numbers from 16 to 30, column three has 4 of the numbers from 31 to 45, column four has 5 of the numbers from 46 to 60, and column five has 5 of the numbers from 61 to 75, how many different bingo cards could be constructed? (*Hint:* Order matters!)

76. Suppose a box contains 3 red and 3 blue balls. A ball is selected at random and removed, without observing its color. The box now contains either 3 red and 2 blue balls or 2 red and 3 blue balls. *Source: 40 Puzzles and Problems in Probability and Mathematical Statistics*.

(a) Nate removes a ball at random from the box, observes its color, and puts the ball back. He performs this experiment a total of 6 times, and each time the ball is blue. What is the probability that a red ball was initially removed from the box? (*Hint:* Use Bayes' Theorem.)

(b) Ray removes a ball at random from the box, observes its color, and puts the ball back. He performs this experiment a total of 80 times. Out of these, the ball was blue 44 times and red 36 times. What is the probability that a red ball was initially removed from the box?

(c) Many people intuitively think that Nate's experiment gives more convincing evidence than Ray's experiment that a red ball was removed. Explain why this is wrong.

YOUR TURN ANSWERS
1. 1/5   2. 0.3483   3. 0.7455
4. 0.0006095   5. 1/210; 1/343   6. 9.514×10^{-6}

8.4 Binomial Probability

APPLY IT What is the probability that 3 out of 6 randomly selected college students attend more than one institution during their college career? *We will calculate this probability in Example 2.*

The question above involves an experiment that is repeated 6 times. Many probability problems are concerned with experiments in which an event is repeated many times. Other examples include finding the probability of getting 7 heads in 8 tosses of a coin, of hitting a target 6 times out of 6, and of finding 1 defective item in a sample of 15 items. Probability problems of this kind are called **Bernoulli trials** problems, or **Bernoulli processes**, named after the Swiss mathematician Jakob Bernoulli (1654–1705), who is well known for his work in probability theory. In each case, some outcome is designated a success and any other outcome is considered a failure. This labeling is arbitrary and does not necessarily have anything to do with real success or failure. Thus, if the probability of a success in a single trial is p, the probability of failure will be $1 - p$. A Bernoulli trials problem, or **binomial experiment**, must satisfy the following conditions.

> ## Binomial Experiment
>
> 1. The same experiment is repeated a fixed number of times.
> 2. There are only two possible outcomes, success and failure.
> 3. The repeated trials are independent, so that the probability of success remains the same for each trial.

EXAMPLE 1   Sleep

The chance that an American falls asleep with the TV on at least three nights a week is 1/4. Suppose a researcher selects 5 Americans at random and is interested in the probability that all 5 are "TV sleepers." *Source: Harper's Magazine.*

SOLUTION   Here the experiment, selecting a person, is repeated 5 times. If selecting a TV sleeper is labeled a success, then getting a "non-TV sleeper" is labeled a failure. The 5 trials are almost independent. There is a very slight dependence; if, for example, the first person selected is a TV sleeper, then there is one less TV sleeper to choose from when we select the next person (assuming we never select the same person twice). When selecting a small sample out of a large population, however, the probability changes negligibly, so researchers consider such trials to be independent. Thus, the probability that all 5 in our sample are sleepers is

$$\frac{1}{4} \cdot \frac{1}{4} \cdot \frac{1}{4} \cdot \frac{1}{4} \cdot \frac{1}{4} = \left(\frac{1}{4}\right)^5 \approx 0.0009766.$$

FOR REVIEW

Recall that if A and B are independent events,

$$P(A \text{ and } B) = P(A)P(B).$$

Now suppose the problem in Example 1 is changed to that of finding the probability that exactly 4 of the 5 people in the sample are TV sleepers. This outcome can occur in more than one way, as shown below, where s represents a success (a TV sleeper) and f represents a failure (a non-TV sleeper).

outcome 1:	s	s	s	s	f
outcome 2:	s	s	s	f	s
outcome 3:	s	s	f	s	s
outcome 4:	s	f	s	s	s
outcome 5:	f	s	s	s	s

Keep in mind that since the probability of success is 1/4, the probability of failure is $1 - 1/4 = 3/4$. The probability, then, of each of these 5 outcomes is

$$\left(\frac{1}{4}\right)^4\left(\frac{3}{4}\right).$$

Since the 5 outcomes represent mutually exclusive events, add the 5 identical probabilities, which is equivalent to multiplying the above probability by 5. The result is

$$P(4 \text{ of the 5 people are TV sleepers}) = 5\left(\frac{1}{4}\right)^4\left(\frac{3}{4}\right) = \frac{15}{4^5} \approx 0.01465.$$

In the same way, we can compute the probability of selecting 3 TV sleepers in our sample of 5. The probability of any one way of achieving 3 successes and 2 failures will be

$$\left(\frac{1}{4}\right)^3\left(\frac{3}{4}\right)^2.$$

Rather than list all the ways of achieving 3 successes out of 5 trials, we will count this number using combinations. The number of ways to select 3 elements out of a set of 5 is $C(5, 3) = 5!/(2! \, 3!) = 10$, giving

$$P(3 \text{ of the 5 people are TV sleepers}) = 10\left(\frac{1}{4}\right)^3\left(\frac{3}{4}\right)^2 = \frac{90}{4^5} \approx 0.08789.$$

A similar argument works in the general case.

Binomial Probability

If p is the probability of success in a single trial of a binomial experiment, the probability of x successes and $n - x$ failures in n independent repeated trials of the experiment, known as **binomial probability**, is

$$P(x \text{ successes in } n \text{ trials}) = C(n, x) \cdot p^x \cdot (1 - p)^{n-x}.$$

EXAMPLE 2   College Students

A recent survey found that 59% of college students attend more than one institution during their college career. Suppose a sample of 6 students is chosen. Assuming that each student's college attendance pattern is independent of the others, find the probability of each of the following. *Source: The New York Times.*

(a) Exactly 3 of the 6 students attend more than one institution.

APPLY IT

   SOLUTION   Think of the 6 students chosen as 6 independent trials. A success occurs if the student attends more than one institution. Then this is a binomial experiment with $n = 6$ and $p = P$ (attend more than one institution) $= 0.59$. To find the probability that exactly 3 students attend more than one institution, let $x = 3$ and use the binomial probability formula.

$$\begin{aligned} P(\text{exactly 3 of 6 students}) &= C(6, 3)(0.59)^3(1 - 0.59)^{6-3} \\ &= 20(0.59)^3(0.41)^3 \\ &= 20(0.2054)(0.06892) \\ &\approx 0.2831 \end{aligned}$$

(b) None of the 6 students attend more than one institution.

YOUR TURN 1 Find the probability that exactly 2 of the 6 students in Example 2 attend more than 1 institution.

   SOLUTION   Let $x = 0$.

$$\begin{aligned} P(\text{exactly 0 of 6 students}) &= C(6, 0)(0.59)^0(1 - 0.59)^6 \\ &= 1(1)(0.41)^6 \approx 0.00475 \end{aligned}$$

TRY YOUR TURN 1

EXAMPLE 3   Checkout Scanners

The Federal Trade Commission (FTC) monitors pricing accuracy to ensure that consumers are charged the correct price at the checkout. According to the FTC, 29% of stores that use checkout scanners do not accurately charge customers. *Source: Federal Trade Commission.*

(a) If you shop at 3 stores that use checkout scanners, what is the probability that you will be incorrectly charged in at least one store?

   SOLUTION   We can treat this as a binomial experiment, letting $n = 3$ and $p = 0.29$. We need to find the probability of "at least 1" incorrect charge, which means 1 or 2 or 3 incorrect charges. To make our calculation simpler, we will use the complement.

We will find the probability of being charged incorrectly in none of the 3 stores, that is, $P(0$ incorrect charges$)$, and then find $1 - P(0$ incorrect charges$)$.

$$P(0 \text{ incorrect charges}) = C(3, 0)(0.29)^0(0.71)^3$$
$$= 1(1)(0.357911) \approx 0.3579$$
$$P(\text{at least one}) = 1 - P(0 \text{ incorrect charges})$$
$$\approx 1 - 0.3579 = 0.6421$$

(b) If you shop at 3 stores that use checkout scanners, what is the probability that you will be incorrectly charged in at most one store?

YOUR TURN 2 In Example 3, if you shop at 4 stores that use checkout scanners, find the probability that you will be charged incorrectly in at least one store.

SOLUTION "At most one" means 0 or 1, so

$$P(0 \text{ or } 1) = P(0) + P(1)$$
$$= C(3, 0)(0.29)^0(0.71)^3 + C(3, 1)(0.29)^1(0.71)^2$$
$$= 1(1)(0.357911) + 3(0.29)(0.5041) \approx 0.7965.$$

TRY YOUR TURN 2

The triangular array of numbers shown below is called **Pascal's triangle** in honor of the French mathematician Blaise Pascal (1623–1662), who was one of the first to use it extensively. The triangle was known long before Pascal's time and appears in Chinese and Islamic manuscripts from the eleventh century.

Pascal's Triangle

```
                    1
                1       1
            1       2       1
        1       3       3       1
    1       4       6       4       1
1       5      10      10       5       1
    :       :       :       :       :
```

The array provides a quick way to find binomial probabilities. The nth row of the triangle, where $n = 0, 1, 2, 3, \ldots$, gives the coefficients $C(n, r)$ for $r = 0, 1, 2, 3, \ldots, n$. For example, for $n = 4$, $1 = C(4, 0)$, $4 = C(4, 1)$, $6 = C(4, 2)$, and so on. Each number in the triangle is the sum of the two numbers directly above it. For example, in the row for $n = 4$, 1 is the sum of 1, the only number above it, 4 is the sum of 1 and 3, 6 is the sum of 3 and 3, and so on. Adding in this way gives the sixth row:

$$1 \quad 6 \quad 15 \quad 20 \quad 15 \quad 6 \quad 1.$$

Notice that Pascal's triangle tells us, for example, that $C(4, 1) + C(4, 2) = C(5, 2)$ (that is, $4 + 6 = 10$). Using the combinations formula, it can be shown that, in general, $C(n, r) + C(n, r + 1) = C(n + 1, r + 1)$. This is left as an exercise.

EXAMPLE 4 Pascal's Triangle

Use Pascal's triangle to find the probability in Example 3 that if you shop at 6 stores that use checkout scanners, at least 3 will charge you incorrectly

SOLUTION The probability of success is 0.29. Since at least 3 means 3, 4, 5, or 6,

$$P(\text{at least 3}) = P(3) + P(4) + P(5) + P(6)$$
$$= C(6, 3)(0.29)^3(0.71)^3 + C(6, 4)(0.29)^4(0.71)^2$$
$$+ C(6, 5)(0.29)^5(0.71)^1 + C(6, 6)(0.29)^6(0.71)^0.$$

Use the sixth row of Pascal's triangle for the combinations to get

YOUR TURN 3 In Example 3, find the probability that if you shop at 6 stores with checkout scanners, at most 3 stores will charge you incorrectly.

$$P(\text{at least } 3) = 20(0.29)^3(0.71)^3 + 15(0.29)^4(0.71)^2$$
$$+ 6(0.29)^5(0.71)^1 + 1(0.29)^6(0.71)^0$$
$$= 0.1746 + 0.0535 + 0.0087 + 0.0006$$
$$= 0.2374.$$

TRY YOUR TURN 3

EXAMPLE 5   Independent Jury

If each member of a 9-person jury acts independently of each other and makes the correct determination of guilt or innocence with probability 0.65, find the probability that the majority of jurors will reach a correct verdict. *Source: Frontiers in Economics.*

SOLUTION

**Method 1
Calculating by Hand**

Since the jurors in this particular situation act independently, we can treat this as a binomial experiment. Thus, the probability that the majority of the jurors will reach the correct verdict is given by

$$P(\text{at least } 5) = C(9, 5)(0.65)^5(0.35)^4 + C(9, 6)(0.65)^6(0.35)^3$$
$$+ C(9, 7)(0.65)^7(0.35)^2 + C(9, 8)(0.65)^8(0.35)^1 + C(9, 9)(0.65)^9$$
$$= 0.2194 + 0.2716 + 0.2162 + 0.1004 + 0.0207$$
$$= 0.8283.$$

**Method 2
Graphing Calculator**

Some graphing calculators provide binomial probabilities. On a TI-84 Plus, for example, the command `binompdf(9,.65,5)`, found in the DISTR menu, gives 0.219386301, which is the probability that $x = 5$. (On a TI-84 Plus C, after DISTR-binompdf, put 9 after trials, .65 after p, and 5 after x value. Then, when the cursor is on Paste, press ENTER.) Alternatively, the command `binomcdf(9,.65,4)` gives 0.1717192855 as the probability that 4 or fewer jurors will make the correct decision. Subtract 0.1717192855 from 1 to get 0.8282807145 as the probability that the majority of the jurors will make the correct decision. This value rounds to 0.8283, which is in agreement with Method 1. Often, graphing calculators are more accurate than calculations by hand due to the accumulation of rounding errors when doing successive calculations by hand.

**Method 3
Spreadsheet**

Some spreadsheets also provide binomial probabilities. In Microsoft Excel, for example, the command "=BINOMDIST(5,9,.65,0)" gives 0.219386301, which is the probability that $x = 5$. Alternatively, the command "=BINOMDIST(4,9,.65,1)" gives 0.171719286 as the probability that 4 or fewer jurors will make the correct decision. Subtract 0.171719286 from 1 to get 0.828280714 as the probability that the majority of the jurors will make the correct decision. This value agrees with the value found in Methods 1 and 2.

8.4 WARM-UP EXERCISES

W1. How many ways can a committee of 10 senators be formed out of 100 senators?   *(Sec. 8.2)*

W2. How many ways can a sample of 8 items be chosen from a batch of 32?   *(Sec. 8.2)*

8.4 EXERCISES

Suppose that a family has 5 children. Also, suppose that the probability of having a girl is 1/2. Find the probabilities that the family has the following children.

1. Exactly 2 girls and 3 boys

2. Exactly 3 girls and 2 boys

3. No girls

4. No boys

5. At least 4 girls

6. At least 3 boys

7. No more than 3 boys

8. No more than 4 girls

A die is rolled 12 times. Find the probabilities of rolling the following.

9. Exactly 12 ones

10. Exactly 6 ones

11. Exactly 1 one

12. Exactly 2 ones

13. No more than 3 ones

14. No more than 1 one

15. How do you identify a probability problem that involves a binomial experiment?

16. How is Pascal's triangle used to find probabilities?

17. Using the definition of combination in Section 8.2, prove that

$$C(n, r) + C(n, r + 1) = C(n + 1, r + 1).$$

(This is the formula underlying Pascal's triangle.)

In Exercises 18 and 19, argue that the use of binomial probabilities is not applicable and, thus, the probabilities that are computed are not correct.

18. In England, a woman was found guilty of smothering her two infant children. Much of the Crown's case against the lady was based on the testimony from a pediatrician who indicated that the chances of two crib deaths occurring in both siblings was only about 1 in 73 million. This number was calculated by assuming that the probability of a single crib death is 1 in 8543 and the probability of two crib deaths is 1 in 8543^2 (i.e., binomial). (See Chapter 7 Review Exercise 118.) *Source: Science.*

19. A contemporary radio station in Boston has a contest in which a caller is asked his or her date of birth. If the caller's date of birth, including the day, month, and year of birth, matches a predetermined date, the caller wins $1 million. Assuming that there were 36,525 days in the 20th century and the contest was run 51 times on consecutive days, the probability that the grand prize will be won is

$$1 - \left(1 - \frac{1}{36,525}\right)^{51} \approx 0.0014.$$

Source: Chance News.

APPLICATIONS

Business and Economics

Management The survey discussed in Example 3 also found that customers are charged incorrectly for 1 out of every 30 items, on average. Suppose a customer purchases 15 items. Find the following probabilities.

20. A customer is charged incorrectly on 3 items.

21. A customer is not charged incorrectly for any item.

22. A customer is charged incorrectly on at least one item.

23. A customer is charged incorrectly on at least 2 items.

24. A customer is charged incorrectly on at most 2 items.

Credit Cards A survey of consumer finance found that 25.4% of credit-card-holding families hardly ever pay off the balance. Suppose a random sample of 20 credit-card-holding families is taken. Find the probabilities of each of the following results. *Source: Statistical Abstract of the United States.*

25. Exactly 6 families hardly ever pay off the balance.

26. Exactly 9 families hardly ever pay off the balance.

27. At least 4 families hardly ever pay off the balance.

28. At most 5 families hardly ever pay off the balance.

Quality Control A factory tests a random sample of 20 transistors for defects. The probability that a particular transistor will be defective has been established by past experience as 0.05.

29. What is the probability that there are no defective transistors in the sample?

30. What is the probability that the number of defective transistors in the sample is at most 2?

31. **Quality Control** The probability that a certain machine turns out a defective item is 0.05. Find the probabilities that in a run of 75 items, the following results are obtained.

    (a) Exactly 5 defective items

    (b) No defective items

    (c) At least 1 defective item

32. **Survey Results** A company is taking a survey to find out whether people like its product. Its last survey indicated that 70% of the population like the product. Based on that, in a sample of 58 people, find the probabilities of the following.

    (a) All 58 like the product.

    (b) From 28 to 30 (inclusive) like the product.

33. **Pecans** Pecan producers blow air through the pecans so that the lighter ones are blown out. The lighter-weight pecans are generally bad and the heavier ones tend to be better. These "blow outs" and "good nuts" are often sold to tourists along the highway. Suppose 60% of the "blow outs" are good, and 80% of the "good nuts" are good. *Source: Irvin R. Hentzel.*

(a) What is the probability that if you crack and check 20 "good nuts" you will find 8 bad ones?

(b) What is the probability that if you crack and check 20 "blow outs" you will find 8 bad ones?

(c) If we assume that 70% of the roadside stands sell "good nuts," and that out of 20 nuts we find 8 that are bad, what is the probability that the nuts are "blow outs"?

34. Hurricane Insurance A company prices its hurricane insurance using the following assumptions:

(i) In any calendar year, there can be at most one hurricane.

(ii) In any calendar year, the probability of a hurricane is 0.05.

(iii) The number of hurricanes in any calendar year is independent of the number of hurricanes in any other calendar year.

Using the company's assumptions, calculate the probability that there are fewer than 3 hurricanes in a 20-year period. Choose one of the following. *Source: Society of Actuaries.*

(a) 0.06   (b) 0.19   (c) 0.38   (d) 0.62   (e) 0.92

Life Sciences

Breast Cancer A recent study found that 85% of breast-cancer cases are detectable by mammogram. Suppose a random sample of 15 women with breast cancer are given mammograms. Find the probability of each of the following results, assuming that detection in the cases is independent. *Source: Harper's Index.*

35. All of the cases are detectable.

36. None of the cases are detectable.

37. Not all cases are detectable.

38. More than half of the cases are detectable.

Births of Twins The probability that a birth will result in twins is 0.012. Assuming independence (perhaps not a valid assumption), what are the probabilities that out of 100 births in a hospital, there will be the following numbers of sets of twins?

39. Exactly 2 sets of twins

40. At most 2 sets of twins

41. Births In 2012, the University of Minnesota Medical Center had a string of 19 births, all of whom were boys. *Source: CBS Minnesota.*

(a) Assuming boy and girl births are equally likely, what is the probability of 19 births in a row being boys?

(b) There are about 4 million births per year in the United States and about 5700 hospitals. For the sake of simplicity, suppose the births over a ten-year period were evenly distributed over all the hospitals, and suppose each of those hospitals divided their births into strings of 19 consecutive births. What is the probability, in any one of those hospitals, of having a string of all boys?

(c) Based on your answer to part (b), what is the probability that at least one of those 5700 hospitals would have a string of all boys?

(d) Explain why the actual probability of a hospital seeing a string of 19 boy births somewhere in the United States over a 10-year period is higher than the value calculated in part (c).

42. Births In Clay County, North Carolina, 54 out of 84 births in 2012, or about 64%, were male, while in Macon County, 201 out of 346 births, or about 58%, were male. *Source: North Carolina State Center for Health Statistics.*

(a) Which of these two events seems less likely to you? Now compute the probability of at least 54 out of 84 births being male, and at least 201 out of 346 births being male, assuming male and female births are equally likely. Does this surprise you?

(b) Explain why the Macon County births are more unusual, even though the Clay County births have a higher percentage of males.

(c) Explain why, in part (a), we calculated the probability of at least 54 births out of 84 being male, rather than the probability that exactly 54 births out of 84 are male.

43. Color Blindness The probability that a male will be color-blind is 0.042. Find the probabilities that in a group of 53 men, the following will be true.

(a) Exactly 5 are color-blind.

(b) No more than 5 are color-blind.

(c) At least 1 is color-blind.

44. Pharmacology In placebo-controlled trials of Pravachol®, a drug that is prescribed to lower cholesterol, 7.3% of the patients who were taking the drug experienced nausea/vomiting, whereas 7.1% of the patients who were taking the placebo experienced nausea/vomiting. *Source: Bristol-Myers Squibb Company.*

(a) If 100 patients who are taking Pravachol® are selected, what is the probability that 10 or more will experience nausea/vomiting?

(b) If a second group of 100 patients receives a placebo, what is the probability that 10 or more will experience nausea/vomiting?

(c) Since 7.3% is larger than 7.1%, do you believe that the Pravachol® causes more people to experience nausea/vomiting than a placebo? Explain.

45. Genetic Fingerprinting The use of DNA has become an integral part of many court cases. When DNA is extracted from cells and body fluids, genetic information is represented by bands of information, which look similar to a bar code at a grocery store. It is generally accepted that in unrelated people, the probability of a particular band matching is 1 in 4. *Source: University of Exeter.*

(a) If 5 bands are compared in unrelated people, what is the probability that all 5 of the bands match? (Express your answer in terms of "1 chance in ?".)

(b) If 20 bands are compared in unrelated people, what is the probability that all 20 of the bands match? (Express your answer in terms of "1 chance in ?".)

(c) If 20 bands are compared in unrelated people, what is the probability that 16 or more bands match? (Express your answer in terms of "1 chance in ?".)

(d) If you were deciding paternity and there were 16 matches out of 20 bands compared, would you believe that the person being tested was the father? Explain.

46. Salmonella According to *The Salt Lake Tribune*, the Coffee Garden in Salt Lake City ran into trouble because of their four-egg quiche:

"A Salt Lake County Health Department inspector paid a visit recently and pointed out that research by the Food and Drug Administration indicates that one in four eggs carries *Salmonella* bacterium, so restaurants should never use more than three eggs when preparing quiche.

The manager on duty wondered aloud if simply throwing out three eggs from each dozen and using the remaining nine in four-egg quiches would serve the same purpose.

The inspector wasn't sure, but she said she would research it." *Source: The Salt Lake Tribune.*

(a) Assuming that one in four eggs carries *Salmonella*, and that the event that any one egg is infected is independent of whether any other egg is infected, find the probability that at least one of the eggs in a four-egg quiche carries *Salmonella.*

(b) Repeat part (a) for a three-egg quiche.

(c) Discuss whether the assumption of independence is justified.

(d) Discuss whether the inspector's reasoning makes sense.

47. Herbal Remedies According to Dr. Peter A.G.M. De Smet of the Netherlands, "If an herb caused an adverse reaction in 1 in 1,000 users, a traditional healer would have to treat 4,800 patients with that herb (i.e., one new patient every single working day for more than 18 years) to have a 95 percent chance of observing the reaction in more than one user." Verify this calculation by finding the probability of observing more than one reaction in 4800 patients, given that 1 in 1000 has a reaction. *Source: The New England Journal of Medicine.*

48. Vaccines A hospital receives 1/5 of its flu vaccine shipments from Company X and the remainder of its shipments from other companies. Each shipment contains a very large number of vaccine vials. For Company X's shipments, 10% of the vials are ineffective. For every other company, 2% of the vials are ineffective. The hospital tests 30 randomly selected vials from a shipment and finds that one vial is ineffective. What is the probability that this shipment came from Company X? Choose one of the following. (*Hint:* Find the probability that one out of 30 vials is ineffective, given that the shipment came from Company X and that the shipment came from other companies. Then use Bayes' theorem.) *Source: Society of Actuaries.*

(a) 0.10 (b) 0.14 (c) 0.37 (d) 0.63 (e) 0.86

49. Health Study A study is being conducted in which the health of two independent groups of ten policyholders is being monitored over a one-year period of time. Individual participants in the study drop out before the end of the study with probability 0.2 (independently of the other participants). What is the probability that at least 9 participants complete the study in one of the two groups, but not in both groups? Choose one of the following. *Source: Society of Actuaries.*

(a) 0.096 (b) 0.192 (c) 0.235 (d) 0.376 (e) 0.469

Social Sciences

50. Women Working A recent study found that 60% of working mothers would prefer to work part-time if money were not a concern. Find the probability that if 10 working mothers are selected at random, at least 3 of them would prefer to work part-time. *Source: Pew Research Center.*

Volunteering A recent survey found that 83% of first-year college students were involved in volunteer work at least occasionally. Suppose a random sample of 12 college students is taken. Find the probabilities of each of the following results. *Source: The New York Times.*

51. Exactly 7 students volunteered at least occasionally.

52. Exactly 9 students volunteered at least occasionally.

53. At least 9 students volunteered at least occasionally.

54. At most 9 students volunteered at least occasionally.

55. Minority Enrollment According to the U.S. Department of Education, 32.2% of all students enrolled in degree-granting institutions (those that grant associate's or higher degrees) belong to minorities. Find the probabilities of the following results in a random sample of 10 students enrolled in degree-granting institutions. *Source: National Center for Education Statistics.*

(a) Exactly 2 belong to a minority.

(b) Three or fewer belong to a minority.

(c) Exactly 5 do not belong to a minority.

(d) Six or more do not belong to a minority.

56. Cheating According to a poll conducted by *U.S. News and World Report*, 84% of college students believe they need to cheat to get ahead in the world today. *Source: U.S. News and World Report.*

(a) Do the results of this poll indicate that 84% of all college students cheat? Explain.

(b) If this result is accurate and 100 college students are asked if they believe that cheating is necessary to get ahead in the world, what is the probability that 90 or more of the students will answer affirmatively to the question?

57. Education A study by Cleveland Clinic tracked a cohort of very-low-birth-weight infants for twenty years. The results of the study indicated that 74% of the very-low-birth-weight babies graduated from high school during this time period. The study also reported that 83% of the comparison group of normal-birth-weight babies graduated from high school during the same period. *Source: The New England Journal of Medicine.*

(a) If 40 very-low-birth-weight babies were tracked through high school, what is the probability that at least 30 will graduate from high school by age 20?

(b) If 40 babies from the comparison group were tracked through high school, what is the probability that at least 30 will graduate from high school by age 20?

58. War Dead A newspaper article questioned whether soldiers and marines from some states bear greater risks in Afghanistan and Iraq than those from others. Out of 644,066 troops deployed as of the time of the article, 1174 had been killed, for a probability of being killed of $p = 1174/644,066$. Assume the deaths are independent.* *Source: Valley News.*

(a) Vermont had 9 deaths out of 1613 troops deployed. Find the probability of at least this many deaths.

*For further statistical analysis, see www.dartmouth.edu/~chance/ForWiki/GregComments.pdf.

(b) Massachusetts had 28 deaths out of 7146 troops deployed. Find the probability of at least this many deaths.

(c) Florida had 54 deaths out of 62,572 troops deployed. Find the probability of at most this many deaths.

(d) Discuss why the assumption of independence may be questionable.

59. Sports In many sports championships, such as the World Series in baseball and the Stanley Cup final series in hockey, the winner is the first team to win four games. For this exercise, assume that each game is independent of the others, with a constant probability p that one specified team (say, the National League team) wins.

(a) Find the probability that the series lasts for four, five, six, and seven games when $p = 0.5$. (*Hint:* Suppose the National League wins the series, so they must win the last game. Consider how the previous games might come out. Then consider the probability that the American League wins.)

(b) Morrison and Schmittlein have found that the Stanley Cup finals can be described by letting $p = 0.73$ be the probability that the better team wins each game. Find the probability that the series lasts for four, five, six, and seven games. *Source: Chance.*

(c) Some have argued that the assumption of independence does not apply. Discuss this issue. *Source: Mathematics Magazine.*

YOUR TURN ANSWERS

1. 0.1475   **2.** 0.7459   **3.** 0.9372

8.5 Probability Distributions; Expected Value

APPLY IT   What is the expected payback for someone who buys one ticket in a raffle?
In Example 4, we will calculate the expected payback or expected value of this raffle.

We shall see that the *expected value* of a probability distribution is a type of average. Probability distributions were introduced briefly in Chapter 7 on Sets and Probability. Now we take a more complete look at probability distributions. A probability distribution depends on the idea of a *random variable*, so we begin with that.

Random Variables   When researchers carry out an experiment it is necessary to quantify the possible outcomes of the experiment. This process will enable the researcher to recognize individual outcomes and analyze the data. The most common way to keep track of the individual outcomes of the experiment is to assign a numerical value to each of the different possible outcomes of the experiment. For example, if a coin is tossed 2 times, the possible outcomes are: *hh, ht, th,* and *tt.* For each of these possible outcomes, we could record the number of heads. Then the outcome, which we will label x, is one of the numbers 0, 1, or 2. Of course, we could have used other numbers, like 00, 01, 10, and 11, to indicate these same outcomes, but the values of 0, 1, and 2 are simpler and provide an immediate description of the exact outcome of the experiment. Notice that using this random variable also gives us a way to readily know how many tails occurred in the experiment. Thus, in some sense, the values of x are random, so x is called a **random variable**.

Random Variable
A **random variable** is a function that assigns a real number to each outcome of an experiment.

Probability Distribution A table that lists the possible values of a random variable, together with the corresponding probabilities, is called a **probability distribution**. The sum of the probabilities in a probability distribution must always equal 1. (The sum in some distributions may vary slightly from 1 because of rounding.)

EXAMPLE 1 Computer Monitors

A shipment of 12 computer monitors contains 3 broken monitors. A shipping manager checks a sample of four monitors to see if any are broken. Give the probability distribution for the number of broken monitors that the shipping manager finds.

SOLUTION Let x represent the random variable "number of broken monitors found by the manager." Since there are 3 broken monitors, the possible values of x are 0, 1, 2, and 3. We can calculate the probability of each x using the methods of Section 8.3. There are 3 broken monitors, and 9 unbroken monitors, so the number of ways of choosing 0 broken monitors (which implies 4 unbroken monitors) is $C(3, 0) \cdot C(9, 4)$. The number of ways of choosing a sample of 4 monitors is $C(12, 4)$. Therefore, the probability of choosing 0 broken monitors is

$$P(0) = \frac{C(3, 0) \cdot C(9, 4)}{C(12, 4)} = \frac{1\left(\dfrac{9 \cdot 8 \cdot 7 \cdot 6}{4 \cdot 3 \cdot 2 \cdot 1}\right)}{\left(\dfrac{12 \cdot 11 \cdot 10 \cdot 9}{4 \cdot 3 \cdot 2 \cdot 1}\right)} = \frac{126}{495} = \frac{14}{55}.$$

Similarly, the probability of choosing 1 broken monitor is

$$P(1) = \frac{C(3, 1) \cdot C(9, 3)}{C(12, 4)} = \frac{3 \cdot 84}{495} = \frac{252}{495} = \frac{28}{55}.$$

The probability of choosing 2 broken monitors is

$$P(2) = \frac{C(3, 2) \cdot C(9, 2)}{C(12, 4)} = \frac{3 \cdot 36}{495} = \frac{108}{495} = \frac{12}{55}.$$

The probability of choosing 3 broken monitors is

$$P(3) = \frac{C(3, 3) \cdot C(9, 1)}{C(12, 4)} = \frac{1 \cdot 9}{495} = \frac{9}{495} = \frac{1}{55}.$$

The results can be put in a table, called a probability distribution.

YOUR TURN 1 Suppose the inspector in Example 1 chose only two monitors to inspect. Find the probability distribution for the number of broken monitors.

Probability Distribution of Broken Monitors in Sample			
x	0	1	2	3
$P(x)$	14/55	28/55	12/55	1/55

TRY YOUR TURN 1

Instead of writing the probability distribution as a table, we could write the same information as a set of ordered pairs:

$$\{(0, 14/55), (1, 28/55), (2, 12/55), (3, 1/55)\}.$$

There is just one probability for each value of the random variable. Thus, a probability distribution defines a function, called a **probability distribution function**, or simply a **probability function**. We shall use the terms "probability distribution" and "probability function" interchangeably.

The information in a probability distribution is often displayed graphically as a special kind of bar graph called a **histogram**. The bars of a histogram all have the same width, usually 1. (The widths might be different from 1 when the values of the random variable are not consecutive integers.) The heights of the bars are determined by the probabilities. A histogram for the data in Example 1 is given in Figure 8. A histogram shows important

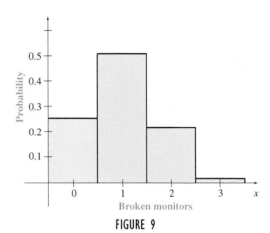

FIGURE 8   FIGURE 9

characteristics of a distribution that may not be readily apparent in tabular form, such as the relative sizes of the probabilities and any symmetry in the distribution.

The area of the bar above $x = 0$ in Figure 8 is the product of 1 and 14/55, or $1 \cdot 14/55 = 14/55$. Since each bar has a width of 1, its area is equal to the probability that corresponds to that value of x. The probability that a particular value will occur is thus given by the area of the appropriate bar of the graph. For example, the probability that one or more monitors is broken is the sum of the areas for $x = 1$, $x = 2$, and $x = 3$. This area, shown in pink in Figure 9, corresponds to 41/55 of the total area, since

$$P(x \geq 1) = P(x = 1) + P(x = 2) + P(x = 3)$$
$$= 28/55 + 12/55 + 1/55 = 41/55.$$

EXAMPLE 2   Probability Distributions

(a) Give the probability distribution for the number of heads showing when two coins are tossed.

SOLUTION   Let x represent the random variable "number of heads." Then x can take on the values 0, 1, or 2. Now find the probability of each outcome. To find the probability of 0, 1, or 2 heads, we can either use binomial probability, or notice that there are 4 outcomes in the sample space: $\{hh, ht, th, tt\}$. The results are shown in the table with Figure 10.

Probability Distribution of Heads			
x	0	1	2
$P(x)$	1/4	1/2	1/4

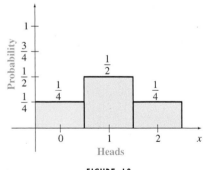

FIGURE 10

YOUR TURN 2 Find the probability distribution and draw a histogram for the number of tails showing when three coins are tossed.

(b) Draw a histogram for the distribution in the table. Find the probability that at least one coin comes up heads.

SOLUTION   The histogram is shown in Figure 10. The portion in pink represents

$$P(x \geq 1) = P(x = 1) + P(x = 2)$$
$$= \frac{3}{4}.$$

TRY YOUR TURN 2

Expected Value   In working with probability distributions, it is useful to have a concept of the typical or average value that the random variable takes on. In Example 2, for instance, it seems reasonable that, on the average, one head shows when two coins are tossed. This does not tell what will happen the next time we toss two coins; we may get two heads, or we may get none. If we tossed two coins many times, however, we would expect that, in the long run, we would average about one head for each toss of two coins.

A way to solve such problems in general is to imagine flipping two coins 4 times. Based on the probability distribution in Example 2, we would expect that 1 of the 4 times we would get 0 heads, 2 of the 4 times we would get 1 head, and 1 of the 4 times we would get 2 heads. The total number of heads we would get, then, is

$$0 \cdot 1 + 1 \cdot 2 + 2 \cdot 1 = 4.$$

The expected numbers of heads per toss is found by dividing the total number of heads by the total number of tosses, or

$$\frac{0 \cdot 1 + 1 \cdot 2 + 2 \cdot 1}{4} = 0 \cdot \frac{1}{4} + 1 \cdot \frac{1}{2} + 2 \cdot \frac{1}{4} = 1.$$

Notice that the expected number of heads turns out to be the sum of the three values of the random variable x multiplied by their corresponding probabilities. We can use this idea to define the *expected value* of a random variable as follows.

Expected Value

Suppose the random variable x can take on the n values $x_1, x_2, x_3, \ldots, x_n$. Also, suppose the probabilities that these values occur are, respectively, $p_1, p_2, p_3, \ldots, p_n$. Then the **expected value** of the random variable is

$$E(x) = x_1 p_1 + x_2 p_2 + x_3 p_3 + \cdots + x_n p_n.$$

EXAMPLE 3   **Computer Monitors**

In Example 1, find the expected number of broken monitors that the shipping manager finds.

SOLUTION   Using the values in the first table in this section and the definition of expected value, we find that

$$E(x) = 0 \cdot \frac{14}{55} + 1 \cdot \frac{28}{55} + 2 \cdot \frac{12}{55} + 3 \cdot \frac{1}{55} = 1.$$

On average, the shipping manager will find 1 broken monitor in the sample of 4. On reflection, this seems natural; 3 of the 12 monitors, or 1/4 of the total, are broken. We should expect, then, that 1/4 of the sample of 4 monitors are broken.   ▬

Physically, the expected value of a probability distribution represents a balance point. If we think of the histogram in Figure 8 as a series of weights with magnitudes represented by the heights of the bars, then the system would balance if supported at the point corresponding to the expected value.

EXAMPLE 4   **Symphony Orchestra**

Suppose a local symphony decides to raise money by raffling an HD television worth $400, a dinner for two worth $80, and 2 CDs worth $20 each. A total of 2000 tickets are sold at $1 each. Find the expected payback for a person who buys one ticket in the raffle.

APPLY IT

Method 1
Direct Calculation

SOLUTION

Here the random variable represents the possible amounts of payback, where payback equals the amount won minus the cost of the ticket. The payback of the person winning the television is $400 (amount won) − $1 (cost of ticket) = $399. The payback for each losing ticket is $0 − $1 = −$1.

The paybacks of the various prizes, as well as their respective probabilities, are shown in the table below. The probability of winning $19 is 2/2000 because there are 2 prizes worth $20. We have not reduced the fractions in order to keep all the denominators equal. Because there are 4 winning tickets, there are 1996 losing tickets, so the probability of winning −$1 is 1996/2000.

Probability Distribution of Prize Winnings			
x	$399	$79	$19	−$1
$P(x)$	1/2000	1/2000	2/2000	1996/2000

The expected payback for a person buying one ticket is

$$399\left(\frac{1}{2000}\right) + 79\left(\frac{1}{2000}\right) + 19\left(\frac{2}{2000}\right) + (-1)\left(\frac{1996}{2000}\right) = -\frac{1480}{2000}$$
$$= -0.74.$$

On average, a person buying one ticket in the raffle will lose $0.74, or 74¢.

It is not possible to lose 74¢ in this raffle: Either you lose $1, or you win a prize worth $400, $80, or $20, minus the $1 you pay to play. But if you bought tickets in many such raffles over a long period of time, you would lose 74¢ per ticket on average. It is important to note that the expected value of a random variable may be a number that can never occur in any one trial of the experiment.

Method 2
Alternate Procedure

An alternative way to compute expected value in this and other examples is to calculate the expected amount won and then subtract the cost of the ticket afterward. The amount won is either $400 (with probability 1/2000), $80 (with probability 1/2000), $20 (with probability 2/2000), or $0 (with probability 1996/2000). The expected payback for a person buying one ticket is then

$$400\left(\frac{1}{2000}\right) + 80\left(\frac{1}{2000}\right) + 20\left(\frac{2}{2000}\right) + 0\left(\frac{1996}{2000}\right) - 1 = -\frac{1480}{2000}$$
$$= -0.74.$$

YOUR TURN 3 Suppose that there is a $5 raffle with prizes worth $1000, $500, and $250. Suppose 1000 tickets are sold and you purchase a ticket. Find your expected payback for this raffle.

TRY YOUR TURN 3

EXAMPLE 5 Friendly Wager

Each day Donna and Mary toss a coin to see who buys coffee ($1.20 a cup). One tosses and the other calls the outcome. If the person who calls the outcome is correct, the other buys the coffee; otherwise the caller pays. Find Donna's expected payback.

SOLUTION Assume that an honest coin is used, that Mary tosses the coin, and that Donna calls the outcome. The possible results and corresponding probabilities are shown below.

	Possible Results			
Result of Toss	Heads	Heads	Tails	Tails
Call	Heads	Tails	Heads	Tails
Caller Wins?	Yes	No	No	Yes
Probability	1/4	1/4	1/4	1/4

Donna wins a $1.20 cup of coffee whenever the results and calls match, and she loses a $1.20 cup when there is no match. Her expected payback is

$$(1.20)\left(\frac{1}{4}\right) + (-1.20)\left(\frac{1}{4}\right) + (-1.20)\left(\frac{1}{4}\right) + (1.20)\left(\frac{1}{4}\right) = 0.$$

This implies that, over the long run, Donna neither wins nor loses.

A game with an expected value of 0 (such as the one in Example 5) is called a **fair game**. Casinos do not offer fair games. If they did, they would win (on average) $0, and have a hard time paying the help! Casino games have expected winnings for the house that vary from 1.5 cents per dollar to 60 cents per dollar. Exercises 47–52 at the end of the section ask you to find the expected payback for certain games of chance.

The idea of expected value can be very useful in decision making, as shown by the next example.

EXAMPLE 6 Life Insurance

At age 50, you receive a letter from Mutual of Mauritania Insurance Company. According to the letter, you must tell the company immediately which of the following two options you will choose: take $20,000 at age 60 (if you are alive, $0 otherwise) or $30,000 at age 70 (again, if you are alive, $0 otherwise). Based *only* on the idea of expected value, which should you choose?

SOLUTION Life insurance companies have constructed elaborate tables showing the probability of a person living a given number of years into the future. From a recent such table, the probability of living from age 50 to 60 is 0.88, while the probability of living from age 50 to 70 is 0.64. The expected values of the two options are given below.

$$\text{First option: } (20,000)(0.88) + (0)(0.12) = 17,600$$
$$\text{Second option: } (30,000)(0.64) + (0)(0.36) = 19,200$$

Based strictly on expected values, choose the second option.

EXAMPLE 7 Bachelor's Degrees

According to the National Center for Education Statistics, 79.4% of those earning bachelor's degrees in education in the United States in 2011–2012 were female. Suppose 5 holders of bachelor's degrees in education from 2011 to 2012 are picked at random. *Source: National Center for Education Statistics.*

(a) Find the probability distribution for the number that are female.

SOLUTION We first note that each of the 5 people in the sample is either female (with probability 0.794) or male (with probability 0.206). As in the previous section, we may assume that the probability for each member of the sample is independent of that of any other. Such a situation is described by binomial probability with $n = 5$ and $p = 0.794$, for which we use the binomial probability formula

$$P(x \text{ successes in } n \text{ trials}) = C(n, x) \cdot p^x \cdot (1 - p)^{n-x},$$

where x is the number of females in the sample. For example, the probability of 0 females is

$$P(x = 0) = C(5, 0)(0.794)^0(0.206)^5 \approx 0.0004.$$

Similarly, we could calculate the probability that x is any value from 0 to 5, resulting in the probability distribution below (with all probabilities rounded to four places).

Probability Distribution of Female Education Graduate					
x	0	1	2	3	4	5
$P(x)$	0.0004	0.0071	0.0551	0.2124	0.4094	0.3156

YOUR TURN 4 In the same survey quoted in Example 7, 80.9% of those earning bachelor's degrees in engineering were male. Suppose 5 holders of bachelor's degrees in engineering were picked at random, find the expected number of male engineers.

(b) Find the expected number of females in the sample of 5 people.

SOLUTION Using the formula for expected value, we have

$$E(x) = 0(0.0004) + 1(0.0071) + 2(0.0551) + 3(0.2124)$$
$$+ 4(0.4094) + 5(0.3156) = 3.9701.$$

On average, 3.970 of the people in the sample of 5 will be female.

TRY YOUR TURN 4

There is another way to get the answer in part (b) of the previous example. Because 79.4% of those earning bachelor's degrees in education in the United States in 2011–2012 are female, it is reasonable to expect 79.4% of our sample to be female. Thus, 79.4% of 5 is $5(0.794) = 3.970$. Notice that what we have done is to multiply n by p. It can be shown that this method always gives the expected value for binomial probability.

> **Expected Value for Binomial Probability**
> For binomial probability, $E(x) = np$. In other words, the expected number of successes is the number of trials times the probability of success in each trial.

EXAMPLE 8   Female Children

Suppose a family has 3 children.

(a) Find the probability distribution for the number of girls.

SOLUTION Assuming girls and boys are equally likely, the probability distribution is binomial with $n = 3$ and $p = 1/2$. Letting x be the number of girls in the formula for binomial probability, we find, for example,

$$P(x = 0) = C(3, 0)\left(\frac{1}{2}\right)^0\left(\frac{1}{2}\right)^3 = \frac{1}{8}.$$

The other values are found similarly, and the results are shown in the following table.

Probability Distribution of Number of Girls			
x	0	1	2	3
$P(x)$	1/8	3/8	3/8	1/8

We can verify this by noticing that in the sample space S of all 3-child families, there are eight equally likely outcomes: $S = \{ggg, ggb, gbg, gbb, bgg, bgb, bbg, bbb\}$. One of the outcomes has 0 girls, three have 1 girl, three have 2 girls, and one has 3 girls.

(b) Find the expected number of girls in a 3-child family using the distribution from part (a).

SOLUTION Using the formula for expected value, we have

$$\text{Expected number of girls} = 0\left(\frac{1}{8}\right) + 1\left(\frac{3}{8}\right) + 2\left(\frac{3}{8}\right) + 3\left(\frac{1}{8}\right)$$
$$= \frac{12}{8} = 1.5.$$

On average, a 3-child family will have 1.5 girls. This result agrees with our intuition that, on average, half the children born will be girls.

(c) Find the expected number of girls in a 3-child family using the formula for expected value for binomial probability.

SOLUTION Using the formula $E(x) = np$ with $n = 3$ and $p = 1/2$, we have

YOUR TURN 5 Find the expected number of girls in a family of a dozen children.

$$\text{Expected number of girls} = 3\left(\frac{1}{2}\right) = 1.5.$$

This agrees with our answer from part (b), as it must.   TRY YOUR TURN 5

8.5 WARM-UP EXERCISES

W1. A die is rolled 5 times. Find the probability of getting exactly 0, 1, 2, 3, 4, and 5 sixes. *(Sec. 8.4)*

W2. Four cards are drawn one at a time, with replacement, from an ordinary deck. Find the probability of getting exactly 0, 1, 2, 3, and 4 spades. *(Sec. 8.4)*

8.5 EXERCISES

For each experiment described below, let x determine a random variable, and use your knowledge of probability to prepare a probability distribution.

1. Four coins are tossed, and the number of heads is noted.

2. Two dice are rolled, and the total number of points is recorded.

3. Three cards are drawn from a deck. The number of aces is counted.

4. Two balls are drawn from a bag in which there are 4 white balls and 2 black balls. The number of black balls is counted.

Draw a histogram for the following, and shade the region that gives the indicated probability.

5. Exercise 1; $P(x \leq 2)$

6. Exercise 2; $P(x \geq 11)$

7. Exercise 3; $P(\text{at least one ace})$

8. Exercise 4; $P(\text{at least one black ball})$

Find the expected value for each random variable.

9.

x	2	3	4	5
$P(x)$	0.1	0.4	0.3	0.2

10.

y	4	6	8	10
$P(y)$	0.4	0.4	0.05	0.15

11.

z	9	12	15	18	21
$P(z)$	0.14	0.22	0.38	0.19	0.07

12.

x	30	32	36	38	44
$P(x)$	0.31	0.29	0.26	0.09	0.05

Find the expected value for the random variable x having the probability function shown in each graph.

13.

14.

15.

16.

17. For the game in Example 5, find Mary's expected payback. Is it a fair game?

18. Suppose one day Mary brings a 2-headed coin and uses it to toss for the coffee. Since Mary tosses, Donna calls.

(a) Is this still a fair game?

(b) What is Donna's expected payback if she calls heads?

(c) What is Donna's expected payback if she calls tails?

Solve each exercise. Many of these exercises require the use of combinations.

19. Suppose 3 marbles are drawn without replacement from a bag containing 3 yellow and 4 white marbles.

(a) Draw a histogram for the number of yellow marbles in the sample.

(b) What is the expected number of yellow marbles in the sample?

20. Suppose 5 apples in a barrel of 25 apples are known to be rotten.

(a) Draw a histogram for the number of rotten apples in a sample of 2 apples.

(b) What is the expected number of rotten apples in a sample of 2 apples?

21. Suppose a die is rolled 4 times.

(a) Find the probability distribution for the number of times 1 is rolled.

(b) What is the expected number of times 1 is rolled?

22. A delegation of 3 is selected from a city council made up of 5 liberals and 6 conservatives.

(a) What is the expected number of liberals in the delegation?

(b) What is the expected number of conservatives in the delegation?

23. From a group of 3 women and 5 men, a delegation of 2 is selected. Find the expected number of women in the delegation.

24. In a club with 20 senior and 10 junior members, what is the expected number of junior members on a 4-member committee?

25. If 2 cards are drawn at one time from a deck of 52 cards, what is the expected number of diamonds?

26. Suppose someone offers to pay you $5 if you draw 2 diamonds in the game in Exercise 25. He says that you should pay 50 cents for the chance to play. Is this a fair game?

27. Your friend missed class the day probability distributions were discussed. How would you explain probability distribution to him?

28. Explain what expected value means in your own words.

29. Four slips of paper numbered 2, 3, 4, and 5 are in a hat. You draw a slip, note the result, and then draw a second slip and note the result (without replacing the first).

(a) Find the probability distribution for the sum of the two slips.

(b) Draw a histogram for the probability distribution in part (a).

(c) Find the odds that the sum is even.

(d) Find the expected value of the sum.

APPLICATIONS

Business and Economics

30. Complaints   A local used-car dealer gets complaints about his cars as shown in the table below. Find the expected number of complaints per day.

Number of Complaints per Day	0	1	2	3	4	5	6
Probability	0.02	0.06	0.16	0.25	0.32	0.13	0.06

31. Payout on Insurance Policies   An insurance company has written 100 policies for $100,000, 500 policies for $50,000, and 1000 policies for $10,000 for people of age 20. If experience shows that the probability that a person will die at age 20 is 0.0012, how much can the company expect to pay out during the year the policies were written?

32. Device Failure   An insurance policy on an electrical device pays a benefit of $4000 if the device fails during the first year. The amount of the benefit decreases by $1000 each successive year until it reaches 0. If the device has not failed by the beginning of any given year, the probability of failure during that year is 0.4. What is the expected benefit under this policy? Choose one of the following. *Source: Society of Actuaries*.

(a) $2234   (b) $2400   (c) $2500   (d) $2667   (e) $2694

33. Pecans   Refer to Exercise 33 in Section 8.4. Suppose that 60% of the pecan "blow outs" are good, and 80% of the "good nuts" are good.

(a) If you purchase 50 pecans, what is the expected number of good nuts you will find if you purchase "blow outs"?

(b) If you purchase 50 pecans, what is the expected number of bad nuts you will find if you have purchased "good nuts"?

34. Rating Sales Accounts   Levi Strauss and Company uses expected value to help its salespeople rate their accounts. For each account, a salesperson estimates potential additional volume and the probability of getting it. The product of these figures gives the expected value of the potential, which is added to the existing volume. The totals are then classified as A, B, or C, as follows: $40,000 or below, class C; from $40,000 up to and including $55,000, class B; above $55,000, class A. Complete the table on the next page for one salesperson. *Source: James McDonald*.

Account Number	Existing Volume	Potential Additional Volume	Probability of Getting It	Expected Value of Potential	Existing Volume + Expected Value of Potential	Class
1	$15,000	$10,000	0.25	$2500	$17,500	C
2	$40,000	$0	—	—	$40,000	C
3	$20,000	$10,000	0.20			
4	$50,000	$10,000	0.10			
5	$5000	$50,000	0.50			
6	$0	$100,000	0.60			
7	$30,000	$20,000	0.80			

35. Tour Bus A tour operator has a bus that can accommodate 20 tourists. The operator knows that tourists may not show up, so he sells 21 tickets. The probability that an individual tourist will not show up is 0.02, independent of all other tourists. Each ticket costs $50, and is non-refundable if a tourist fails to show up. If a tourist shows up and a seat is not available, the tour operator has to pay $100 (ticket cost $+$ $50 penalty) to the tourist. What is the expected revenue of the tour operator? Choose one of the following. *Source: Society of Actuaries.*

(a) $935 (b) $950 (c) $967 (d) $976 (e) $985

Life Sciences

36. Animal Offspring In a certain animal species, the probability that a healthy adult female will have no offspring in a given year is 0.29, while the probabilities of 1, 2, 3, or 4 offspring are, respectively, 0.23, 0.18, 0.16, and 0.14. Find the expected number of offspring.

37. Ear Infections Otitis media, or middle ear infection, is initially treated with an antibiotic. Researchers have compared two antibiotics, amoxicillin and cefaclor, for their cost effectiveness. Amoxicillin is inexpensive, safe, and effective. Cefaclor is also safe. However, it is considerably more expensive and it is generally more effective. Use the tree diagram below (where the costs are estimated as the total cost of medication, office visit, ear check, and hours of lost work) to answer the following. *Source: Journal of Pediatric Infectious Disease.*

(a) Find the expected cost of using each antibiotic to treat a middle ear infection.

(b) To minimize the total expected cost, which antibiotic should be chosen?

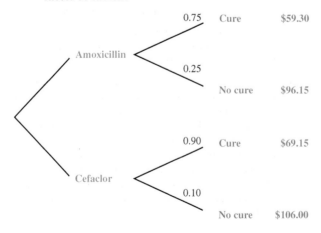

38. Hospitalization Insurance An insurance policy pays an individual $100 per day for up to 3 days of hospitalization and $25 per day for each day of hospitalization thereafter. The number of days of hospitalization, X, is a discrete random variable with probability function

$$P(X = k) = \begin{cases} \dfrac{6 - k}{15} & \text{for } k = 1, 2, 3, 4, 5 \\ 0 & \text{otherwise.} \end{cases}$$

Calculate the expected payment for hospitalization under this policy. Choose one of the following. *Source: Society of Actuaries.*

(a) $85 (b) $163 (c) $168 (d) $213 (e) $255

Social Sciences

39. Education Recall from Exercise 57 in Section 8.4 that a study from Cleveland Clinic reported that 74% of very-low-birth-weight babies graduate from high school by age 20. If 250 very-low-birth-weight babies are followed through high school, how many would you expect to graduate from high school? *Source: The New England Journal of Medicine.*

40. Cheating Recall from Exercise 56 in Section 8.4 that a poll conducted by *U.S. News and World Report* reported that 84% of college students believe they need to cheat to get ahead in the world today. If 500 college students were surveyed, how many would you expect to say that they need to cheat to get ahead in the world today? *Source: U.S. News and World Report.*

41. Samuel Alito When Supreme Court Justice Samuel Alito was on the U.S. Court of Appeals for the 3rd Circuit, he dissented in the successful appeal of a first-degree murder case. The prosecution used its peremptory challenges to eliminate all African Americans from the jury, as it had in three other first-degree murder trials in the same county that year. According to a majority of the judges, "An amateur with a pocket calculator can calculate the number of blacks that would have served had the State used its strikes in a racially proportionate manner. In the four capital cases there was a total of 82 potential jurors on the venires who were not removed for cause, of whom eight, or 9.76%, were black. If the prosecution had used its peremptory challenges in a manner proportional to the percentage of blacks in the overall venire, then only 3 of the 34 jurors peremptorily struck (8.82%) would have been black and 5 of the 48 actual jurors (10.42%) would have been black. Instead, none of the 48 jurors were black. Admittedly, there was no statistical analysis of these figures presented by either side in the post-conviction proceeding. But is it really necessary to have a sophisticated analysis by a statistician to conclude that there is little chance of randomly selecting four consecutive all white juries?" *Source: findlaw.com.*

(a) Using binomial probability, calculate the probability that no African Americans would be selected out of 48 jurors if the percentage of African Americans is 9.76%.

(b) Binomial probability is not entirely accurate in this case, because the jurors were selected without replacement, so the selections were not independent. Recalculate the probability in part (a) using combinations.

(c) In his dissent, Judge Alito wrote, "Statistics can be very revealing—and also terribly misleading in the hands of 'an amateur with a pocket calculator.' . . . Although only about 10% of the population is left-handed, left-handers have won five of the last six presidential elections. Our 'amateur with a calculator' would conclude that 'there is little chance of randomly selecting' left-handers in five out of six presidential elections. But does it follow that the voters cast their ballots based on whether a candidate was right- or left-handed?" Given the figures quoted by Judge Alito, what is the probability that at least 5 out of the last 6 presidents elected would be left-handed?

(d) The majority of the judges, in disagreeing with Judge Alito, said, "The dissent has overlooked the obvious fact that there is no provision in the Constitution that protects persons from discrimination based on whether they are right-handed or left handed." Furthermore, according to *Chance News*, only 2 of the last 6 men elected president were left-handed. What is the probability that at least 2 out of the last 6 presidents elected would be left-handed? *Source: Chance News.*

Physical Sciences

42. **Seeding Storms** One of the few methods that can be used in an attempt to cut the severity of a hurricane is to *seed* the storm. In this process, silver iodide crystals are dropped into the storm. Unfortunately, silver iodide crystals sometimes cause the storm to *increase* its speed. Wind speeds may also increase or decrease even with no seeding. Use the table below to answer the following. *Source: American Association for the Advancement of Science.*

(a) Find the expected amount of damage under each option, "seed" and "do not seed."

(b) To minimize total expected damage, what option should be chosen?

	Change in wind speed	Probability	Property damage (millions of dollars)
Seed	+32%	0.038	335.8
	+16%	0.143	191.1
	0	0.392	100.0
	−16%	0.255	46.7
	−34%	0.172	16.3
Do not seed	+32%	0.054	335.8
	+16%	0.206	191.1
	0	0.480	100.0
	−16%	0.206	46.7
	+34%	0.054	16.3

General Interest

43. **Zilch** In the dice game of Zilch, a player rolls up to 6 dice and receives points based upon what is rolled. If some of the dice are worth points, the player may then roll the remaining dice again. *Source: playr.co.uk.*

(a) Suppose a player rolls only two dice. The player gets 50 points for each 5 and 100 points for each 1 rolled. Find the expected value of the game. (*Hint:* There are 6 cases to consider.)

(b) Suppose a player rolls three dice. Now find the expected value of a roll with three dice. (*Hint:* There are 10 cases to consider.)

(c) The game with three dice is actually more complicated than we considered in part (b), in that three 1's, 2's, 3's, 4's, 5's, or 6's earn 1000, 200, 300, 400, 500, or 600 points, respectively. Now find the expected value of a roll with three dice.

44. **Postal Service** Mr. Statistics (a feature in *Fortune* magazine) investigated the claim of the U.S. Postal Service that 83% of first class mail in New York City arrives by the next day. (The figure is 87% nationwide.) He mailed a letter to himself on 10 consecutive days; only 4 were delivered by the next day. *Source: Fortune.*

(a) Find the probability distribution for the number of letters delivered by the next day if the overall probability of next-day delivery is 83%.

(b) Using your answer to part (a), find the probability that 4 or fewer out of 10 letters would be delivered by the next day.

(c) Based on your answer to part (b), do you think it is likely that the 83% figure is accurate? Explain.

(d) Find the number of letters out of 10 that you would expect to be delivered by the next day if the 83% figure is accurate.

45. **Raffle** A raffle offers a first prize of $400 and 3 second prizes of $80 each. One ticket costs $2, and 500 tickets are sold. Find the expected payback for a person who buys 1 ticket. Is this a fair game?

46. **Raffle** A raffle offers a first prize of $1000, 2 second prizes of $300 each, and 20 third prizes of $10 each. If 10,000 tickets are sold at 50¢ each, find the expected payback for a person buying 1 ticket. Is this a fair game?

Find the expected payback for the games of chance described in Exercises 47–52.

47. **Lottery** A state lottery requires you to choose 4 cards from an ordinary deck: 1 heart, 1 club, 1 diamond, and 1 spade in that order from the 13 cards in each suit. If all four choices are selected by the lottery, you win $5000. It costs $1 to play.

48. **Lottery** If exactly 3 of the 4 choices in Exercise 47 are selected, the player wins $200. (Ignore the possibility that all 4 choices are selected. It still costs $1 to play.)

49. **Roulette** In one form of roulette, you bet $1 on "even." If 1 of the 18 even numbers comes up, you get your dollar back, plus another one. If 1 of the 20 noneven (18 odd, 0, and 00) numbers comes up, you lose your dollar.

50. Roulette In another form of roulette, there are only 19 non-even numbers (no 00).

51. Numbers *Numbers* is a game in which you bet $1 on any three-digit number from 000 to 999. If your number comes up, you get $500.

52. Keno In one form of the game *Keno*, the house has a pot containing 80 balls, each marked with a different number from 1 to 80. You buy a ticket for $1 and mark one of the 80 numbers on it. The house then selects 20 numbers at random. If your number is among the 20, you get $3.20 (for a net winning of $2.20).

53. Contests A magazine distributor offers a first prize of $100,000, two second prizes of $40,000 each, and two third prizes of $10,000 each. A total of 2,000,000 entries are received in the contest. Find the expected payback if you submit one entry to the contest. If it would cost you $1 in time, paper, and stamps to enter, would it be worth it?

54. Contests A contest at a fast-food restaurant offered the following cash prizes and probabilities of winning on one visit. Suppose you spend $1 to buy a bus pass that lets you go to 25 different restaurants in the chain and pick up entry forms. Find your expected value.

Prize	Probability
$100,000	1/176,402,500
$25,000	1/39,200,556
$5000	1/17,640,250
$1000	1/1,568,022
$100	1/282,244
$5	1/7056
$1	1/588

55. The Hog Game In the hog game, each player states the number of dice that he or she would like to roll. The player then rolls that many dice. If a 1 comes up on any die, the player's score is 0. Otherwise, the player's score is the sum of the numbers rolled. *Source: Mathematics Teacher.*

(a) Find the expected value of the player's score when the player rolls one die.

(b) Find the expected value of the player's score when the player rolls two dice.

(c) Verify that the expected nonzero score of a single die is 4, so that if a player rolls n dice that do not result in a score of 0, the expected score is $4n$.

(d) Verify that if a player rolls n dice, there are 5^n possible ways to get a nonzero score, and 6^n possible ways to roll the dice. Explain why the expected value, E, of the player's score when the player rolls n dice is then

$$E = \frac{5^n(4n)}{6^n}.$$

56. Football After a team scores a touchdown, it can either attempt to kick an extra point or attempt a two-point conversion. During the 2013 NFL season, two-point conversions were successful 47.8% of the time and the extra-point kicks were successful 99.6% of the time. *Source: Sporting Charts.*

(a) Calculate the expected value of each strategy.

(b) Which strategy, over the long run, will maximize the number of points scored?

(c) Using this information, should a team always only use one strategy? Explain.

57. Baseball The 2013 National League batting champion was Michael Cuddyer, with an average of 0.331. This can be interpreted as a probability of 0.331 of getting a hit whenever he bats. Assume that each time at bat is an independent event. Suppose he goes to bat four times in a game. *Source: baseball-reference.com.*

(a) Find the probability distribution for the number of hits.

(b) What is the expected number of hits that Michael Cuddyer gets in a game?

YOUR TURN ANSWERS ▬

1.

x	0	1	2
$P(x)$	6/11	9/22	1/22

2.

x	0	1	2	3
$P(x)$	1/8	3/8	3/8	1/8

3. −$3.25 **4.** 4.045 **5.** 6

8 CHAPTER REVIEW

SUMMARY

In this chapter we continued our study of probability by introducing some elementary principles of counting. Our primary tool is the multiplication principle:

If n choices must be made, with m_1 ways to make choice 1, and for each of these ways, m_2 ways to make choice 2, and so on, with m_n ways to make choice n, then there are $m_1 \cdot m_2 \cdot \ldots \cdot m_n$ ways to make the entire sequence of choices.

We learned two counting ideas to efficiently count the number of ways we can select a number of objects without replacement:

- permutations (when order matters), and
- combinations (when order doesn't matter).

We also considered distinguishable permutations, in which some of the objects are indistinguishable. All of these concepts were then used to calculate the numerator and denominator of various probabilities. We next explored binomial probability, in which the following conditions were satisfied:

- the same experiment is repeated a fixed number of times (n),
- there are only two possible outcomes (success and failure), and
- the trials are independent, so the probability of success remains constant (p).

We showed how to quickly calculate an entire set of combinations for binomial probability using Pascal's triangle. Finally, we introduced the following terms regarding probability distributions:

- random variable (a function assigning a real number to each outcome of an experiment),
- probability distribution (the possible values of a random variable, along with the corresponding probabilities),
- histogram (a bar graph displaying a probability distribution), and
- expected value (the average value of a random variable that we would expect in the long run).

In the next chapter, we will see how probability forms the basis of the field known as statistics.

Factorial Notation	$n! = n(n - 1)(n - 2) \cdots (3)(2)(1)$ $0! = 1$
Permutations	$P(n, r) = \dfrac{n!}{(n - r)!}$
Distinguishable Permutations	If there are n_1 objects of type 1, n_2 of type 2, and so on for r different types, then the number of distinguishable permutations is $$\dfrac{n!}{n_1! n_2! \cdots n_r!}.$$
Combinations	$C(n, r) = \dfrac{n!}{(n - r)! \, r!}$
Binomial Probability	$P(x) = C(n, x) \, p^x (1 - p)^{n-x}$
Expected Value	$E(x) = x_1 p_1 + x_2 p_2 + x_3 p_3 + \cdots + x_n p_n$ For binomial probability, $E(x) = np$.

KEY TERMS

8.1
multiplication principle
factorial notation
permutations
distinguishable permutations

8.2
combinations

8.4
Bernoulli trials
binomial experiment

binomial probability
Pascal's triangle

8.5
random variable
probability distribution

probability function
histogram
expected value
fair game

REVIEW EXERCISES

CONCEPT CHECK

Determine whether each of the following statements is true or false, and explain why.

1. Permutations provide a way of counting possibilities when order matters.

2. Combinations provide a way of counting possibilities when order doesn't matter.

3. The number of distinguishable permutations of n objects, when r are indistinguishable and the remaining $n - r$ are also indistinguishable, is the same as the number of combinations of r objects chosen from n.

4. Calculating the numerator or the denominator of a probability can involve either permutations or combinations.

5. The probability of at least 2 occurrences of an event is equal to the probability of 1 or fewer occurrences.

6. The probability of at least two people in a group having the same birthday is found by subtracting the probability of the complement of the event from 1.

7. The trials in binomial probability must be independent.

8. Binomial probability can be used when each trial has three possible outcomes.

9. A random variable can have negative values.

10. The expected value of a random variable must equal one of the values that the random variable can have.

11. The probabilities in a probability distribution must add up to 1.

12. A fair game can have an expected value that is greater than 0.

PRACTICE AND EXPLORATIONS

13. In how many ways can 6 shuttle vans line up at the airport?

14. How many variations in first-, second-, and third-place finishes are possible in a 100-yd dash with 6 runners?

15. In how many ways can a sample of 3 oranges be taken from a bag of a dozen oranges?

16. In how many ways can a committee of 4 be selected from a club with 10 members?

17. If 2 of the 12 oranges in Exercise 15 are rotten, in how many ways can the sample of 3 include

    (a) exactly 1 rotten orange?

    (b) exactly 2 rotten oranges?

    (c) no rotten oranges?

    (d) at most 2 rotten oranges?

18. If 6 of the 10 club members in Exercise 16 are males, in how many ways can the sample of 4 include

    (a) exactly 3 males?

    (b) no males?

    (c) at least 2 males?

19. Five different pictures will be arranged in a row on a wall.

    (a) In how many ways can this be done?

    (b) In how many ways can this be done if a certain one must be first?

20. In how many ways can the 5 pictures in Exercise 19 be arranged if 2 are landscapes and 3 are puppies and if

    (a) like types must be kept together?

    (b) landscapes and puppies must be alternated?

21. In a Chinese restaurant the menu lists 8 items in column A and 6 items in column B.

    (a) To order a dinner, the diner is told to select 3 items from column A and 2 from column B. How many dinners are possible?

    (b) How many dinners are possible if the diner can select up to 3 from column A and up to 2 from column B? Assume at least one item must be included from either A or B.

22. A representative is to be selected from each of 3 departments in a small college. There are 7 people in the first department, 5 in the second department, and 4 in the third department.

    (a) How many different groups of 3 representatives are possible?

    (b) How many groups are possible if any number (at least 1) up to 3 representatives can form a group? (Each department is still restricted to at most one representative.)

23. Explain under what circumstances a permutation should be used in a probability problem, and under what circumstances a combination should be used.

24. Discuss under what circumstances the binomial probability formula should be used in a probability problem.

A basket contains 4 black, 2 blue, and 7 green balls. A sample of 3 balls is drawn. Find the probabilities that the sample contains the following.

25. All black balls

26. All blue balls

27. 2 black balls and 1 green ball

28. Exactly 2 black balls

29. Exactly 1 blue ball

30. 2 green balls and 1 blue ball

Suppose a family plans 6 children, and the probability that a particular child is a girl is 1/2. Find the probabilities that the 6-child family has the following children.

31. Exactly 3 girls

32. All girls

33. At least 4 girls

34. No more than 2 boys

Suppose 2 cards are drawn without replacement from an ordinary deck of 52. Find the probabilities of the following results.

35. Both cards are red.

36. Both cards are spades.

37. At least 1 card is a spade.

38. One is a face card and the other is not.

39. At least one is a face card.

40. At most one is a queen.

In Exercises 41 and 42, (a) give a probability distribution, (b) sketch its histogram, and (c) find the expected value.

41. A coin is tossed 3 times and the number of heads is recorded.

42. A pair of dice is rolled and the sum of the results for each roll is recorded.

In Exercises 43 and 44, give the probability that corresponds to the shaded region of each histogram.

43.

44.

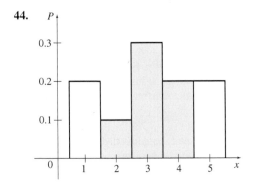

45. You pay $6 to play in a game where you will roll a die, with payoffs as follows: $8 for a 6, $7 for a 5, and $4 for any other results. What are your expected winnings? Is the game fair?

46. Find the expected number of girls in a family of 5 children.

47. Three cards are drawn from a standard deck of 52 cards.

   (a) What is the expected number of aces?

   (b) What is the expected number of clubs?

48. Suppose someone offers to pay you $100 if you draw 3 cards from a standard deck of 52 cards and all the cards are clubs. What should you pay for the chance to win if it is a fair game?

49. Six students will decide which of them are on a committee by flipping a coin. Each student flips the coin and is on the committee if he or she gets a head. What is the probability that someone is on the committee, but not all 6 students?

50. Find the probability that at most 2 students from Exercise 49 are on the committee.

51. In this exercise we study the connection between sets (from Chapter 7) and combinations (from Chapter 8).

   (a) Given a set with n elements, what is the number of subsets of size 0? of size 1? of size 2? of size n?

   (b) Using your answer from part (a), give an expression for the total number of subsets of a set with n elements.

   (c) Using your answer from part (b) and a result from Chapter 7, explain why the following equation must be true:
   $$C(n, 0) + C(n, 1) + C(n, 2) + \cdots + C(n, n) = 2^n.$$

   (d) Verify the equation in part (c) for $n = 4$ and $n = 5$.

   (e) Explain what the equation in part (c) tells you about Pascal's triangle.

In the following exercise, find the digit (0 through 9) that belongs in each box. This exercise is from the 1990 University Entrance Center Examination, given in Japan to all applicants for public universities. *Source: Japanese University Entrance Examination Problems in Mathematics.*

52. The numbers 1 through 9 are written individually on nine cards. Choose three cards from the nine, letting x, y, and z denote the numbers of the cards arranged in increasing order.

   (a) There are $\square\square$ such x, y, and z combinations.

   (b) The probability of having x, y, and z all even is $\dfrac{\square}{\square\square}$.

   (c) The probability of having x, y, and z be consecutive numbers is $\dfrac{\square}{\square\square}$.

   (d) The probability of having $x = 4$ is $\dfrac{\square}{\square\square}$.

   (e) Possible values of x range from $\square$ to $\square$. If k is an integer such that $\square \le k \le \square$, the probability that $x = k$ is $\dfrac{(\square - k)(\square - k)}{\square\square\square}$. The expected value of x is $\dfrac{\square}{\square}$.

APPLICATIONS

Business and Economics

53. Music Players   A popular music player is manufactured in 3 different sizes, 8 different colors, and with or without a camera. How many different varieties of this music player are available?

54. Job Qualifications   Of the 12 people applying for an entry level position, 9 are qualified and 3 are not. The personnel manager will hire 4 of the applicants.

   (a) In how many different ways can she hire the 4 applicants if the jobs are considered the same?

   (b) In how many ways can she hire 4 applicants that are qualified?

   (c) In how many ways can she hire at most 1 unqualified applicant?

   (d) In how many ways can she hire the 4 applicants if the jobs are not the same?

Identity Theft   According to a survey by Javelin Strategy and Research, 1 out of 6 adults in Arizona were victims of identity theft. Suppose that 12 adults are randomly selected from Arizona. Find the probabilities of each of the following results. *Source: The New York Times.*

55. None of the adults were victims of identity theft.

56. All of the adults were victims of identity theft.

57. Exactly 10 of the adults were victims of identity theft.

58. Exactly 2 of the adults were victims of identity theft.

59. At least 2 of the adults were victims of identity theft.

60. At most 3 of the adults were victims of identity theft.

61. Find the expected number of victims of identity theft in a sample of 12 adults in Arizona.

62. Land Development   A developer can buy a piece of property that will produce a profit of $26,000 with probability 0.7, or a loss of $9000 with probability 0.3. What is the expected profit?

63. Insurance Claims   An insurance company determines that N, the number of claims received in a week, is a random variable with $P(N = n) = 1/2^{n+1}$, where $n \ge 0$. The company also determines that the number of claims received in a given week is independent of the number of claims received in any other week. Determine the probability that exactly seven claims will be received during a given two-week period. Choose one of the following. *Source: Society of Actuaries.*

   (a) 1/256   **(b)** 1/128   **(c)** 7/512   **(d)** 1/64   **(e)** 1/32

64. Injury Claims The number of injury claims per month is modeled by a random variable N with

$$P(N = n) = \frac{1}{(n + 1)(n + 2)}, \quad \text{where } n \geq 0.$$

Determine the probability of at least one claim during a particular month, given that there have been at most four claims during that month. Choose one of the following. *Source: Society of Actuaries.*

(a) 1/3 (b) 2/5 (c) 1/2 (d) 3/5 (e) 5/6

65. Product Success A company is considering the introduction of a new product that is believed to have probability 0.5 of being successful and probability 0.5 of being unsuccessful. Successful products pass quality control 80% of the time. Unsuccessful products pass quality control 25% of the time. If the product is successful, the net profit to the company will be $40 million; if unsuccessful, the net loss will be $15 million. Determine the expected net profit if the product passes quality control. Choose one of the following. *Source: Society of Actuaries.*

(a) $23 million (b) $24 million (c) $25 million

(d) $26 million (e) $27 million

66. Sampling Fruit A merchant buys boxes of fruit from a grower and sells them. Each box of fruit is either Good or Bad. A Good box contains 80% excellent fruit and will earn $200 profit on the retail market. A Bad box contains 30% excellent fruit and will produce a loss of $1000. The a priori probability of receiving a Good box of fruit is 0.9. Before the merchant decides to put the box on the market, he can sample one piece of fruit to test whether it is excellent. Based on that sample, he has the option of rejecting the box without paying for it. Determine the expected value of the right to sample. Choose one of the following. (*Hint:* The a priori probability is the probability before sampling a piece of fruit. If the merchant samples the fruit, what are the probabilities of accepting a Good box, accepting a Bad box, and not accepting the box? What are these probabilities if he does not sample the fruit?) *Source: Society of Actuaries.*

(a) 0 (b) $16 (c) $34 (d) $72 (e) $80

67. Overbooking Flights The March 1982 issue of *Mathematics Teacher* included "Overbooking Airline Flights," an article by Joe Dan Austin. In this article, Austin developed a model for the expected income for an airline flight. With appropriate assumptions, the probability that exactly x of n people with reservations show up at the airport to buy a ticket is given by the binomial probability formula. Assume the following: 6 reservations have been accepted for 3 seats, $p = 0.6$ is the probability that a person with a reservation will show up, a ticket costs $400, and the airline must pay $400 to anyone with a reservation who does not get a ticket. Complete the following table.

Number Who Show Up (x)	0	1	2	3	4	5	6
Airline's Income							
$P(x)$							

(a) Use the table to find $E(I)$, the expected airline income from the 3 seats.

(b) Find $E(I)$ for $n = 3$, $n = 4$, and $n = 5$. Compare these answers with $E(I)$ for $n = 6$. For these values of n, how many reservations should the airline book for the 3 seats in order to maximize the expected revenue?

Life Sciences

68. Pharmacology In placebo-controlled trials of Prozac®, a drug that is prescribed to fight depression, 23% of the patients who were taking the drug experienced nausea, whereas 10% of the patients who were taking the placebo experienced nausea. *Source: The New England Journal of Medicine.*

(a) If 50 patients who are taking Prozac® are selected, what is the probability that 10 or more will experience nausea?

(b) Of the 50 patients in part (a), what is the expected number of patients who will experience nausea?

(c) If a second group of 50 patients receives a placebo, what is the probability that 10 or fewer will experience nausea?

(d) If a patient from a study of 1000 people, who are equally divided into two groups (those taking a placebo and those taking Prozac®), is experiencing nausea, what is the probability that he/she is taking Prozac®?

(e) Since 0.23 is more than twice as large as 0.10, do you think that people who take Prozac® are more likely to experience nausea than those who take a placebo? Explain.

Social Sciences

69. Education In Exercise 46 of Section 8.3, we saw that a school in Bangkok requires that students take an entrance examination. After the examination, 5 students are randomly drawn from each group of 40 for automatic acceptance into the school regardless of their performance on the examination. The drawing consists of placing 35 red and 5 green pieces of paper into a box. If the lottery is changed so that each student picks a piece of paper from the box and then returns the piece of paper to the box, find the probability that exactly 5 of the 40 students will choose a green piece of paper. *Source: The Mathematics Teacher.*

General Interest

In Exercises 70–73, (a) give a probability distribution, (b) sketch its histogram, and (c) find the expected value.

70. Candy According to officials of Mars, the makers of M&M Plain Chocolate Candies, 20% of the candies in each bag are orange. Four candies are selected from a bag and the number of orange candies is recorded. *Source: Mars, Inc.*

71. Schools In 2011, 48% of U.S. schools made progress under the No Child Left Behind mandate. Suppose 5 schools are picked at random and the number of schools making progress is recorded. *Source: The World Almanac and Book of Facts 2014.*

72. Race In the mathematics honors society at a college, 2 of the 8 members are African American. Three members are selected at random to be interviewed by the student newspaper, and the number of African Americans is noted.

73. Homework In a small class of 10 students, 3 did not do their homework. The professor selects half of the class to present solutions to homework problems on the board, and records how many of those selected did not do their homework.

74. Moneyball In the 2011 movie *Moneyball*, Billy Beane is shown reading a paper in which we see the following:

"Since Chesbro's team was 51–47, or .520, then I figured him by the formula

$$\frac{53!}{41!12!}(.520)^{41}(.480)^{12}.\text{"}$$

Based on what you've learned in this chapter, discuss what the author of the paper might have been calculating.

75. Contests At one time, game boards for a United Airlines contest could be obtained by sending a self-addressed, stamped envelope to a certain address. The prize was a ticket for any city to which United flies. Assume that the value of the ticket was $2000 (we might as well go first-class), and that the probability that a particular game board would win was 1/8000. If the stamps to enter the contest cost 49¢ and envelopes cost 4¢ each, find the expected payback for a person ordering 1 game board. (Notice that 2 stamps and envelopes were required to enter.)

76. Lottery On June 23, 2003, an interesting thing happened in the Pennsylvania Lottery's Big 4, in which a four-digit number from 0000 to 9999 is chosen twice a day. On this day, the number 3199 was chosen both times. *Source: Pennsylvania Lottery*.

(a) What is the probability of the same number being chosen twice in one day?

(b) What is the probability of the number 3199 being chosen twice in one day?

77. Lottery In the Pennsylvania Lottery's Daily Number (Evening) game, a three-digit number between 000 and 999 is chosen each day. The favorite number among players is 000, which on May 16, 2011, was the winning number for the 15th time since 1980. *Source: Pennsylvania Lottery*.

(a) Find the number of times that 000 would be expected to win in 32 years of play. (Assume that the game is played 365 days a year.)

(b) In 2003, a Daily Number (Midday) drawing was added. The number 000 has occurred four times. Find the number of times that 000 would be expected to win in 10 years of play. (Assume that the game is played 365 days a year.)

78. Lottery New York has a lottery game called Quick Draw, in which the player can pick anywhere from 1 up to 10 numbers from 1 to 80. The computer then picks 20 numbers, and how much you win is based on how many of your numbers match the computer's. For simplicity, we will consider only the two cases in which you pick 4 or 5 numbers. The payoffs for each dollar that you bet are given in the table below.

	How Many Numbers Match the Computer's Numbers					
	0	1	2	3	4	5
You Pick 4	0	0	1	5	55	
You Pick 5	0	0	0	2	20	300

(a) According to the Quick Draw playing card, the "Overall Chances of Winning" when you pick 4 are "1:3.86," while the chances when you pick 5 are "1:10.34." Verify these figures.

(b) Find the expected value when you pick 4 and when you pick 5, betting $1 each time.

(c) Based on your results from parts (a) and (b), are you better off picking 4 numbers or picking 5? Explain your reasoning.

79. Murphy's Law Robert Matthews wrote an article about Murphy's Law, which says that if something can go wrong, it will. He considers Murphy's Law of Odd Socks, which says that if an odd sock can be created it will be, in a drawer of 10 loose pairs of socks. *Source: Sunday Telegraph*.

(a) Find the probability of getting a matching pair when the following numbers of socks are selected at random from the drawer.

   (i) 5 socks   **(ii)** 6 socks

(b) Matthews says that it is necessary to rummage through 30% of the socks to get a matching pair. Using your answers from part (a), explain precisely what he means by that.

(c) Matthews claims that if you lose 6 socks at random from the drawer, then it is 100 times more likely that you will be left with the worst possible outcome—6 odd socks—than with a drawer free of odd socks. Verify this calculation by finding the probability that you will be left with 6 odd socks and the probability that you will have a drawer free of odd socks.

80. Baseball The number of runs scored in 16,456 half-innings of the 1986 National League Baseball season was analyzed by Hal Stern. Use the table to answer the following questions. *Source: Chance News*.

(a) What is the probability that a given team scored 5 or more runs in any given half-inning during the 1986 season?

(b) What is the probability that a given team scored fewer than 2 runs in any given half-inning of the 1986 season?

(c) What is the expected number of runs that a team scored during any given half-inning of the 1986 season? Interpret this number.

Runs	Frequency	Probability
0	12,087	0.7345
1	2451	0.1489
2	1075	0.0653
3	504	0.0306
4	225	0.0137
5	66	0.0040
6	29	0.0018
7	12	0.0007
8	5	0.0003
9	2	0.0001

81. St. Petersburg Paradox Suppose you play a gambling game in which you flip a coin until you get a head. If you get a head on the first toss, you win $2. You win $4 if the first head occurs on the second toss, $8 if it occurs on the the third toss, and so forth, with a prize of 2^n if the first head occurs on the nth toss. Show that the expected value of this game is infinite. Explain why this is a paradox.*

*Many articles have been written in an attempt to explain this paradox, first posed by the Swiss mathematician Daniel Bernoulli when he lived in St. Petersburg. For example, see Székely, Gábor and Donald St. P. Richards, "The St. Petersburg Paradox and the Crash of High-Tech Stocks in 2000," *The American Statistician*, Vol. 58, No. 3, Aug. 2004, pp. 225–231.

82. Pit The card game of Pit was introduced by Parker Brothers in 1904 and is still popular. In the version owned by one of the authors of this book, there are 10 suits of 9 identical cards, plus the Bull and the Bear card, for a total of 92 cards. (Newer versions of the game have only 8 suits of cards.) For this problem, assume that all 92 cards are used, and you are dealt 9 cards.

(a) What is the probability that you have one card from each of 9 different suits, but neither the Bull nor the Bear?

(b) What is the probability that you have a pair of cards from one suit and one card from each of 7 other suits, but neither the Bull nor the Bear?

(c) What is the probability that you have two pairs of cards from two different suits and one card from each of 5 other suits, but neither the Bull nor the Bear?

EXTENDED APPLICATION

OPTIMAL INVENTORY FOR A SERVICE TRUCK

For many different items it is difficult or impossible to take the item to a central repair facility when service is required. Washing machines, large television sets, office copiers, and computers are only a few examples of such items. Service for items of this type is commonly performed by sending a repair person to the item, with the person driving to the location in a truck containing various parts that might be required in repairing the item. Ideally, the truck should contain all the parts that might be required. However, most parts would be needed only infrequently, so that inventory costs for the parts would be high.

An optimum policy for deciding on which parts to stock on a truck would require that the probability of not being able to repair an item without a trip back to the warehouse for needed parts be as low as possible, consistent with minimum inventory costs. An analysis similar to the one below was developed at the Xerox Corporation.

To set up a mathematical model for deciding on the optimum truck-stocking policy, let us assume that a broken machine might require one of 5 different parts (we could assume any number of different parts—we use 5 to simplify the notation). Suppose also that the probability that a particular machine requires part 1 is p_1; that it requires part 2 is p_2; and so on. Assume also that failures of different part types are independent, and that at most one part of each type is used on a given job.

Suppose that, on the average, a repair person makes N service calls per time period. If the repair person is unable to make a repair because at least one of the parts is unavailable, there is a penalty cost, L, corresponding to wasted time for the repair person, an extra trip to the parts depot, customer unhappiness, and so on. For each of the parts carried on the truck, an average inventory cost is incurred. Let H_i be the average inventory cost for part i, where $1 \leq i \leq 5$.

Let M_1 represent a policy of carrying only part 1 on the repair truck, M_{24} represent a policy of carrying only parts 2 and 4, with

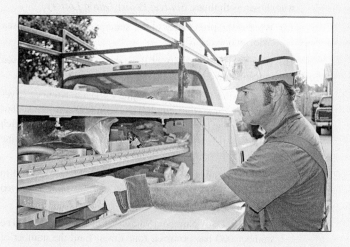

M_{12345} and M_0 representing policies of carrying all parts and no parts, respectively.

For policy M_{35}, carrying parts 3 and 5 only, the expected cost per time period per repair person, written $C(M_{35})$, is

$$C(M_{35}) = (H_3 + H_5) + NL[1 - (1 - p_1)(1 - p_2)(1 - p_4)].$$

(The expression in brackets represents the probability of needing at least one of the parts not carried, 1, 2, or 4 here.) As further examples,

$$C(M_{125}) = (H_1 + H_2 + H_5) + NL[1 - (1 - p_3)(1 - p_4)],$$

while

$$C(M_{12345}) = (H_1 + H_2 + H_3 + H_4 + H_5) + NL[1 - 1]$$
$$= H_1 + H_2 + H_3 + H_4 + H_5,$$

and

$$C(M_0) = NL[1 - (1 - p_1)(1 - p_2)(1 - p_3)(1 - p_4)(1 - p_5)].$$

To find the best policy, evaluate $C(M_0)$, $C(M_1)$, ..., $C(M_{12345})$, and choose the smallest result. (A general solution method is in the *Management Science* paper.) **Source: Management Science.**

EXAMPLE 1

Suppose that for a particular item, only 3 possible parts might need to be replaced. By studying past records of failures of the item, and finding necessary inventory costs, suppose that the following values have been found.

p_1	p_2	p_3	H_1	H_2	H_3
0.09	0.24	0.17	$15	$40	$9

Suppose $N = 3$ and L is $54. Then, as an example,

$$\begin{aligned} C(M_1) &= H_1 + NL[1 - (1 - p_2)(1 - p_3)] \\ &= 15 + 3(54)[1 - (1 - 0.24)(1 - 0.17)] \\ &= 15 + 3(54)[1 - (0.76)(0.83)] \\ &\approx 15 + 59.81 = 74.81. \end{aligned}$$

Thus, if policy M_1 is followed (carrying only part 1 on the truck), the expected cost per repair person per time period is $74.81. Also,

$$\begin{aligned} C(M_{23}) &= H_2 + H_3 + NL[1 - (1 - p_1)] \\ &= 40 + 9 + 3(54)(0.09) = 63.58, \end{aligned}$$

so that M_{23} is a better policy than M_1. By finding the expected values for all other possible policies (see the exercises), the optimum policy may be chosen.

EXERCISES

1. Refer to the example and find the following.

    (a) $C(M_0)$ (b) $C(M_2)$ (c) $C(M_3)$

    (d) $C(M_{12})$ (e) $C(M_{13})$ (f) $C(M_{123})$

2. Which policy leads to the lowest expected cost?

3. In the example, $p_1 + p_2 + p_3 = 0.09 + 0.24 + 0.17 = 0.50$. Why is it not necessary that the probabilities add up to 1?

4. Suppose an item to be repaired might need one of n different parts. How many different policies would then need to be evaluated?

DIRECTIONS FOR GROUP PROJECT

Suppose you and three others are employed as service repair persons and that you have some disagreement with your supervisor as to the quantity and type of parts to have on hand for your service calls. Use the answers to Exercises 1–4 to prepare a report with a recommendation to your boss on optimal inventory. Make sure that you describe each concept well, since your boss is not mathematically minded.

9 Statistics

To understand the economics of large-scale farming, analysts look at historical data on the farming industry. In an exercise in Section 1 you will calculate basic descriptive statistics for U.S. wheat prices and production levels over a recent decade. Later sections in this chapter develop more sophisticated techniques for extracting useful information from this kind of data.

S tatistics is a branch of mathematics that deals with the collection and summarization of data. Methods of statistical analysis make it possible for us to draw conclusions about a population based on data from a sample of the population. Statistical models have become increasingly useful in manufacturing, government, agriculture, medicine, the social sciences, and all types of research. In this chapter we give a brief introduction to some of the key topics from statistical theory.

9.1 Frequency Distributions; Measures of Central Tendency

APPLY IT How can the results of a survey of business executives on the number of college credits in management needed by a business major best be organized to provide useful information?

Frequency distributions will provide an answer to this question in Example 1.

Often, a researcher wishes to learn something about a characteristic of a population, but because the population is very large or mobile, it is not possible to examine all of its elements. Instead, a limited sample drawn from the population is studied to determine the characteristics of the population. For these inferences to be correct, the sample chosen must be a **random sample**. Random samples are representative of the population because they are chosen so that every element of the population is equally likely to be selected. A hand dealt from a well-shuffled deck of cards is a random sample.

A random sample can be difficult to obtain in real life. For example, suppose you want to take a random sample of voters in your congressional district to see which candidate they prefer in the next election. If you do a telephone survey, you have a random sample of people who are at home to answer the telephone, underrepresenting those who work a lot of hours and are rarely home to answer the phone, or those who have an unlisted number, or those who cannot afford a telephone, or those who only have a cell phone, or those who refuse to answer telephone surveys. Such people may have a different opinion than those you interview.

A famous example of an inaccurate poll was made by the *Literary Digest* in 1936. Their survey indicated that Alfred Landon would win the presidential election; in fact, Franklin Roosevelt won with 62% of the popular vote. The *Digest's* major error was mailing their surveys to a sample of those listed in telephone directories. During the Depression, many poor people did not have telephones, and the poor voted overwhelmingly for Roosevelt. Modern pollsters use sophisticated techniques to ensure that their sample is as random as possible.

Frequency Distribution

Once a sample has been chosen and all data of interest are collected, the data must be organized so that conclusions may be more easily drawn. One method of organization is to group the data into intervals; equal intervals are usually chosen.

EXAMPLE 1 **Business Executives**

A survey asked a random sample of 30 business executives for their recommendations as to the number of college credits in management that a business major should have. The results are shown below. Group the data into intervals and find the frequency of each interval.

$$
\begin{array}{cccccccccc}
3 & 25 & 22 & 16 & 0 & 9 & 14 & 8 & 34 & 21 \\
15 & 12 & 9 & 3 & 8 & 15 & 20 & 12 & 28 & 19 \\
17 & 16 & 23 & 19 & 12 & 14 & 29 & 13 & 24 & 18
\end{array}
$$

APPLY IT

SOLUTION The highest number in the list is 34 and the lowest is 0; one convenient way to group the data is in intervals of size 5, starting with 0–4 and ending with 30–34. This gives an interval for each number in the list and results in seven equal intervals of a convenient size. Too many intervals of smaller size would not simplify the data enough, while too few intervals of larger size would conceal information that the data might provide. A rule of thumb is to use from 6 to 15 intervals.

First tally the number of college credits falling into each interval. Then total the tallies in each interval as in the following table. This table is an example of a **grouped frequency distribution**.

Grouped Frequency Distribution		
College Credits	Tally	Frequency
0–4	|||	3
5–9	||||	4
10–14	||||		6
15–19	|||| |||	8
20–24	||||	5
25–29	|||	3
30–34			1
		Total: 30

The frequency distribution in Example 1 shows information about the data that might not have been noticed before. For example, the interval with the largest number of recommended credits is 15–19, and 19 executives (more than half) recommended between 10 and 24 credits, inclusive. Also, the frequency in each interval increases rather evenly (up to 8) and then decreases at about the same pace. However, some information has been lost; for example, we no longer know how many executives recommended 12 credits.

The information in a grouped frequency distribution can be displayed in a histogram similar to the histograms for probability distributions in Chapter 8. The intervals determine the widths of the bars; if equal intervals are used, all the bars have the same width. The heights of the bars are determined by the frequencies.

A **frequency polygon** is another form of graph that illustrates a grouped frequency distribution. The polygon is formed by joining consecutive midpoints of the tops of the histogram bars with straight line segments. The midpoints of the first and last bars are joined to endpoints on the horizontal axis where the next midpoint would appear.

NOTE   In this section, the heights of the histogram bars give the frequencies. The histograms in Chapter 8 were for probability distributions, and so the heights gave the probabilities.

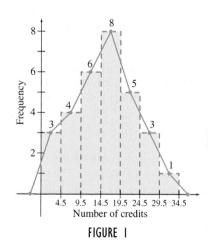

FIGURE 1

EXAMPLE 2   **Histogram and Frequency Polygon**

A grouped frequency distribution of college credits was found in Example 1. Draw a histogram and a frequency polygon for this distribution.

SOLUTION   First draw a histogram, shown in red in Figure 1. To get a frequency polygon, connect consecutive midpoints of the tops of the bars. The frequency polygon is shown in blue.

Many graphing calculators have the capability of drawing a histogram. On a TI-84 Plus C calculator, enter the data by selecting STAT EDIT and then typing the entries in L_1. To create a histogram, select STATPLOT and 1:Plot1. Turn the plot ON and select the histogram icon in the Type row, as shown in Figure 2(a). Be sure that L_1 is entered for Xlist.

Select WINDOW to set up the intervals, as shown in Figure 2(b). The Xscl value gives the width of each interval. To draw the histogram, select GRAPH. Figure 2(c) shows the histogram for the data of Example 1. See the *Graphing Calculator and Excel Spreadsheet Manual* available with this text.

(a)   (b)   (c)

FIGURE 2

Measures of Central Tendency

As we have seen, the frequency distribution, histogram, and frequency polygon give us a picture of the data. We also use mathematics to summarize and quantify some of the characteristics or tendencies of the data.

In Example 1, business executives were asked how many college credits in management business students should complete. If we want to use these data to develop a recommendation, we would need to summarize the responses into a single number. We could look at the histogram and see that our value should be near the center of the data, which is somewhere in the range of 15 to 19 credits. Of course, the frequency distribution and the histogram don't indicate exactly what that number should be.

Three mathematical quantities are used to describe the "average" value of a set of data. These values are said to measure the central tendency of a set of data and are called the mean, median, and mode.

Mean

The most important of the measures of central tendency is the mean, which is similar to the expected value of a probability distribution.

The **arithmetic mean** (the **mean**) of a set of numbers is the sum of the numbers, divided by the total number of numbers. Recall from Section 1.3 that we can write the sum of n numbers $x_1, x_2, x_3, \ldots, x_n$ in a compact way using *summation notation*:

$$x_1 + x_2 + x_3 + \cdots + x_n = \Sigma x.$$

The symbol $\bar{x}$ (read x-bar) is used to represent the mean of a sample.

Mean

The **mean** of the n numbers $x_1, x_2, x_3, \ldots, x_n$ is

$$\bar{x} = \frac{\Sigma x}{n}.$$

Bankruptcies	
Year	Petitions Filed (thousands)
2008	1118
2009	1474
2010	1593
2011	1411
2012	1221
2013	1072

YOUR TURN 1 Find the mean of the following data: 12, 17, 21, 25, 27, 38, 49.

EXAMPLE 3 Bankruptcy

The table to the left lists the number of bankruptcy petitions (in thousands) filed in the United States in the years 2008–2013. Find the mean number of bankruptcy petitions filed annually during this period. *Source: U.S. Courts.*

SOLUTION Let $x_1 = 1118$, $x_2 = 1474$, and so on. Here, $n = 6$, since there are six numbers.

$$\bar{x} = \frac{1118 + 1474 + 1593 + 1411 + 1221 + 1072}{6}$$

$$\bar{x} = \frac{7889}{6} \approx 1315$$

The mean number of bankruptcy petitions filed per year during the given years is about 1,315,000. **TRY YOUR TURN 1**

As another example, the mean response for the number of college credits in management that a business major should have, based on the sample of 30 business executives described in Example 1, is

$$\bar{x} = \frac{3 + 25 + 22 + \cdots + 18}{30} = \frac{478}{30} = 15.93.$$

EXAMPLE 4 Mean for Frequency Distributions

Find the mean for the data shown in the following frequency distribution.

Calculations for Frequency Distribution		
Value, x	Frequency, f	Product, xf
30	6	$30 \cdot 6 = 180$
32	9	$32 \cdot 9 = 288$
33	7	$33 \cdot 7 = 231$
37	12	$37 \cdot 12 = 444$
42	6	$42 \cdot 6 = 252$
	Total: 40	Total: 1395

SOLUTION The value 30 appears six times, 32 nine times, and so on. To find the mean, first multiply 30 by 6, 32 by 9, and so on.

A new column, "Product, xf" has been added to the frequency distribution. Adding the products from this column gives a total of 1395. The total from the frequency column is 40, so $n = 40$. The mean is

$$\bar{x} = \frac{1395}{40} = 34.875.$$

The mean of grouped data is found in a similar way. For grouped data, intervals are used, rather than single values. To calculate the mean, it is assumed that all these values are located at the midpoint of the interval. The letter x is used to represent the midpoints and f represents the frequencies, as shown in the next example.

EXAMPLE 5   **Business Executives**

Listed below is the grouped frequency distribution for the 30 business executives described in Example 1. Find the mean from the grouped frequency distribution.

Grouped Frequency Distribution for College Credits			
Interval	Midpoint, x	Frequency, f	Product, xf
0–4	2	3	6
5–9	7	4	28
10–14	12	6	72
15–19	17	8	136
20–24	22	5	110
25–29	27	3	81
30–34	32	1	32
		Total: 30	Total: 465

SOLUTION   A column for the midpoint of each interval has been added. The numbers in this column are found by adding the endpoints of each interval and dividing by 2. For the interval 0–4, the midpoint is $(0 + 4)/2 = 2$. The numbers in the product column on the right are found by multiplying each frequency by its corresponding midpoint. Finally, we divide the total of the product column by the total of the frequency column to get

$$\bar{x} = \frac{465}{30} = 15.5.$$

Notice that this mean is slightly different from the earlier mean of 15.93. The reason for this difference is that we have acted as if each piece of data is at the midpoint, which is not true here, and is not true in most cases. Information is always lost when the data are grouped. It is more accurate to use the original data, rather than the grouped frequency, when calculating the mean, but the original data might not be available. Furthermore, the mean based upon the grouped data is typically not too far from the mean based upon the original data, and there may be situations in which the extra accuracy is not worth the extra effort.

TRY YOUR TURN 2

YOUR TURN 2   Find the mean of the following grouped frequency.

Interval	Frequency
0–6	2
7–13	4
14–20	7
21–27	10
28–34	3
35–41	1

The formula for the mean of a grouped frequency distribution is given below.

Mean of a Grouped Distribution

The mean of a distribution, where x represents the midpoints, f the frequencies, and $n = \Sigma f$, is

$$\bar{x} = \frac{\Sigma xf}{n}.$$

The mean of a random sample is a random variable, and for this reason it is sometimes called the **sample mean**. The sample mean is a random variable because it assigns a number to the experiment of taking a random sample. If a different random sample were taken, the mean would probably have a different value, with some values more probable than others. If another set of 30 business executives were selected in Example 1, the mean number of college credits in management recommended for a business major might be 13.22 or 17.69. It is unlikely that the mean would be as small as 1.21 or as large as 32.75, although these values are remotely possible.

NOTE
1. The midpoint of the intervals in a grouped frequency distribution may be values that the data cannot take on. For example, if we grouped the data for the 30 business executives into the intervals 0–5, 6–11, 12–17, 18–23, 24–29, and 30–35, the midpoints would be 2.5, 8.5, 14.5, 20.5, 26.5, and 32.5, even though all the data are whole numbers.
2. If we used different intervals in Example 5, the mean would come out to be a slightly different number. Verify that with the intervals 0–5, 6–11, 12–17, 18–23, 24–29, and 30–35, the mean in Example 5 is 16.1.

We saw in Section 8.5 how to calculate the expected value of a random variable when we know its probability distribution. The expected value is sometimes called the **population mean**, denoted by the Greek letter μ. In other words,

$$E(x) = \mu.$$

Furthermore, it can be shown that the expected value of $\bar{x}$ is also equal to μ; that is,

$$E(\bar{x}) = \mu.$$

For instance, consider again the 30 business executives in Example 1. We found that $\bar{x} = 15.93$, but the value of μ, the average for all possible business executives, is unknown. If a good estimate of μ were needed, the best guess (based on this data) is 15.93.

Median Asked by a reporter to give the average height of the players on his team, a Little League coach lined up his 15 players by increasing height. He picked the player in the middle and pronounced that player to be of average height. This kind of average, called the **median**, is defined as the middle entry in a set of data arranged in either increasing or decreasing order. If there is an even number of entries, the median is defined to be the mean of the two center entries.

Calculating the Median	
Odd Number of Entries	**Even Number of Entries**
1	2
3	3
Median = 4	4 } Median = $\dfrac{4+7}{2}$ = 5.5
7	7 }
8	9
	15

EXAMPLE 6 **Median**

Find the median for each list of numbers.

(a) 11, 12, 17, 20, 23, 28, 29

SOLUTION The median is the middle number; in this case, 20. (Note that the numbers are already arranged in numerical order.) In this list, three numbers are smaller than 20 and three are larger.

(b) 15, 13, 7, 11, 19, 30, 39, 5, 10

SOLUTION First arrange the numbers in numerical order, from smallest to largest.

$$5, 7, 10, 11, 13, 15, 19, 30, 39$$

The middle number, or median, can now be determined; it is 13.

(c) 47, 59, 32, 81, 74, 153

SOLUTION Write the numbers in numerical order.

$$32, 47, 59, 74, 81, 153$$

There are six numbers here; the median is the mean of the two middle numbers.

$$\text{Median} = \frac{59 + 74}{2} = \frac{133}{2} = 66\frac{1}{2}$$

YOUR TURN 3 Find the median of the data in Your Turn 1.

TRY YOUR TURN 3

Mode Katie's scores on ten class quizzes include one 7, two 8's, six 9's, and one 10 (out of 10 points possible). She claims that her average grade on quizzes is 9, because most of her scores are 9's. This kind of "average," found by selecting the most frequent entry, is called the **mode**.

EXAMPLE 7 Mode

Find the mode for each list of numbers.

(a) 57, 38, 55, 55, 80, 87, 98, 55, 57

   SOLUTION The number 55 occurs more often than any other, so it is the mode. It is not necessary to place the numbers in numerical order when looking for the mode.

(b) 182, 185, 183, 185, 187, 187, 189

   SOLUTION Both 185 and 187 occur twice. This list has *two* modes.

(c) 10,708; 11,519; 10,972; 17,546; 13,905; 12,182

   SOLUTION No number occurs more than once. This list has no mode.

EXAMPLE 8 Seed Storage

Seeds that are dried, placed in an airtight container, and stored in a cool, dry place remain ready to be planted for a long time. The table below gives the amount of time that each type of seed can be stored and still remain viable for planting. *Source: The Handy Science Answer Book.*

Storage Time			
Vegetable	**Years**	**Vegetable**	**Years**
Beans	3	Cucumbers	5
Cabbage	4	Melons	4
Carrots	1	Peppers	2
Cauliflower	4	Pumpkin	4
Corn	2	Tomatoes	3

Find the mean, median, and mode of the information in the table.

SOLUTION

**Method 1
Calculating by Hand**

The mean amount of time that the seeds can be stored is

$$\bar{x} = \frac{3 + 4 + 1 + 4 + 2 + 5 + 4 + 2 + 4 + 3}{10} = 3.2 \text{ years.}$$

After the numbers are arranged in order from smallest to largest, the average of the two middle numbers, or median, is found; it is 3.5.

The number 4 occurs more often than any other, so it is the mode.

**Method 2
Graphing Calculator**

Most scientific calculators have some statistical capability and can calculate the mean of a set of data; graphing calculators can often calculate the median as well. For example, Figure 3 shows the mean and the median for the data above calculated on a TI-84 Plus C, where the data were stored in the list L_1. These commands are found under the LIST-MATH menu. This calculator does not include a command for finding the mode.

mean(L1)	
	3.2
median(L1)	
	3.5

FIGURE 3

Method 3
Spreadsheet

Using Microsoft Excel, place the data in cells A1 through A10. To find the mean of these data, type "=AVERAGE(A1:A10)" in cell A11, or any other unused cell, and then press Enter. The result of 3.2 will appear in cell A11. To find the median of these data, type "=MEDIAN(A1:A10)" in cell A12, or any other unused cell, and press Enter. The result of 3.5 will appear in cell A12. To find the mode of these data, type "=MODE(A1:A10)" in cell A13, or any other unused cell, and press Enter. The result of 4 will appear in cell A13.

The mean, median, and mode are examples of a **statistic**, which is simply a number that gives information about a sample. All three are a measure of the center, or "average," of the data.

The mean is the most commonly used measure of central tendency. Its advantages are that it is easy to compute, it takes all the data into consideration, and it is reliable—that is, repeated samples are likely to give very similar means. A disadvantage of the mean is that it is influenced by extreme values, as will be illustrated in Example 9.

The median can be easy to compute and is influenced very little by extremes. Another advantage is that the median can be found in situations where the data are not numerical. For example, in a taste test, people are asked to rank five soft drinks from the one they like best to the one they like least. The combined rankings then produce an ordered sample, from which the median can be identified. A disadvantage of the median is the need to rank the data in order; this can be difficult when the number of items is large.

The mode has the advantages of being easily found and not being influenced by data that are very large or very small compared to the rest of the data. It is often used in samples where the data to be "averaged" are not numerical. A major disadvantage of the mode is that we cannot always locate exactly one mode for a set of values. There can be more than one mode, in the case of ties, or there can be no mode if all entries occur with the same frequency.

The final example shows a situation in which one data value is much larger than the rest of the data. In this case, the median gives a truer representation than the mean.

EXAMPLE 9 **Salaries**

An office has 2 secretaries, 4 salespersons, 1 sales manager, and Jeff Weidenaar, who owns the business. Their annual salaries are as follows:

Each of the two secretaries earns $35,000;

each of the four salespersons earns $45,000;

the sales manager earns $55,000;

and the owner earns $300,000.

(a) Calculate the mean salary of those working in the office.

SOLUTION The mean salary is

$$\bar{x} = \frac{(35,000)2 + (45,000)4 + 55,000 + 300,000}{8} = \$75,625.$$

Notice that 7 people earn less than this mean and only 1 (the owner) earns more. The owner's salary is much higher than the rest of the salaries, and this extreme value has a pronounced effect on the mean. In this case, the mean does not seem very representative of the center, or "average," of the office salaries.

(b) Calculate the median salary of those working in the office.

SOLUTION The median salary is found by ranking the salaries by size:

$35,000, $35,000, $45,000, $45,000, $45,000, $45,000, $55,000, $300,000.

Because there are 8 salaries (an even number) in the list, the mean of the fourth and fifth entries will give the value of the median. The fourth and fifth entries are both $45,000, so the median is $45,000. In this example, the median gives a truer representation of the office salaries than the mean.

9.1 EXERCISES

For Exercises 1–4, do the following:

(a) **Group the data as indicated.**

(b) **Prepare a frequency distribution with a column for intervals and frequencies.**

(c) **Construct a histogram.**

(d) **Construct a frequency polygon.**

1. Use six intervals, starting with 0–24.

7	105	116	73	129	26
29	44	126	82	56	137
43	73	65	141	79	74
121	12	46	37	85	82
2	99	85	95	90	38
86	147	32	84	13	100

2. Use seven intervals, starting with 30–39.

79	71	78	87	69	50	63	51
60	46	65	65	56	88	94	56
74	63	87	62	84	76	82	67
59	66	57	81	93	93	54	88
55	69	78	63	63	48	89	81
98	42	91	66	60	70	64	70
61	75	82	65	68	39	77	81
67	62	73	49	51	76	94	54
83	71	94	45	73	95	72	66
71	77	48	51	54	57	69	87

3. Repeat Exercise 1 using eight intervals, starting with 0–19.

4. Repeat Exercise 2 using six intervals, starting with 39–48.

5. How does a frequency polygon differ from a histogram?

6. Discuss the advantages and disadvantages of the mean as a measure of central tendency.

Find the mean for each list of numbers.

7. 8, 10, 16, 21, 25

8. 67, 89, 75, 86, 100, 93

9. 30,200; 23,700; 33,320; 29,410; 24,600; 27,750; 27,300; 32,680

10. 38,500; 39,720; 42,183; 21,982; 43,250

11. 9.4, 11.3, 10.5, 7.4, 9.1, 8.4, 9.7, 5.2, 1.1, 4.7

12. 15.3, 27.2, 14.8, 16.5, 31.8, 40.1, 18.9, 28.4, 26.3, 35.3

Find the mean for the following.

13.

Value	Frequency
4	6
6	1
9	3
15	2

14.

Value	Frequency
9	3
12	5
15	1
18	1

15. Find the mean for the data in Exercise 1 from the grouped frequency distribution found in each of the following exercises.

(a) Exercise 1

(b) Exercise 3

16. Find the mean for the data in Exercise 2 from the grouped frequency distribution found in each of the following exercises.

(a) Exercise 2

(b) Exercise 4

Find the median for each list of numbers.

17. 27, 35, 39, 42, 47, 51, 54

18. 596, 604, 612, 683, 719

19. 100, 114, 125, 135, 150, 172

20. 359, 831, 904, 615, 211, 279, 505

21. 28.4, 9.1, 3.4, 27.6, 59.8, 32.1, 47.6, 29.8

22. 0.2, 1.4, 0.6, 0.2, 2.5, 1.9, 0.8, 1.5

Use a graphing calculator or spreadsheet to calculate the mean and median for the data in the indicated exercises.

23. Exercise 1   **24.** Exercise 2

Find the mode or modes for each list of numbers.

25. 4, 9, 8, 6, 9, 2, 1, 3

26. 16, 15, 13, 15, 14, 13, 11, 15, 14

27. 55, 62, 62, 71, 62, 55, 73, 55, 71

28. 158, 162, 165, 162, 165, 157, 163

29. 6.8, 6.3, 6.3, 6.9, 6.7, 6.4, 6.1, 6.0

30. 22.35, 14.90, 17.85, 15.46, 14.91, 17.85, 21.35

31. When is the median the most appropriate measure of central tendency?

32. Under what circumstances would the mode be an appropriate measure of central tendency?

For grouped data, the *modal class* is the interval containing the most data values. Find the modal class for each collection of grouped data.

33. Use the distribution in Exercise 1.

34. Use the distribution in Exercise 2.

35. To predict the outcome of the next congressional election, you take a survey of your friends. Is this a random sample of the voters in your congressional district? Explain why or why not.

APPLICATIONS

Business and Economics

Wheat Production   U.S. wheat prices and production figures for recent years are given in the following table. *Source: USDA.*

Year	Price ($ per bushel)	Production (millions of bushels)
2004	3.40	2157
2005	3.42	2103
2006	4.26	1808
2007	6.48	2051
2008	6.78	2499
2009	4.87	2218
2010	5.70	2207
2011	7.24	1999
2012	7.77	2266
2013	6.87	2130

Find the mean and median for the following.

36. Price per bushel of wheat

37. Wheat production

38. Salaries   The total compensation (in millions of dollars) for the 10 highest paid CEOs in 2013 is given in the table at the top of the next column. *Source: The Huffington Post.*

Person, Company	Total Compensation
Anthony Petrello, Nabors Industries	68.2
Leslie Moonves, CBS	65.6
Richard Adkerson, Freeport-McMoRan Copper & Gold	55.3
Stephen Kaufer, TripAdvisor	39.0
Philippe Dauman, Viacom	37.2
Leonard Schleifer, Regeneron Pharmaceuticals	36.3
Robert Iger, Walt Disney	34.3
David Zaslav, Discovery Communications	33.3
Jeffrey Bewkes, Time Warner	32.5
Brian Roberts, Comcast	31.4

(a) Find the mean total compensation for this group of people.

(b) Find the median total compensation for this group of people.

39. Household Income   The total income for African American households making under $250,000 in 2012 is given in the following table. *Source: U.S. Census Bureau.*

Income Range	Midpoint Salary	Frequency (in thousands)
Under $20,000	$10,000	5037
$20,000–$39,999	$30,000	3936
$40,000–$59,999	$50,000	2593
$60,000–$79,999	$70,000	1583
$80,000–$99,999	$90,000	1031
$100,000–$149,999	$125,000	1151
$150,000–$199,999	$175,000	327
$200,000–$249,999	$225,000	132

Use the table to estimate the mean income for African American households in 2012.

40. Household Income   The total income for white households making under $250,000 in 2012 is given in the following table. *Source: U.S. Census Bureau.*

Income Range	Midpoint Salary	Frequency (in thousands)
Under $20,000	$10,000	16,431
$20,000–$39,999	$30,000	20,501
$40,000–$59,999	$50,000	16,183
$60,000–$79,999	$70,000	12,780
$80,000–$99,999	$90,000	9097
$100,0000–$149,999	$125,000	12,859
$150,000–$199,999	$175,000	5186
$200,000–$249,999	$225,000	2160

(a) Use this table to estimate the mean income for white households in 2012.

(b) Compare this estimate with the estimate found in Exercise 39. Discuss whether this provides evidence that white American households have higher earnings than African American households.

41. Airlines   The number of consumer complaints against the top U.S. airlines in 2013 is given in the following table. *Source: U.S. Department of Transportation.*

Airline	Complaints	Complaints per 100,000 Passengers Boarding
Southwest Airlines	397	0.34
Alaska Airlines	86	0.44
Delta Airlines	713	0.59
JetBlue Airways	192	0.63
AirTran Airways	130	0.73
SkyWest Airlines	217	0.80
Mesa Airlines	71	0.85
Endeavor Air	113	0.86
ExpressJet Airlines	319	0.96
Hawaiian Airlines	105	1.06
Virgin America	81	1.28
US Airways	806	1.42
American Eagle Airlines	303	1.70
American Airlines	1730	1.99
United Airlines	1935	2.14
Frontier Airlines	316	3.09

(a) By considering the numbers in the column labeled "Complaints," calculate the mean and median number of complaints per airline.

(b) Explain why the averages found in part (a) are not meaningful.

(c) Find the mean and median of the numbers in the column labeled "Complaints per 100,000 Passengers Boarding." Discuss whether these averages are meaningful.

42. Housing Prices   An Erie, PA, newspaper advertised homes for sale in different areas of the region. In Summit Township, seven homes were advertised at the following listing prices: $199,000, $109,000, $229,000, $169,900, $219,900, $25,500, and $207,000. In the rural area south of Summit, six homes were advertised at the following listing prices: $749,000, $352,400, $314,900, $165,000, $175,000, and $215,000.

(a) Find the mean and median housing prices for Summit Township.

(b) Find the mean and median housing prices for the rural area.

(c) Discuss the differences between the mean and median for each region. Which gives a truer representation of the average housing price for each region?

43. New Housing Sales   The number (in thousands) of new houses sold each month in the United States from 2010 to 2013 is given in the following table. *Source: U.S. Census.*

	2010	2011	2012	2013
Jan.	24	21	23	32
Feb.	27	22	30	36
Mar.	36	28	34	41
Apr.	41	30	34	43
May	26	28	35	40
June	28	28	34	43
July	26	27	33	33
Aug.	23	25	31	31
Sept.	25	24	30	31
Oct.	23	25	29	36
Nov.	20	23	28	32
Dec.	23	24	28	31

(a) Prepare a frequency distribution with a column for intervals and frequencies. Use six intervals, starting with 20–23.

(b) Sketch a histogram and a frequency polygon, using the intervals in part (a).

(c) Find the mean for the original data.

(d) Find the mean using the grouped data from part (a).

(e) Explain why your answers to parts (c) and (d) are different.

(f) Find the median and mode for the original data.

Life Sciences

44. Pandas   The size of the home ranges (in square kilometers) of a group of pandas were surveyed over a year's time, with the following results.

Home Range	Frequency
0.1–0.5	11
0.6–1.0	12
1.1–1.5	7
1.6–2.0	6
2.1–2.5	2
2.6–3.0	1
3.1–3.5	1

(a) Sketch a histogram and frequency polygon for the data.

(b) Find the mean for the data.

45. Blood Types The number of recognized blood types varies by species, as indicated by the table below. Find the mean, median, and mode of this data. *Source: The Handy Science Answer Book.*

Animal	Number of Blood Types
Pig	16
Cow	12
Chicken	11
Horse	9
Human	8
Sheep	7
Dog	7
Rhesus monkey	6
Mink	5
Rabbit	5
Mouse	4
Rat	4
Cat	2

General Interest

46. Temperature The following table gives the number of days in June and July of recent years in which the temperature reached 90 degrees or higher in New York's Central Park. *Source: The National Weather Service.*

Year	Days	Year	Days	Year	Days
1985	4	1995	14	2005	12
1986	8	1996	0	2006	5
1987	14	1997	10	2007	4
1988	21	1998	5	2008	10
1989	10	1999	24	2009	0
1990	6	2000	3	2010	20
1991	21	2001	4	2011	17
1992	4	2002	13	2012	15
1993	25	2003	11	2013	13
1994	16	2004	1	2014	3

(a) Prepare a frequency distribution with a column for intervals and frequencies. Use six intervals, starting with 0–4.

(b) Sketch a histogram and a frequency polygon, using the intervals in part (a).

(c) Find the mean for the original data.

(d) Find the mean using the grouped data from part (a).

(e) Explain why your answers to parts (c) and (d) are different.

(f) Find the median and the mode for the original data.

47. Temperature The table at the top of the next column gives the average monthly temperatures in degrees Fahrenheit for a certain area.

Month	Maximum	Minimum
January	39	16
February	39	18
March	44	21
April	50	26
May	60	32
June	69	37
July	79	43
August	78	42
September	70	37
October	51	31
November	47	24
December	40	20

Find the mean and median for the following.

(a) The maximum temperature

(b) The minimum temperature

48. Olympics The number of nations participating in the Winter Olympic games, from 1968 to 2014, is given below. Find the following measures for the data. *Source: Sports-Reference.*

Year	Nations Participating	Year	Nations Participating
1968	37	1994	67
1972	35	1998	72
1976	37	2002	77
1980	37	2006	85
1984	49	2010	82
1988	57	2014	89
1992	64		

(a) Mean   (b) Median   (c) Mode

49. Personal Wealth When Russian billionaire Roman Abramovich became governor of the Russian province Chukotka (in the Bering Straits, opposite Alaska), it instantly became the fourth most prosperous region in Russia, even though its 80,000 other residents are poor. Mr. Abramovich was then worth $5.7 billion. Suppose each of the 80,000 other residents of Chukotka was worth $100. *Source: National Public Radio.*

(a) Calculate the average worth of a citizen of Chukotka.

(b) What does this example tell you about the use of the mean to describe an average?

50. Personal Wealth *Washington Post* writer John Schwartz pointed out that if Microsoft Corp. cofounder Bill Gates, who, at the time, was reportedly worth $10 billion, lived in a town with 10,000 totally penniless people, the average personal wealth in the town would make it seem as if everyone were a millionaire. *Source: The Washington Post.*

(a) Verify Schwartz's statement.

(b) What would be the median personal wealth in this town?

(c) What would be the mode for the personal wealth in this town?

(d) In this example, which average is most representative: the mean, the median, or the mode?

51. **Baseball Salaries** The Major League Baseball team with the lowest payroll in 2014 was the Houston Astros. The following table gives the salary of each Astro in 2014. *Source: ESPN.*

Name	Salary
Scott Feldman	$12,000,000
Jose Veras	$3,850,000
Chad Qualls	$2,750,000
Jason Castro	$2,450,000
Jose Altuve	$1,437,500
Jesus Guzman	$1,300,000
Matt Dominguez	$510,100
Chris Carter	$510,000
Dallas Keuchel	$508,700
Josh Fields	$506,500
Carlos Corporan	$505,300
Anthony Bass	$505,200
Marwin Gonzalez	$504,500
Robbie Grossman	$504,500
Brad Peacock	$504,300
L. J. Hoes	$502,900
Jared Cosart	$500,000

(a) Find the mean, median, and mode of the salaries.

(b) Which average best describes these data?

(c) Why is there such a difference between the mean and median?

52. **SAT I: Reasoning Test** Given the following sequence of numbers*

$$1, a, a^2, a^3, \ldots, a^n,$$

where n is a positive even integer, with the *additional assumption* that a is a positive number, the median is best described as

(a) greater than $a^{n/2}$;

(b) smaller than $a^{n/2}$;

(c) equal to $a^{n/2}$.

(d) The relationship cannot be determined from the information given.

YOUR TURN ANSWERS

1. 27

2. 19.85

3. 25

*Permission to reprint SAT materials does not constitute review or endorsement by Educational Testing Service or the College Board of this publication as a whole or of any other questions or testing information it may contain. This problem appeared, minus the *additional assumption*, on an SAT in 1996. Colin Rizzio, a high school student at the time, became an instant celebrity when he noticed that the additional assumption was needed to complete the problem. *Source: The New York Times.*

9.2 Measures of Variation

APPLY IT How can we tell when a manufacturing process is out of control?
To answer this question, which we will do in Example 6, we need to understand measures of variation, which tell us how much the numbers in a sample vary from the mean.

The mean gives a measure of central tendency of a list of numbers but tells nothing about the *spread* of the numbers in the list. For example, suppose three inspectors each inspect a sample of five restaurants in their region and record the number of health violations they find in each restaurant. Their results are recorded in the table to the left.

Each of these three samples has a mean of 4, and yet they are quite different; the amount of dispersion or variation within the samples is different. Therefore, in addition to a measure of central tendency, another kind of measure is needed that describes how much the numbers vary.

Three Sets of Data				
I	3	5	6	3	3
II	4	4	4	4	4
III	10	1	0	0	9

Range The largest number in sample I is 6, while the smallest is 3, a difference of 3. In sample II this difference is 0; in sample III, it is 10. The difference between the largest and smallest number in a sample is called the **range**, one example of a measure of variation.

The range of sample I is 3, of sample II, 0, and of sample III, 10. The range has the advantage of being very easy to compute, and gives a rough estimate of the variation among the data in the sample. It depends only on the two extremes, however, and tells nothing about how the other data are distributed between the extremes.

EXAMPLE 1   Range

Find the range for each list of numbers.

(a) 12, 27, 6, 19, 38, 9, 42, 15

   SOLUTION   The highest number here is 42; the lowest is 6. The range is the difference between these numbers, or $42 - 6 = 36$.

(b) 74, 112, 59, 88, 200, 73, 92, 175

   SOLUTION

$$\text{Range} = 200 - 59 = 141$$

Variance and Standard Deviation

The most useful measure of variation is the *standard deviation*. Before defining it, however, we must find the **deviations from the mean**, the differences found by subtracting the mean from each number in a sample.

EXAMPLE 2   Deviations from the Mean

Find the deviations from the mean for the numbers

$$32, 41, 47, 53, 57.$$

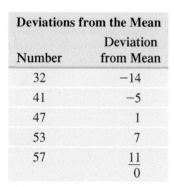

Deviations from the Mean	
Number	Deviation from Mean
32	−14
41	−5
47	1
53	7
57	11
	0

SOLUTION   Adding these numbers and dividing by 5 gives a mean of 46. To find the deviations from the mean, subtract 46 from each number in the list. For example, as shown in the table to the left, the first deviation from the mean is $32 - 46 = -14$; the last is $57 - 46 = 11$.

   To check your work, find the sum of these deviations. It should always equal 0. (The answer is always 0 because the positive and negative numbers cancel each other.)

   To find a measure of variation, we might be tempted to use the mean of the deviations. As mentioned above, however, this number is always 0, no matter how widely the data are dispersed. One way to solve this problem is to use absolute value and find the mean of the absolute values of the deviations from the mean. Absolute value is awkward to work with algebraically, and there is an alternative approach that provides better theoretical results. In this method, the way to get a list of positive numbers is to square each deviation and then find the mean. When finding the mean of the squared deviations, most statisticians prefer to divide by $n - 1$, rather than n. We will give the reason later in this section. For the data above, this gives

$$\frac{(-14)^2 + (-5)^2 + 1^2 + 7^2 + 11^2}{5 - 1} = \frac{196 + 25 + 1 + 49 + 121}{4}$$

$$= 98.$$

This number, 98, is called the *variance* of the sample. Since it is found by averaging a list of squares, the variance of a sample is represented by s^2.

   For a sample of n numbers $x_1, x_2, x_3, \ldots, x_n$, with mean $\bar{x}$, the variance is

$$s^2 = \frac{\Sigma (x - \bar{x})^2}{n - 1}.$$

The following shortcut formula for the variance can be derived algebraically from the formula above. You are asked for this derivation in Exercise 23.

Variance

The **variance** of a sample of n numbers $x_1, x_2, x_3, \ldots, x_n$, with mean $\bar{x}$, is

$$s^2 = \frac{\Sigma x^2 - n\bar{x}^2}{n - 1}.$$

To find the variance, we squared the deviations from the mean, so the variance is in squared units. To return to the same units as the data, we use the *square root* of the variance, called the *standard deviation*.

Standard Deviation

The **standard deviation** of a sample of n numbers $x_1, x_2, x_3, \ldots, x_n$, with mean $\bar{x}$, is

$$s = \sqrt{s^2} = \sqrt{\frac{\Sigma x^2 - n\bar{x}^2}{n - 1}}.$$

As its name indicates, the standard deviation is the most commonly used measure of variation. The standard deviation is a measure of the variation from the mean. The size of the standard deviation tells us something about how spread out the data are from the mean.

EXAMPLE 3 Standard Deviation

Find the standard deviation of the numbers

$$7, 9, 18, 22, 27, 29, 32, 40.$$

SOLUTION

Method 1
Calculating by Hand

The mean of the numbers is

$$\bar{x} = \frac{7 + 9 + 18 + 22 + 27 + 29 + 32 + 40}{8} = 23.$$

Arrange the work in columns, as shown in the table.

Standard Deviation Calculations	
Number, x	Square of the Number, x^2
7	49
9	81
18	324
22	484
27	729
29	841
32	1024
40	1600
	Total: 5132

The total of the second column gives $\Sigma x^2 = 5132$. Now, using the formula for variance with $n = 8$, the variance is

$$s^2 = \frac{\Sigma x^2 - n\bar{x}^2}{n - 1}$$

$$= \frac{5132 - 8(23)^2}{8 - 1} \qquad \Sigma x^2 = 5132, n = 8, \bar{x} = 23$$

$$\approx 128.57,$$

rounded, and the standard deviation is

$$s = \sqrt{128.57} \approx 11.3.$$

Method 2
Graphing Calculator

The data are entered into the L_1 list on a TI-84 Plus C calculator. Figure 4 shows how the variance and standard deviation are then calculated through the LIST-MATH menu. Figure 5 shows an alternative method, going through the STAT menu, which calculates the mean, the standard deviation using both $n - 1$ (indicated by Sx) and n (indicated by σx) in the denominator, and other statistics.

YOUR TURN 1 Find the range, variance, and standard deviation for the following list of numbers: 7, 11, 16, 17, 19, 35.

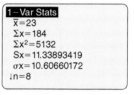

FIGURE 4   FIGURE 5

Method 3
Spreadsheet

The data are entered in cells A1 through A8. Then, in cell A9, type "=VAR(A1:A8)" and press Enter. The standard deviation can be calculated by either taking the square root of cell A9 or by typing "=STDEV(A1:A8)" in cell A10 and pressing Enter.

TRY YOUR TURN 1 ▇▇

CAUTION Be careful to divide by $n - 1$, not n, when calculating the standard deviation of a sample. Many calculators are equipped with statistical keys that compute the variance and standard deviation. Some of these calculators use $n - 1$ and others use n for these computations; some may have keys for both. Check your calculator's instruction book before using a statistical calculator for the exercises.

One way to interpret the standard deviation uses the fact that, for many populations, most of the data are within three standard deviations of the mean. (See Section 9.3.) This implies that, in Example 3, most members of the population from which this sample is taken are between

$$\bar{x} - 3s = 23 - 3(11.3) = -10.9$$

and

$$\bar{x} + 3s = 23 + 3(11.3) = 56.9.$$

This has important implications for quality control. If the sample in Example 3 represents measurements of a product that the manufacturer wants to be between 5 and 45, the standard deviation is too large, even though all the numbers in the sample are within these bounds.

We saw in the previous section that the mean of a random sample is a random variable. It should not surprise you, then, to learn that the variance and standard deviation are also random variables. We will refer to the variance and standard deviation of a random sample as the **sample variance** and **sample standard deviation**.

Recall from the previous section that the sample mean $\bar{x}$ is not the same as the population mean μ, which is defined by $\mu = E(x)$, but that $\bar{x}$ gives a good approximation to μ because $E(\bar{x}) = \mu$. Similarly, there is a **population variance**, denoted σ^2, defined by $\sigma^2 = E(x - \mu)^2$, which measures the amount of variation in a population. The **population standard deviation** is simply σ, the square root of the population variance σ^2. (The Greek letter σ is the lowercase version of sigma. You have already seen Σ, the uppercase version.) In more advanced courses in statistics, it is shown that $E(s^2) = \sigma^2$. The reason many statisticians prefer $n - 1$ in the denominator of the standard deviation formula is that it makes $E(s^2) = \sigma^2$ true; this is not true if n is used in the denominator. It may surprise you, then, that $E(s) = \sigma$ is *false,* whether n or $n - 1$ is used. If n is large, the difference between $E(s)$ and σ is slight, so, in practice, the sample standard deviation s gives a good estimate of the population standard deviation σ.

For data in a grouped frequency distribution, a slightly different formula for the standard deviation is used.

FOR REVIEW

Recall from Section 8.5 that a random variable is a function that assigns a real number to each outcome of an experiment. When the experiment consists of drawing a random sample, the standard deviation and the variance are two real numbers assigned to each outcome. Every time the experiment is performed, the standard deviation and variance will most likely have different values, with some values more probable than others.

Standard Deviation for a Grouped Distribution

The standard deviation for a distribution with mean $\bar{x}$, where x is an interval midpoint with frequency f, and $n = \Sigma f$, is

$$s = \sqrt{\frac{\Sigma fx^2 - n\bar{x}^2}{n - 1}}.$$

CAUTION

In calculating the standard deviation for either a grouped or ungrouped distribution, using a rounded value for the mean may produce an inaccurate value.

The formula indicates that the product fx^2 is to be found for each interval. Then these products are summed, n times the square of the mean is subtracted, and the difference is divided by one less than the total frequency; that is, by $n - 1$. The square root of this result is s, the standard deviation.

EXAMPLE 4　Standard Deviation for Grouped Data

Find the standard deviation for the grouped data of Example 5, Section 9.1.

SOLUTION　Begin by forming columns for x (the midpoint of the interval), x^2, and fx^2. Then sum the f and fx^2 columns. Recall from Example 5 of Section 9.1 that $\bar{x} = 15.5$.

Standard Deviation for Grouped Data				
Interval	x	x^2	f	fx^2
0–4	2	4	3	12
5–9	7	49	4	196
10–14	12	144	6	864
15–19	17	289	8	2312
20–24	22	484	5	2420
25–29	27	729	3	2187
30–34	32	1024	1	1024
			Total: 30	Total: 9015

YOUR TURN 2 Find the standard deviation for the following grouped frequency distribution.

Interval	Frequency
0–6	2
7–13	4
14–20	7
21–27	10
28–34	3
35–41	1

The total of the fourth column gives $n = \Sigma f = 30$, and the total of the last column gives $\Sigma f x^2 = 9015$. Use the formula for standard deviation for a grouped distribution to find s.

$$s = \sqrt{\frac{\Sigma f x^2 - n\bar{x}^2}{n - 1}}$$

$$= \sqrt{\frac{9015 - 30(15.5)^2}{30 - 1}} \qquad \Sigma f x^2 = 9015, n = 30, \bar{x} = 15.5$$

$$\approx 7.89$$

Verify that the standard deviation of the original, ungrouped data in Example 1 of Section 9.1 is 7.92. **TRY YOUR TURN 2**

EXAMPLE 5 Nathan's Hot Dog Eating Contest

Since 1916, Nathan's Famous Hot Dogs has held an annual hot dog eating contest, in which each contestant attempts to consume as many hot dogs with buns as possible in a set time period. The following table contains a list of each year's winners since 2000. In what percent of the contests did the number of hot dogs eaten by the winner fall within one standard deviation of the mean number of hot dogs? Within two standard deviations? Within three standard deviations? *Source: Wikipedia.*

Hot Dog Eating Contest Winners		
Year	Winner	Hot Dogs Eaten
2000	Kazutoyo Arai	25.125
2001	Takeru Kobayashi	50
2002	Takeru Kobayashi	50.5
2003	Takeru Kobayashi	44.5
2004	Takeru Kobayashi	53.5
2005	Takeru Kobayashi	49
2006	Takeru Kobayashi	53.75
2007	Joey Chestnut	66
2008	Joey Chestnut	59
2009	Joey Chestnut	68
2010	Joey Chestnut	54
2011	Joey Chestnut	62
2012	Joey Chestnut	68
2013	Joey Chestnut	69
2014	Joey Chestnut	61

SOLUTION First, using the formulas for $\bar{x}$ and s, we calculate the mean and standard deviation:

$$\bar{x} \approx 55.56 \quad \text{and} \quad s \approx 11.46.$$

Subtracting one standard deviation from the mean and then adding one standard deviation to the mean, we find the lower and upper limits:

$$\bar{x} - s = 55.56 - 11.46 = 44.10 \quad \text{(lower)}$$

and

$$\bar{x} + s = 55.56 + 11.46 = 67.02. \quad \text{(upper)}$$

In 11 of the 15 contests, the number of hot dogs eaten by the winner was between 44.10 and 67.02. Therefore, in about 73% $(11/15 \approx 0.73)$ of the recent contests, the number of hot dogs consumed by the winner was within one standard deviation of the mean.

Likewise, subtracting 2 standard deviations from the mean and adding 2 standard deviations to the mean, we get a lower limit of 32.64 and an upper limit of 78.48. In 14 of the 15 contests, or about 93% $(14/15 \approx 0.93)$ of the contests, the winning number of consumed hot dogs was within two standard deviations of the mean.

Finally, subtracting 3 standard deviations from the mean and adding 3 standard deviations to the mean gives an interval of 21.18 to 89.94. The winning numbers in all fifteen contests fall in this interval, so in 100% of the recent contests the number of hot dogs eaten by the winner was within three standard deviations from the mean. ▬▬

EXAMPLE 6 Quality Assurance

APPLY IT *Statistical process control* is a method of determining when a manufacturing process is out of control, producing defective items. The procedure involves taking samples of a measurement on a product over a production run and calculating the mean and standard deviation of each sample. These results are used to determine when the manufacturing process is out of control. For example, three sample measurements from a manufacturing process on each of four days are given in the table below. The mean $\bar{x}$ and standard deviation s are calculated for each sample.

Samples from a Manufacturing Process											
Day	1			2			3			4		
Sample Number	1	2	3	1	2	3	1	2	3	1	2	3
Measurements	−3	0	4	5	−2	4	3	−1	0	4	−2	1
	0	5	3	4	0	3	−2	0	0	3	0	3
	2	2	2	3	1	4	0	1	−2	3	−1	0
$\bar{x}$	−1/3	7/3	3	4	−1/3	11/3	1/3	0	−2/3	10/3	−1	4/3
s	2.5	2.5	1	1	1.5	0.6	2.5	1	1.2	0.6	1	1.5

Next, the mean of the 12 sample means, $\overline{X}$, and the mean of the 12 sample standard deviations, $\bar{s}$, are found (using the formula for $\bar{x}$). Here, these measures are

$$\overline{X} = 1.3 \quad \text{and} \quad \bar{s} = 1.41.$$

The control limits for the sample means are given by

$$\overline{X} \pm k_1 \cdot \bar{s},$$

where k_1 is a constant that depends on the sample size, and can be found from a manual. For samples of size 3, $k_1 = 1.954$, so the control limits for the sample means are

$$1.3 \pm (1.954)(1.41).$$

The upper control limit is 4.06, and the lower control limit is −1.46.

Similarly, the control limits for the sample standard deviations are given by $k_2 \cdot \bar{s}$ and $k_3 \cdot \bar{s}$, where k_2 and k_3 also are values given in the same manual. Here, $k_2 = 2.568$ and $k_3 = 0$, with the upper and lower control limits for the sample standard deviations equal to $2.568(1.41)$ and $0(1.41)$, or 3.62 and 0. As long as the sample means are between −1.46 and 4.06 and the sample standard deviations are between 0 and 3.62, the process is in control. *Source: Statistical Process Control.* ▬▬

9.2 EXERCISES

 1. How are the variance and the standard deviation related?

2. Why can't we use the sum of the deviations from the mean as a measure of dispersion of a distribution?

Find the range and standard deviation for each set of numbers.

3. 72, 61, 57, 83, 52, 66, 85

4. 122, 132, 141, 158, 162, 169, 180

5. 241, 248, 251, 257, 252, 287

6. 51, 58, 62, 64, 67, 71, 74, 78, 82, 93

7. 3, 7, 4, 12, 15, 18, 19, 27, 24, 11

8. 17, 57, 48, 13, 26, 3, 36, 21, 9, 40

 Use a graphing calculator or spreadsheet to calculate the standard deviation for the data in the indicated exercises.

9. Exercise 1 from Section 9.1   **10.** Exercise 2 from Section 9.1

Find the standard deviation for the following grouped data.

11. (From Exercise 1, Section 9.1)

Interval	Frequency
0–24	4
25–49	8
50–74	5
75–99	10
100–124	4
125–149	5

12. (From Exercise 2, Section 9.1)

Interval	Frequency
30–39	1
40–49	6
50–59	13
60–69	22
70–79	17
80–89	13
90–99	8

Chebyshev's theorem states that for any set of numbers, the fraction that will lie within k standard deviations of the mean (for $k > 1$) is at least

$$1 - \frac{1}{k^2}.$$

For example, at least $1 - 1/2^2 = 3/4$ of any set of numbers lie within 2 standard deviations of the mean. Similarly, for any probability distribution, the probability that a number will lie within k standard deviations of the mean is at least $1 - 1/k^2$. For example, if the mean is 100 and the standard deviation is 10, the probability that a number will lie within 2 standard deviations of 100, or between 80 and 120, is at least 3/4. Use Chebyshev's theorem to find the fraction of all the numbers of a data set that must lie within the following numbers of standard deviations from the mean.

13. 3   **14.** 4

15. 5   **16.** 6

In a certain distribution of numbers, the mean is 60 with a standard deviation of 8. Use Chebyshev's theorem to tell the probability that a number lies in each interval.

17. Between 36 and 84   **18.** Between 48 and 72

19. Less than 36 or more than 84

20. Less than 48 or more than 72

21. Discuss what the standard deviation tells us about a distribution.

22. Explain the difference between the sample mean and standard deviation, and the population mean and standard deviation.

23. Derive the shortcut formula for the variance

$$s^2 = \frac{\Sigma x^2 - n\bar{x}^2}{n - 1}$$

from the formula

$$s^2 = \frac{\Sigma(x - \bar{x})^2}{n - 1}$$

and the following summation formulas, in which c is a constant:

$$\Sigma cx = c\Sigma x, \quad \Sigma c = nc, \quad \text{and} \quad \Sigma(x \pm y) = \Sigma x \pm \Sigma y.$$

(*Hint:* Multiply out $(x - \bar{x})^2$.)

24. Consider the set of numbers 9,999,999, 10,000,000, and 10,000,001.

(a) Calculate the variance by hand using the formula
$$s^2 = \frac{\Sigma(x - \bar{x})^2}{n - 1}.$$

(b) Calculate the variance using your calculator and the shortcut formula $s^2 = \frac{\Sigma x^2 - n\bar{x}^2}{n - 1}$.

(c) There may be a discrepancy between your answers to parts (a) and (b) because of roundoff. Explain this discrepancy, and then discuss advantages and disadvantages of the shortcut formula.

APPLICATIONS

Business and Economics

25. Battery Life Forever Power Company analysts conducted tests on the life of its batteries and those of a competitor (Brand X). They found that their batteries had a mean life (in hours) of 26.2, with a standard deviation of 4.1. Their results for a sample of 10 Brand X batteries were as follows: 15, 18, 19, 23, 25, 25, 28, 30, 34, 38.

(a) Find the mean and standard deviation for the sample of Brand X batteries.

(b) Which batteries have a more uniform life in hours?

(c) Which batteries have the highest average life in hours?

26. Sales Promotion The Quaker Oats Company conducted a survey to determine whether a proposed premium, to be included in boxes of cereal, was appealing enough to generate new sales. Four cities were used as test markets, where the cereal was distributed with the premium, and four cities as control markets, where the cereal was distributed without the premium. The eight cities were chosen on the basis of their similarity in terms of population, per capita income, and total cereal purchase volume. The results were as follows. *Source: Quaker Oats Company.*

	City	Percent Change in Average Market Share per Month
Test Cities	1	+18
	2	+15
	3	+7
	4	+10
Control Cities	1	+1
	2	−8
	3	−5
	4	0

(a) Find the mean of the change in market share for the four test cities.

(b) Find the mean of the change in market share for the four control cities.

(c) Find the standard deviation of the change in market share for the test cities.

(d) Find the standard deviation of the change in market share for the control cities.

(e) Find the difference between the means of parts (a) and (b). This difference represents the estimate of the percent change in sales due to the premium.

(f) The two standard deviations from parts (c) and (d) were used to calculate an "error" of ±7.95 for the estimate in part (e). With this amount of error, what are the smallest and largest estimates of the increase in sales?

On the basis of the interval estimate of part (f), the company decided to mass-produce the premium and distribute it nationally.

27. Process Control The following table gives 10 samples of three measurements, made during a production run.

Sample Number									
1	2	3	4	5	6	7	8	9	10
2	3	−2	−3	−1	3	0	−1	2	0
−2	−1	0	1	2	2	1	2	3	0
1	4	1	2	4	2	2	3	2	2

Use the techniques in Example 6 to find the following.

(a) Find the mean $\bar{x}$ for each sample of three measurements.

(b) Find the standard deviation s for each sample of three measurements.

(c) Find the mean $\bar{X}$ of the sample means.

(d) Find the mean $\bar{s}$ of the sample standard deviations.

(e) Using $k_1 = 1.954$, find the upper and lower control limits for the sample means.

(f) Using $k_2 = 2.568$ and $k_3 = 0$, find the upper and lower control limits for the sample standard deviations.

28. Process Control Given the following measurements from later samples on the process in Exercise 27, decide whether the process is out of control. (*Hint:* Use the results of Exercise 27(e) and (f).)

Sample Number					
1	2	3	4	5	6
3	−4	2	5	4	0
−5	2	0	1	−1	1
2	1	1	−4	−2	−6

29. Washer Thickness An assembly-line machine turns out washers with the following thicknesses (in millimeters).

1.20	1.01	1.25	2.20	2.58	2.19	1.29	1.15
2.05	1.46	1.90	2.03	2.13	1.86	1.65	2.27
1.64	2.19	2.25	2.08	1.96	1.83	1.17	2.24

Find the mean and standard deviation of these thicknesses.

30. Unemployment The number of unemployed workers in the United States in recent years (in millions) is given below. *Source: Bureau of Labor Statistics.*

Year	Number Unemployed
2004	8.15
2005	7.59
2006	7.00
2007	7.08
2008	8.92
2009	14.27
2010	14.83
2011	13.75
2012	12.51
2013	11.46

(a) Find the mean number unemployed (in millions) in this period. Which years had unemployment closest to the mean?

(b) Find the range (in millions) of the data.

(c) Find the standard deviation (in millions) for the data.

(d) In how many of these years is unemployment within 1 standard deviation of the mean?

(e) In how many of these years is unemployment within 2 standard deviations of the mean?

31. New Housing Sales In Exercise 43, Section 9.1, the number (in thousands) of new houses sold each month in the United States from 2010 to 2013 was given. *Source: U.S. Census.*

(a) Find the standard deviation of the data.

(b) In what percent of the months did new housing sales fall within one standard deviation of the mean? Within two standard deviations? Within three?

32. New Housing Sales The following grouped frequency distribution, from Exercise 43, Section 9.1, gives the number (in thousands) of new houses sold each month in the United States from 2010 to 2013. The mean of the grouped data was found to be 29.75 thousand. Find the standard deviation of the grouped data. Compare the answer with the answer to part (a) of the previous exercise. *Source: U.S. Census.*

New Houses Sold per Month (in thousands)	Midpoint, x	f
20–23	21.5	8
24–27	25.5	10
28–31	29.5	14
32–35	33.5	8
36–39	37.5	3
40–43	41.5	5

33. Home-Based Workers Because of advancements in communication and information technologies, workers are increasingly able to work at home. The following grouped frequency distribution gives the number (in millions) of employed people who work at home for various age groups in 2010. (Assume the midpoint for the last interval is 69.5.) *Source: U.S. Census Bureau.*

Age (in years)	Midpoint, x	Frequency, f
15–24	19.5	0.4
25–34	29.5	1.3
35–44	39.5	2.1
45–54	49.5	2.5
55–64	59.5	2.0
Over 65	69.5	1.0

(a) Find the mean age of employed people who work at home.

(b) Find the standard deviation for the data.

Life Sciences

34. Blood Types The number of recognized blood types between species is given in the following table. In Exercise 45 of the previous section, the mean was found to be 7.38. *Source: The Handy Science Answer Book.*

Animal	Number of Blood Types
Pig	16
Cow	12
Chicken	11
Horse	9
Human	8
Sheep	7
Dog	7
Rhesus monkey	6
Mink	5
Rabbit	5
Mouse	4
Rat	4
Cat	2

(a) Find the variance and the standard deviation of these data.

(b) How many of these animals have blood types that are within 1 standard deviation of the mean?

35. Tumor Growth The amount of time that it takes for various slow-growing tumors to double in size are listed in the following table. *Source: American Journal of Roentgen.*

Type of Cancer	Doubling Time (days)
Breast cancer	84
Rectal cancer	91
Synovioma	128
Skin cancer	131
Lip cancer	143
Testicular cancer	153
Esophageal cancer	164

(a) Find the mean and standard deviation of these data.

(b) How many of these cancers have doubling times that are within 2 standard deviations of the mean?

(c) If a person had a nonspecified tumor that was doubling every 200 days, discuss whether this particular tumor is growing at a rate that would be expected.

36. Blood pH A medical laboratory tested 21 samples of human blood for acidity on the pH scale, with the following results.

7.1	7.5	7.3	7.4	7.6	7.2	7.3
7.4	7.5	7.3	7.2	7.4	7.3	7.5
7.5	7.4	7.4	7.1	7.3	7.4	7.4

(a) Find the mean and standard deviation.

(b) What percentage of the data is within 2 standard deviations of the mean?

General Interest

37. Temperature In Exercise 46, Section 9.1, the number of days in June and July of recent years in which the temperature reached 90 degrees or higher in New York's Central Park was given. The mean was found to be 10.43 days. *Source: The National Weather Service.*

(a) Find the standard deviation of the data.

(b) In what percent of the years did the number of 90 plus degree days in June and July fall within one standard deviation of the mean? Within two standard deviations? Within three?

38. Temperature The following grouped frequency distribution, from Exercise 46, Section 9.1, gives the number of days in June and July of recent years in which the temperature reached 90 degrees or higher in New York's Central Park. The mean of the grouped data was found to be 10.67 days. Find the standard deviation of the grouped data. Compare the answer with the answer to part (a) of the previous exercise. *Source: The National Weather Service.*

Interval	Frequency, f
0–4	9
5–9	4
10–14	9
15–19	3
20–24	4
25–29	1

39. Baseball Salaries The table in Exercise 51, Section 9.1, lists the salary for each player on the Houston Astros baseball team in 2014. The mean was found to be $1,726,441. *Source: ESPN.*

(a) Calculate the range of the salaries.

(b) Calculate the standard deviation of these data.

(c) How many of the 2014 Houston Astros players have salaries that are beyond 3 standard deviations from the mean?

(d) What does your answer to part (c) suggest?

40. Box Office Receipts The table below lists the 20 films in which actor Will Smith has starred through 2013, along with the gross domestic box office receipts and the year for each movie. *Source: The Movie Times.*

Movie	Domestic Box Office Receipts
After Earth, 2013	$27,520,040
Men in Black 3, 2012	$179,020,854
Hancock, 2008	$227,946,274
Seven Pounds, 2008	$69,951,824
I Am Legend, 2007	$256,386,216
The Pursuit of Happyness, 2006	$162,586,036
Hitch, 2005	$177,575,142
Shark Tale, 2004	$161,412,000
I, Robot, 2004	$144,801,023
Bad Boys II, 2003	$138,540,870
Men in Black 2, 2002	$190,418,803
Ali, 2001	$58,200,000
The Legend of Bagger Vance, 2000	$30,695,000
Wild Wild West, 1999	$113,745,000
Enemy of the State, 1998	$111,544,000
Men in Black, 1997	$250,107,128
Independence Day, 1996	$306,124,000
Bad Boys, 1995	$65,807,000
Made in America, 1993	$44,942,000
Six Degrees of Separation, 1993	$6,410,000

(a) Find the mean domestic box office receipts for Will Smith's movies. Which movie has box office receipts closest to the mean?

(b) Find the range of the data.

(c) Find the standard deviation for the data.

(d) What percent of the movies have box office receipts within 1 standard deviation of the mean? Within 2 standard deviations of the mean?

41. Cookies Marie Revak and Jihan Williams performed an experiment to determine whether Oreo Double Stuf cookies contain twice as much filling as traditional Oreo cookies. The table below gives the results in grams of the amount of filling inside 49 traditional cookies and 52 Double Stuf cookies. *Source: The Mathematics Teacher.*

(a) Find the mean, maximum, minimum, and standard deviation of the weights for traditional Oreo cookies.

(b) Find the mean, maximum, minimum, and standard deviation of the weights for Oreo Double Stuf cookies.

(c) What percent of the data of traditional Oreo cookies is within 2 standard deviations of the Double Stuf Oreo mean? (*Hint:* Use the mean and standard deviation for the Double Stuf data.)

(d) What percent of the data of traditional Oreo cookies, when multiplied by 2, is within 2 standard deviations of the Double Stuf Oreo mean? (*Hint:* Use the mean and standard deviation for the Double Stuf data.)

(e) Is there evidence that Double Stuf Oreos have twice as much filling as the traditional Oreo cookie? Explain.

YOUR TURN ANSWERS

1. 28, 92.7, 9.628
2. 8.52

Traditional	Traditional	Traditional	Double Stuf	Double Stuf	Double Stuf
2.9	2.4	2.7	4.7	6.5	5.8
2.8	2.8	2.8	6.5	6.3	5.9
2.6	3.8	2.6	5.5	4.8	6.2
3.5	3.1	2.6	5.6	3.3	5.9
3.0	2.9	3.0	5.1	6.4	6.5
2.4	3.0	2.8	5.3	5.0	6.5
2.7	2.1	3.5	5.4	5.3	6.1
2.4	3.8	3.3	5.4	5.5	5.8
2.5	3.0	3.3	3.5	5.0	6.0
2.2	3.0	2.8	5.5	6.0	6.2
2.6	2.8	3.1	6.5	5.7	6.2
2.6	2.9	2.6	5.9	6.3	6.0
2.9	2.7	3.5	5.4	6.0	6.8
2.6	3.2	3.5	4.9	6.3	6.2
2.6	2.8	3.1	5.6	6.1	5.4
3.1	3.1	3.1	5.7	6.0	6.6
2.9			5.3	5.8	6.2
			6.9		

9.3 The Normal Distribution

APPLY IT **What is the probability that a salesperson drives between 1200 miles and 1600 miles per month?**
This question will be answered in Example 4 by using the normal probability distribution introduced in this section.

Suppose a bank is interested in improving its services to customers. The manager decides to begin by finding the amount of time tellers spend on each transaction, rounded to the nearest minute. The times for 75 different transactions are recorded with the results shown in the following table. The frequencies listed in the second column are divided by 75 to find the empirical probabilities.

FOR REVIEW

Empirical probabilities, discussed in Section 7.3, are derived from grouped data by dividing the frequency or amount for each group by the total for all the groups. This gives one example of a probability distribution, discussed further in Sections 7.3 and 8.5.

Teller Transaction Times		
Time	Frequency	Probability
1	3	$3/75 = 0.04$
2	5	$5/75 \approx 0.07$
3	9	$9/75 = 0.12$
4	12	$12/75 = 0.16$
5	15	$15/75 = 0.20$
6	11	$11/75 \approx 0.15$
7	10	$10/75 \approx 0.13$
8	6	$6/75 = 0.08$
9	3	$3/75 = 0.04$
10	1	$1/75 \approx 0.01$

Figure 6(a) shows a histogram and frequency polygon for the data. The heights of the bars are the empirical probabilities rather than the frequencies. The transaction times are given to the nearest minute. Theoretically at least, they could have been timed to the nearest tenth of a minute, or hundredth of a minute, or even more precisely. In each case, a histogram and frequency polygon could be drawn. If the times are measured with smaller and smaller units, there are more bars in the histogram, and the frequency polygon begins to look more and more like the curve in Figure 6(b) instead of a polygon. Actually, it is possible for the transaction times to take on any real number value greater than 0. A distribution in which the outcomes can take any real number value within some interval is a **continuous distribution**. The graph of a continuous distribution is a curve.

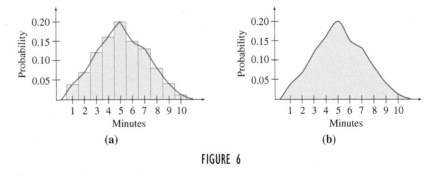

FIGURE 6

The distribution of heights (in inches) of college women is another example of a continuous distribution, since these heights include infinitely many possible measurements, such as 53, 58.5, 66.3, 72.666, . . . , and so on. Figure 7 shows the continuous distribution of heights of college women. Here the most frequent heights occur near the center of the interval shown.

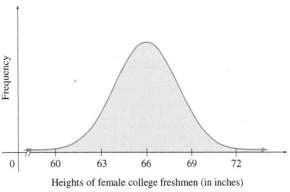

FIGURE 7

Another continuous curve, which approximates the distribution of yearly incomes in the United States, is given in Figure 8. The graph shows that the most frequent incomes are grouped near the low end of the interval. This kind of distribution, where the peak is not at the center, is called **skewed**.

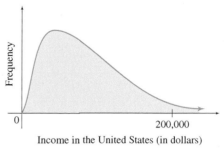

FIGURE 8

Many natural and social phenomena produce continuous probability distributions whose graphs can be approximated very well by bell-shaped curves, such as those shown in Figure 9 below. Such distributions are called **normal distributions** and their graphs are called **normal curves**. Examples of distributions that are approximately normal are the heights of college women and the errors made in filling 1-lb cereal boxes. We use the Greek letters μ (mu) to denote the mean and σ (sigma) to denote the standard deviation of a normal distribution. The definitions of the mean and standard deviation of a continuous distribution require ideas from calculus, but the intuitive ideas are similar to those in the previous section.

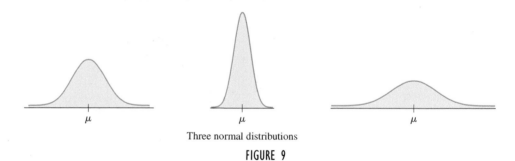

Three normal distributions

FIGURE 9

There are many normal distributions. Some of the corresponding normal curves are tall and thin and others are short and wide, as shown in Figure 9. But every normal curve has the following properties.

1. Its peak occurs directly above the mean μ.

2. The curve is symmetric about the vertical line through the mean (that is, if you fold the page along this line, the left half of the graph will fit exactly on the right half).

3. The curve never touches the x-axis—it extends indefinitely in both directions.

4. The area under the curve (and above the horizontal axis) is always 1. (This agrees with the fact that the sum of the probabilities in any distribution is 1.)

It can be shown that a normal distribution is completely determined by its mean μ and standard deviation σ.* A small standard deviation leads to a tall, narrow curve like the one in

---

*As is shown in more advanced courses, its graph is the graph of the function

$$f(x) = \frac{1}{\sigma\sqrt{2\pi}}e^{-(x-\mu)^2/(2\sigma^2)},$$

where $e \approx 2.71828$ is a real number.

the center of Figure 9. A large standard deviation produces a flat, wide curve, like the one on the right in Figure 9.

Since the area under a normal curve is 1, parts of this area can be used to determine certain probabilities. For instance, Figure 10(a) is the probability distribution of the annual rainfall in a certain region. Calculus can be used to show that the probability that the annual rainfall will be between 25 in. and 35 in. is the area under the curve from 25 to 35. The general case, shown in Figure 10(b), can be stated as follows.

FIGURE 10

Normal Probability
The area of the shaded region under a normal curve from a to b is the probability that an observed data value will be between a and b.

To use normal curves effectively, we must be able to calculate areas under portions of these curves. These calculations have already been done for the normal curve with mean $\mu = 0$ and standard deviation $\sigma = 1$ (which is called the **standard normal curve**) and are available in a table in the Appendix. The following examples demonstrate how to use the table or a calculator or spreadsheet to find such areas. Later we shall see how the standard normal curve may be used to find areas under any normal curve.

EXAMPLE 1   Standard Normal Curve

The horizontal axis of the standard normal curve is usually labeled z. Find the following areas under the standard normal curve.

Method 1
Using a Table

(a) The area to the left of $z = 1.25$

SOLUTION   The normal curve table (located in the Appendix) gives the area (rounded to four decimal places) under the standard normal curve to the left of a value z. To find the area to the left of $z = 1.25$, find 1.2 in the left-hand column and 0.05 at the top, then locate the intersection of the corresponding row and column. The specified area is 0.8944, so the shaded area shown in Figure 11 is 0.8944. This area represents 89.44% of the total area under the normal curve, and so the probability that $z \leq 1.25$ is

$$P(z \leq 1.25) = 0.8944.$$

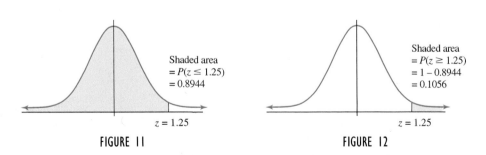

FIGURE 11   FIGURE 12

(b) The area to the right of $z = 1.25$

SOLUTION   From part (a), the area to the left of $z = 1.25$ is 0.8944. The total area under the normal curve is 1, so the area to the right of $z = 1.25$ is

$$1 - 0.8944 = 0.1056.$$

See Figure 12, where the shaded area represents 10.56% of the total area under the normal curve, and the probability that $z \geq 1.25$ is $P(z \geq 1.25) = 0.1056$.

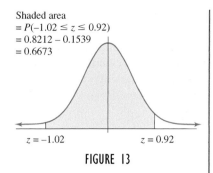

Shaded area
$= P(-1.02 \le z \le 0.92)$
$= 0.8212 - 0.1539$
$= 0.6673$

$z = -1.02$ $z = 0.92$

FIGURE 13

(c) The area between $z = -1.02$ and $z = 0.92$

SOLUTION To find this area, which is shaded in Figure 13, start with the area to the left of $z = 0.92$ and subtract the area to the left of $z = -1.02$. See the two shaded regions in Figure 14. The result is

$$P(-1.02 \le z \le 0.92) = 0.8212 - 0.1539 = 0.6673.$$

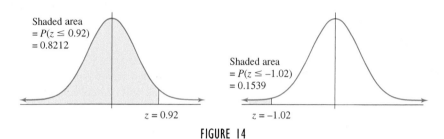

Shaded area
$= P(z \le 0.92)$
$= 0.8212$

$z = 0.92$

Shaded area
$= P(z \le -1.02)$
$= 0.1539$

$z = -1.02$

FIGURE 14

**Method 2
Graphing Calculator**

Because of convenience and accuracy, graphing calculators have made normal curve tables less important. On the TI-84 Plus C calculator, the area under the normal curve can be found using the `normalcdf` command in the DISTR menu. The `normalcdf` command requires you to enter four values: the lower bound, the upper bound, the mean (μ), and the standard deviation (σ). (If the mean and standard deviation are not entered, the calculator assumes the standard normal with $\mu = 0$ and $\sigma = 1$.)

In part (a), we are looking for the area to the left of $z = 1.25$. The lower bound is negative infinity, but the most negative value that the calculator can handle is -1×10^{99}. The area between -1×10^{99} and 1.25 is essentially the same as the area to the left of 1.25, so enter −1 EE 99 for the lower bound. (Note that only one E will show on the screen.) The upper bound is 1.25, the mean is 0, and the standard deviation is 1. See Figure 15.

In part (b), we are looking for the area to the right of $z = 1.25$. The lower bound is 1.25 and the upper bound is infinity. The largest value that the calculator can handle is 1×10^{99}, so enter 1 EE 99. Again, the mean is 0 and the standard deviation is 1. See Figure 15.

In part (c), we are looking for the area between $z = -1.02$ and $z = 0.92$. The command and solution are shown in Figure 15.

```
normalcdf(-1E99, 1.25, 0, 1)
                  .894350161
normalcdf(1.25,1E99,1.25,0,1)
                  .105649839
normalcdf(-1.02,.92, 0, 1)
                  .6673494029
```

FIGURE 15

**Method 3
Spreadsheet**

Statistical software packages are widely used today. These packages are set up in a way that is similar to a spreadsheet, and they can be used to generate normal curve values. In addition, most spreadsheets can also perform a wide range of statistical calculations. For example, Microsoft Excel can be used to generate the answers to parts (a), (b), and (c) of this example. In any cell, type "=NORMDIST(1.25,0,1,1)" and press Enter. The value of 0.894350226 is returned. Notice that this value differs slightly from the value returned by a TI-84 Plus C. The first three input values represent the z value, mean, and standard deviation. The fourth value is always either a 0 or 1. For applications in this text, we will always place a 1 in this position to indicate that we want the area to the left of the first input value. Similarly, by typing "=1-NORMDIST(1.25,0,1,1)" and pressing Enter, we find that the area to the right of $z = 1.25$ is 0.105649774.

YOUR TURN 1 Find the following areas under the standard normal curve. **(a)** The area to the left of $z = -0.76$. **(b)** The area to the right of $z = -1.36$. **(c)** The area between $z = -1.22$ and $z = 1.33$.

TRY YOUR TURN 1

CAUTION

When using a table to calculate normal probabilities, it is wise to draw a normal curve with the mean and the z-scores every time. This will avoid confusion as to whether you should add or subtract probabilities.

NOTE

1. The probability that z is equal to one exact value is zero, because no area is included. For example, $P(z = 1.25) = 0$.

2. The area under the curve is the same, whether we include the endpoint or not. Therefore, $P(z \leq 1.25) = P(z < 1.25)$.

EXAMPLE 2   **Finding a Value of z**

Find a value of z satisfying the following conditions.

Method 1
Using a Table

(a) 12.1% of the area is to the left of z.

SOLUTION   Use the normal curve table (located in the Appendix) backwards. The table gives the area (rounded to four decimal places) under the normal curve to the left of z. The total area under the curve is 1, so 12.1% of 1 is 0.121. Look in the body of the table for an area of 0.1210. The value is in the row -1.1 and the column labeled 0.07. Therefore, $z = -1.17$ corresponds to an area of 0.121.

(b) 20% of the area is to the right of z.

SOLUTION   If 20% of the area is to the right, 80% is to the left. Look in the body of the table for an area of 0.8000. This value is not in the table, so we select the closest value, which is 0.7995. This area corresponds to $z = 0.84$.

 Method 2
Graphing Calculator

On the TI-84 Plus C calculator, the value of z can be found using the `invNorm` command found in the `DISTR` menu. The `invNorm` command requires you to enter three values: the area to the left, the mean (μ), and the standard deviation (σ). (If the mean and standard deviation are not entered, the calculator assumes the standard normal with $\mu = 0$ and $\sigma = 1$.)

In part (a), we are looking for the value of z with 12.1% of the area to the left. We enter .121 for the area, 0 for the mean, and 1 for the standard deviation. The value of z, rounded to two decimal places, is $z = -1.17$. See Figure 16.

In part (b), we are looking for the value of z with 20% of the area to the right. The area to the left then is 80%, so we enter .8 for the area along with 0 for the mean and 1 for the standard deviation. The value of z, rounded to two decimal places, is $z = 0.84$. See Figure 16.

```
invNorm(.121, 0, 1)
                 -1.170002407
invNorm(.8, 0, 1)
                  .8416212335
```

FIGURE 16

Method 3
Spreadsheet

Microsoft Excel can also be used to generate the answers to parts (a) and (b) of this example. In any cell, type "=NORMINV(.121,0,1)" and press Enter. The value of -1.170002408 is returned. Similarly, by typing "=NORMINV(.8,0,1)" and pressing Enter, we find that the corresponding z value is 0.841621234.

TRY YOUR TURN 2

YOUR TURN 2   Find a value of z satisfying the following conditions. **(a)** 2.5% of the area is to the left of z. **(b)** 20.9% of the area is to the right of z

The key to using the normal table to find areas under *any* normal curve is to express each number x on the horizontal axis in terms of standard deviation above or below the mean. The **z-score** for x is the number of standard deviations that x lies from the mean (positive if x is above the mean, negative if x is below the mean).

EXAMPLE 3 z-Scores

If a normal distribution has mean 50 and standard deviation 4, find the following z-scores.

(a) The z-score for $x = 46$

SOLUTION Since 46 is 4 units below 50 and the standard deviation is 4, 46 is 1 standard deviation below the mean. So, its z-score is -1.

(b) The z-score for $x = 60$

SOLUTION The z-score is 2.5 because 60 is 10 units above the mean (since $60 - 50 = 10$), and 10 units is 2.5 standard deviations (since $10/4 = 2.5$).

TRY YOUR TURN 3

YOUR TURN 3 Find the z-score for $x = 20$ if a normal distribution has a mean 35 and standard deviation 20.

In Example 3(b), we found the z-score by taking the difference between 60 and the mean and dividing this difference by the standard deviation. The same procedure works in the general case.

z-Score

If a normal distribution has mean μ and standard deviation σ, then the z-score for the number x is

$$z = \frac{x - \mu}{\sigma}.$$

The importance of z-scores lies in the following fact.

Area Under a Normal Curve

The area under a normal curve between $x = a$ and $x = b$ is the same as the area under the standard normal curve between the z-score for a and the z-score for b.

Therefore, by converting to z-scores and using the table for the standard normal curve, we can find areas under any normal curve. Since these areas are probabilities, we can now handle a variety of applications.

EXAMPLE 4 Sales

Dixie Office Supplies finds that its sales force drives an average of 1200 miles per month per person, with a standard deviation of 150 miles. Assume that the number of miles driven by a salesperson is closely approximated by a normal distribution.

APPLY IT

(a) Find the probability that a salesperson drives more than 1375 miles per month.

Method 1
Using a Table

SOLUTION Here $\mu = 1200$ and $\sigma = 150$, and we must find the area under the normal distribution more than, or to the right of, $x = 1375$. We begin by finding the z-score corresponding to $x = 1375$.

$$z = \frac{x - \mu}{\sigma} = \frac{1375 - 1200}{150} = \frac{175}{150} \approx 1.17$$

From the table, the area to the left of $z = 1.17$ is 0.8790, so the area to the right is

$$1 - 0.8790 = 0.1210.$$

Therefore, the probability that a salesperson drives more than 1375 miles per month is 0.1210. See Figure 17.

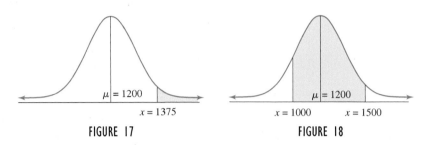

FIGURE 17   FIGURE 18

(b) Find the probability that a salesperson drives between 1000 miles and 1500 miles per month.

SOLUTION   As shown in Figure 18, z-scores for both $x_1 = 1000$ and $x_2 = 1500$ are needed.

For $x_1 = 1000$,   For $x_2 = 1500$,

$$z_1 = \frac{1000 - 1200}{150} \qquad z_2 = \frac{1500 - 1200}{150}$$

$$= \frac{-200}{150} \qquad\qquad = \frac{300}{150}$$

$$z_1 \approx -1.33. \qquad\qquad z_2 = 2.00.$$

From the table, $z_1 = -1.33$ leads to an area of 0.0918, while $z_2 = 2.00$ corresponds to 0.9772. A total of $0.9772 - 0.0918 = 0.8854$, or 88.54%, of the drivers travel between 1000 and 1500 miles per month. The probability that a driver travels between 1000 miles and 1500 miles per month is 0.8854.

(c) Find the shortest and longest distances driven by the middle 95% of the sales force.

SOLUTION   Notice that in parts (a) and (b) we were given different traveling distances and we were asked to find the corresponding probability (or area under the curve). In this part, we are given the probability (or area under the curve) and we are asked to find the distances that bound this area.

First, find the values of z that bound the middle 95% of the data. As Figure 19 illustrates, the lower z value, z_1, has 2.5% of the area to its left, and the higher z value, z_2, has 97.5% of the area to its left. Using the table backwards, we find that $z_1 = -1.96$ and $z_2 = 1.96$.

The shortest distance is, therefore, 1.96 standard deviations *below* the mean, or

$$\text{Shortest} = \mu + z \cdot \sigma = 1200 + (-1.96) \cdot (150) = 906 \text{ miles.}$$

Likewise, the longest distance is 1.96 standard deviations *above* the mean, or

$$\text{Longest} = \mu + z \cdot \sigma = 1200 + (1.96) \cdot (150) = 1494 \text{ miles.}$$

Therefore, the distances driven by the middle 95% of the sales force are between 906 and 1494 miles.

FIGURE 19

Method 2
Graphing Calculator

Graphing calculators and computers can be used to solve Example 4. Because you can enter the mean and standard deviation for any normal curve, it is not necessary to first calculate the z-score.

In part (a), to find the probability that a salesperson drives more than 1375 miles per month on the TI-84 Plus C calculator, we use the `normalcdf` command. We enter 1375 for the lower bound, 1EE99 for the upper bound, 1200 for the mean, and 150 for the standard deviation. The answer, rounded to four decimal places, is 0.1217. This is more accurate than the value of 0.1210 found using the normal curve table, which required rounding the z-score to two decimal places. See Figure 20.

In part (b), the probability that a salesperson drives between 1000 and 1500 miles per month can be found by entering the following command: `normalcdf(1000,1500,1200,150)`. As shown in Figure 20, the answer, rounded to four decimal places, is 0.8860.

In part (c), to find the shortest distance and the longest distance driven that correspond with the middle 95% of the sales force, we use the `invNorm` command. The shortest distance would have 2.5% of the area to its left, so the command would be `invNorm(.025,1200,150)`. The longest distance would have 2.5% of the area to its right, and therefore 97.5% of the area to its left. The command would be `invNorm(.975,1200,150)`. As Figure 20 shows, the distances driven by the middle 95% of the sales force are between 906 miles and 1494 miles.

```
normalcdf(1375,⁻1ᴇ99,1200,▶
                    .1213725608
normalcdf(1000,1500,1200, ▶
                    .8860386561
invNorm(.025, 1200, 150)
                    906.0054021
invNorm(.975, 1200, 150)
                    1493.994598
```

FIGURE 20

YOUR TURN 4 For Example 4, find the probability that a salesperson drives between 1275 and 1425 miles.

TRY YOUR TURN 4

As mentioned above, z-scores are the number of standard deviations from the mean, so $z = 1$ corresponds to 1 standard deviation above the mean, and so on. Looking up $z = 1.00$ and $z = -1.00$ in the table shows that

$$0.8413 - 0.1587 = 0.6826,$$

or 68.3% of the area under a normal curve lies within 1 standard deviation of the mean. Also, looking up $z = 2.00$ and $z = -2.00$ shows that

$$0.9772 - 0.0228 = 0.9544,$$

or 95.4% of the area lies within 2 standard deviations of the mean. These results, summarized in Figure 21, can be used to get a quick estimate of results when working with normal curves.

NOTE The answers given to the exercises in this text are found using a graphing calculator. If you use the normal curve table or a computer program, your answers may differ slightly.

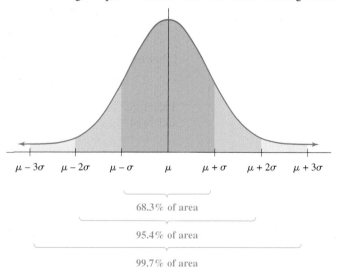

68.3% of area

95.4% of area

99.7% of area

FIGURE 21

9.3 EXERCISES

1. The peak in a normal curve occurs directly above _____.

2. The total area under a normal curve (above the horizontal axis) is _____.

3. How are z-scores found for normal distributions where $\mu \neq 0$ or $\sigma \neq 1$?

4. How is the standard normal curve used to find probabilities for normal distributions?

Find the percent of the area under a normal curve between the mean and the given number of standard deviations from the mean.

5. 1.70

6. 0.93

7. −2.31

8. −1.45

Find the percent of the total area under the standard normal curve between each pair of z-scores.

9. $z = 0.32$ and $z = 3.18$

10. $z = 0.99$ and $z = 2.37$

11. $z = -1.83$ and $z = -0.91$

12. $z = -3.13$ and $z = -2.65$

13. $z = -2.95$ and $z = 2.03$

14. $z = -0.15$ and $z = 0.23$

Find a z-score satisfying the following conditions.

15. 5% of the total area is to the left of z.

16. 1% of the total area is to the left of z.

17. 10% of the total area is to the right of z.

18. 25% of the total area is to the right of z.

19. For any normal distribution, what is the value of $P(x \leq \mu)$? $P(x \geq \mu)$?

20. Compare the probability that a number will lie within 2 standard deviations of the mean of a probability distribution using Chebyshev's theorem and using the normal distribution. (See Exercises 13–20, Section 9.2.) Explain what you observe.

21. Repeat Exercise 20 using 3 standard deviations.

APPLICATIONS

In all of the following applications, assume the distributions are normal. In each case, you should consider whether this is reasonable.

Business and Economics

Life of Light Bulbs A certain type of light bulb has an average life of 500 hours, with a standard deviation of 100 hours. The length of life of the bulb can be closely approximated by a normal curve. An amusement park buys and installs 10,000 such bulbs. Find the total number that can be expected to last for each period of time.

22. At least 500 hours

23. Less than 500 hours

24. Between 680 and 780 hours

25. Between 350 and 550 hours

26. Less than 770 hours

27. More than 440 hours

28. Find the shortest and longest lengths of life for the middle 60% of the bulbs.

Quality Control A box of oatmeal must contain 16 oz. The machine that fills the oatmeal boxes is set so that, on the average, a box contains 16.5 oz. The boxes filled by the machine have weights that can be closely approximated by a normal curve. What fraction of the boxes filled by the machine are underweight if the standard deviation is as follows?

29. 0.5 oz

30. 0.3 oz

31. 0.2 oz

32. 0.1 oz

Quality Control The chickens at Colonel Thompson's Ranch have a mean weight of 1850 g, with a standard deviation of 150 g. The weights of the chickens are closely approximated by a normal curve. Find the percent of all chickens having weights in the following ranges.

33. More than 1700 g

34. Less than 1950 g

35. Between 1750 and 1900 g

36. Between 1600 and 2000 g

37. More than 2100 g or less than 1550 g

38. Find the smallest and largest weights for the middle 95% of the chickens.

39. Annual Bonuses Salespeople of a large corporation received an annual bonus based upon their sales performance. The size of the bonuses was normally distributed with a mean of $12,000 and a standard deviation of $2500.

(a) What percent of the salespeople received an annual bonus in excess of $10,000?

(b) What percent of the salespeople received an annual bonus between $10,000 and $15,000?

(c) What size bonus is exceeded by 75% of all other bonuses?

(d) Find the smallest and largest amounts for the middle 75% of the annual bonuses.

40. Grocery Bills At the Discount Market, the average weekly grocery bill is $74.50, with a standard deviation of $24.30.

(a) What percent of the market's customers spend over $100?

(b) What percent of the market's customers spend less than $50?

(c) What percent of the market's customers spend between $0 and $50?

(d) Based on your answers to parts (b) and (c), discuss whether the amounts that customers spend is likely to be normally distributed. Explain why this might be expected.

(e) What are the smallest and largest amounts spent by the middle 50% of the market's customers?

41. Quality Control A machine that fills quart milk cartons is set up to average 32.2 oz per carton, with a standard deviation of 1.2 oz. What is the probability that a filled carton will contain less than 32 oz of milk?

42. Quality Control A machine produces bolts with an average diameter of 0.25 in. and a standard deviation of 0.02 in. What is the probability that a bolt will be produced with a diameter greater than 0.3 in.?

43. Grading Eggs To be graded extra large, an egg must weigh at least 2.2 oz. If the average weight for an egg is 1.5 oz, with a standard deviation of 0.4 oz, how many eggs in a sample of five dozen would you expect to grade extra large?

Life Sciences

44. Vitamin Requirements In nutrition, the Recommended Daily Allowance of vitamins is a number set by the government as a guide to an individual's daily vitamin intake. Actually, vitamin needs vary drastically from person to person, but the needs are very closely approximated by a normal curve. To calculate the Recommended Daily Allowance, the government first finds the average need for vitamins among people in the population and the standard deviation. The Recommended Daily Allowance is then defined as the mean plus 2.5 times the standard deviation. What percent of the population will receive adequate amounts of vitamins under this plan?

45. Life Spans According to actuarial tables, life spans in the United States are approximately normally distributed with a mean of about 75 years and a standard deviation of about 16 years. *Source: Psychological Science.*

(a) Find the probability that a randomly selected person lives less than 88 years.

(b) Find the probability that a randomly selected person lives more than 67 years.

46. Blood Clotting The mean clotting time of blood is 7.45 seconds, with a standard deviation of 3.6 seconds. What is the probability that an individual's blood clotting time will be less than 7 seconds or greater than 8 seconds?

Social Sciences

Speed Limits New studies by Federal Highway Administration traffic engineers suggest that speed limits on many thoroughfares are set arbitrarily and often are artificially low. According to traffic engineers, the ideal limit should be the "85th percentile speed." This means the speed at or below which 85 percent of the traffic moves. Assuming speeds are normally distributed, find the 85th percentile speed for roads with the following conditions. *Source: Federal Highway Administration.*

47. The mean speed is 52 mph with a standard deviation of 8 mph.

48. The mean speed is 30 mph with a standard deviation of 5 mph.

Education The grading system known as "grading on the curve" is based on the assumption that grades are often distributed according to the normal curve and that a certain percent of a class should receive each grade, regardless of the performance of the class as a whole. The following is how one professor might grade on the curve.

Grade	Total Points
A	Greater than $\mu + (3/2)\sigma$
B	$\mu + (1/2)\sigma$ to $\mu + (3/2)\sigma$
C	$\mu - (1/2)\sigma$ to $\mu + (1/2)\sigma$
D	$\mu - (3/2)\sigma$ to $\mu - (1/2)\sigma$
F	Below $\mu - (3/2)\sigma$

What percent of the students receive the following grades?

49. A   **50.** B   **51.** C

52. Do you think this system would be more likely to be fair in a large freshman class in psychology or in a graduate seminar of five students? Why?

Education A teacher gives a test to a large group of students. The results are closely approximated by a normal curve. The mean is 76, with a standard deviation of 8. The teacher wishes to give A's to the top 8% of the students and F's to the bottom 8%. A grade of B is given to the next 20%, with D's given similarly. All other students get C's. Find the bottom cutoff (rounded to the nearest whole number) for the following grades.

53. A   **54.** B

55. C   **56.** D

57. Standardized Tests David Rogosa, a professor of educational statistics at Stanford University, has calculated the accuracy of tests used in California to abolish social promotion. Dr. Rogosa has claimed that a fourth grader whose true reading score is exactly at reading level (50th percentile—half of all the students read worse and half read better than this student) has a 58% chance of scoring either above the 55th percentile or below the 45th percentile on any one test. Assume that the results of a given test are normally distributed with mean 0.50 and standard deviation 0.09. *Source: The New York Times.*

(a) Verify that Dr. Rogosa's claim is true.

(b) Find the probability that this student will not score between the 40th and 60th percentile.

(c) Using the results of parts (a) and (b), discuss problems with the use of standardized testing to prevent social promotion.

General Interest

58. Christopher Columbus Before Christopher Columbus crossed the ocean, he measured the heights of the men on his three ships and found that they were normally distributed with a mean of 69.10 in. and a standard deviation of 3.50 in. What is the probability that a member of his crew had a height less than 65.46 in.? (The answer has another connection with Christopher Columbus!)

59. Lead Poisoning Historians and biographers have collected evidence that suggests that President Andrew Jackson suffered from lead poisoning. Recently, researchers measured the amount of lead in samples of Jackson's hair from 1815. The results of this experiment showed that Jackson had a mean lead level of 130.5 ppm. *Source: JAMA.*

(a) If levels of lead in hair samples from that time period follow a normal distribution with mean 93 and standard deviation 16, find the probability that a randomly selected person from this time period would have a lead level of 130.5 ppm or higher. Does this provide evidence that Jackson suffered from lead poisoning during this time period?* *Source: Science*.

(b) Today's typical lead levels follow a normal distribution with approximate mean 10 ppm and standard deviation 5 ppm. By these standards, calculate the probability that a randomly selected person from today would have a lead level of 130.5 or higher. (*Note:* These standards may not be valid for this experiment.) *Source: Clinical Chemistry*.

(c) Discuss whether we can conclude that Andrew Jackson suffered from lead poisoning.

60. Mercury Poisoning   Historians and biographers have also collected evidence that suggests that President Andrew Jackson suffered from mercury poisoning. Recently, researchers measured the amount of mercury in samples of Jackson's hair from 1815. The results of this experiment showed that Jackson had a mean mercury level of 6.0 ppm. *Source: JAMA*.

(a) If levels of mercury in hair samples from that time period follow a normal distribution with mean 6.9 and standard deviation 4.6, find the probability that a randomly selected person from that time period would have a mercury level of 6.0 ppm or higher. *Source: Science of the Total Environment*.

(b) Discuss whether this provides evidence that Jackson suffered from mercury poisoning during this time period.

(c) Today's accepted normal mercury levels follow a normal distribution with approximate mean 0.6 ppm and standard deviation 0.3 ppm. By present standards, is it likely that a randomly selected person from today would have a mercury level of 6.0 ppm or higher?

(d) Discuss whether we can conclude that Andrew Jackson suffered from mercury poisoning.

61. Barbie   The popularity and voluptuous shape of Barbie dolls have generated much discussion about the influence these dolls may have on young children, particularly with regard to normal body shape. In fact, many people have speculated as to what Barbie's measurements would be if they were scaled to a common human height. Researchers have done this and have compared Barbie's measurements to the average 18- to 35-year-old woman, labeled Reference, and with the average model. The table at the top of the next column illustrates some of the results of their research, where each measurement is in centimeters. Assume that the distributions of measurements for the models and for the reference group follow a normal distribution with the given mean and standard deviation. *Source: Sex Roles*.

(a) Find the probability of Barbie's head size or larger occurring for the reference group and for the models.

(b) Find the probability of Barbie's neck size or smaller occurring for the reference group and for the models.

Measurement	Models Mean	Models s.d.	Reference Mean	Reference s.d.	Barbie
Head	50.0	2.4	55.3	2.0	55.0
Neck	31.0	1.0	32.7	1.4	23.9
Chest (bust)	87.4	3.0	90.3	5.5	82.3
Wrist	15.0	0.6	16.1	0.8	10.6
Waist	65.7	3.5	69.8	4.7	40.7

(c) Find the probability of Barbie's bust size or larger occurring for the reference group and for the models.

(d) Find the probability of Barbie's wrist size or smaller occurring for the reference group and for the models.

(e) Find the probability of Barbie's waist size or smaller occurring for the reference group and for the models.

(f) Compare the above values and discuss whether Barbie represents either the reference group or models. Any surprises?

62. Ken   The same researchers from Exercise 61 wondered how the famous Ken doll measured up to average males and with Australian football players. The table below illustrates some of the results of their research, where each measurement is in centimeters. Assume that the distributions of measurements for the football players and for the reference group follow a normal distribution with the given mean and standard deviation. *Source: Sex Roles*.

Measurement	Football Mean	Football s.d.	Reference Mean	Reference s.d.	Ken
Head	52.1	2.3	53.7	2.9	53.0
Neck	34.6	1.8	34.2	1.9	32.1
Chest	92.3	3.5	91.2	4.8	75.0
Upper Arm	29.9	1.9	28.8	2.2	27.1
Waist	75.1	3.6	80.9	9.8	56.5

(a) Find the probability of Ken's head size or larger occurring for the reference group and for the football players.

(b) Find the probability of Ken's neck size or smaller occurring for the reference group and for the football players.

(c) Find the probability of Ken's chest size or smaller occurring for the reference group and for the football players.

(d) Find the probability of Ken's upper arm size or smaller occurring for the reference group and for the football players.

(e) Find the probability of Ken's waist size or smaller occurring for the reference group and for the football players.

(f) Compare the above values and discuss whether Ken's measurements are representative of either the reference group or football players. Then compare these results with the results of Exercise 61. Any surprises?

YOUR TURN ANSWERS ■■■
1. (a) 0.2236   **(b)** 0.9131   **(c)** 0.7970
2. (a) −1.96   **(b)** 0.81   **3.** −0.75   **4.** 0.2417

*Although this provides evidence that Andrew Jackson had elevated lead levels, the authors of the paper concluded that Andrew Jackson did not die of lead poisoning.

9.4 Normal Approximation to the Binomial Distribution

APPLY IT What is the probability that at least 40 out of 100 drivers exceed the speed limit by at least 20 mph in Atlanta?

This is a binomial probability problem with a large number of trials (100). In this section we will see how the normal curve can be used to approximate the binomial distribution, allowing us to answer this question in Example 4.

As we saw in Section 8.4 on Binomial Probability, many practical experiments have only two possible outcomes, sometimes referred to as success or failure. Such experiments are called Bernoulli trials or Bernoulli processes. Examples of Bernoulli trials include flipping a coin (with heads being a success, for instance, and tails a failure) or testing a computer chip coming off the assembly line to see whether or not it is defective. A binomial experiment consists of repeated independent Bernoulli trials, such as flipping a coin 10 times or taking a random sample of 20 computer chips from the assembly line. In Section 8.5 on Probability Distributions and Expected Value, we found the probability distribution for several binomial experiments, such as sampling five people with bachelor's degrees in education and counting how many are women. The probability distribution for a binomial experiment is known as a **binomial distribution**.

EXAMPLE 1 Speeding

It was reported in a recent study that 40% of drivers in Atlanta exceed the speed limit by at least 20 mph. *Source: Laser Atlanta.*

(a) Suppose a state trooper wants to verify this statistic and records the speed of 10 randomly selected drivers. The trooper finds that 5 out of 10, or 50%, exceed the speed limit by at least 20 mph. How likely is this if the 40% figure is accurate?

SOLUTION We can answer this question with the binomial probability formula from the previous chapter:

$$C(n, x) \cdot p^x \cdot (1 - p)^{n-x},$$

where n is the size of the sample (10 in this case), x is the number of speeders (5 in this example), and p is the probability that a driver is a speeder (0.40). This gives

$$P(x = 5) = C(10, 5) \cdot 0.40^5 \cdot (1 - 0.40)^5$$
$$= 252(0.01024)(0.07776) \approx 0.2007.$$

The probability is about 20%, so this result is not unusual.

(b) Suppose that the state trooper takes a larger random sample of 100 drivers. What is the probability that 50 or more drivers speed if the 40% figure is accurate?

SOLUTION Calculating $P(x = 50) + P(x = 51) + \cdots + P(x = 100)$ is a formidable task. One solution is provided by graphing calculators or computers. On the TI-84 Plus C, for example, we can first calculate the probability that 49 or fewer drivers exceed the speed limit using the DISTR menu command `binomcdf(100,.40,49)`. Subtracting the answer from 1 gives a probability of 0.0271. ∎

As we saw in Example 1(b), calculators and computers can be used to compute a binomial probability with just a few keystrokes. But this high-tech method fails as n becomes

---

FOR REVIEW

Recall from Chapter 8 that the symbol $C(n, r)$ is defined as $\dfrac{n!}{r!(n - r)!}$. For example,

$$C(10, 5) = \frac{10!}{5! \, 5!}$$
$$= \frac{10 \cdot 9 \cdot 8 \cdot 7 \cdot 6}{5 \cdot 4 \cdot 3 \cdot 2 \cdot 1} = 252.$$

larger; the command `binomcdf(1000000,.40,50000)` gives an error message. On the other hand, there is a low-tech method that works regardless of the size of n. It has further interest because it connects two different distributions: the normal and the binomial. The normal distribution is continuous, since the random variable can take on any real number. The binomial distribution is *discrete*, because the random variable can only take on integer values between 0 and n. Nevertheless, the normal distribution can be used to give a good approximation to binomial probability.

In order to use the normal approximation, we first need to know the mean and standard deviation of the binomial distribution. Recall from Section 8.5 that for the binomial distribution, $E(x) = np$. In Section 9.1, we referred to $E(x)$ as μ, and that notation will be used here. It is shown in more advanced courses in statistics that the standard deviation of the binomial distribution is given by $\sigma = \sqrt{np(1-p)}$.

Mean and Standard Deviation for the Binomial Distribution

For the binomial distribution, the mean and standard deviation are given by

$$\mu = np \qquad \text{and} \qquad \sigma = \sqrt{np(1-p)},$$

where n is the number of trials and p is the probability of success on a single trial.

EXAMPLE 2 Coin Flip

Suppose a fair coin is flipped 15 times.

(a) Find the mean and standard deviation for the number of heads.

SOLUTION Using $n = 15$ and $p = 1/2$, the mean is

$$\mu = np = 15\left(\frac{1}{2}\right) = 7.5.$$

The standard deviation is

$$\sigma = \sqrt{np(1-p)} = \sqrt{15\left(\frac{1}{2}\right)\left(1 - \frac{1}{2}\right)}$$

$$= \sqrt{15\left(\frac{1}{2}\right)\left(\frac{1}{2}\right)} = \sqrt{3.75} \approx 1.94.$$

We expect, on average, to get 7.5 heads out of 15 tosses. Most of the time, the number of heads will be within 3 standard deviations of the mean, or between $7.5 - 3(1.94) = 1.68$ and $7.5 + 3(1.94) = 13.32$.

(b) Find the probability distribution for the number of heads, and draw a histogram of the probabilities.

SOLUTION The probability distribution is found by putting $n = 15$ and $p = 1/2$ into the formula for binomial probability. For example, the probability of 9 heads is given by

$$P(x = 9) = C(15, 9)\left(\frac{1}{2}\right)^9\left(1 - \frac{1}{2}\right)^6 \approx 0.15274.$$

YOUR TURN 1 Suppose a die is rolled 12 times. Find the mean and standard deviation of the number of sixes rolled.

Probabilities for the other values of x between 0 and 15, as well as a histogram of the probabilities, are shown in the table and in Figure 22 on the next page.

TRY YOUR TURN 1

Probability Distribution for Number of Heads	
x	P(x)
0	0.00003
1	0.00046
2	0.00320
3	0.01389
4	0.04166
5	0.09164
6	0.15274
7	0.19638
8	0.19638
9	0.15274
10	0.09164
11	0.04166
12	0.01389
13	0.00320
14	0.00046
15	0.00003

FIGURE 22

In Figure 22, we have superimposed the normal curve with $\mu = 7.5$ and $\sigma = 1.94$ over the histogram of the distribution. Notice how well the normal distribution fits the binomial distribution. This approximation was first discovered in 1733 by Abraham De Moivre (1667–1754) for the case $p = 1/2$. The result was generalized by the French mathematician Pierre-Simon Laplace (1749–1827) in a book published in 1812.* As n becomes larger and larger, a histogram for the binomial distribution looks more and more like a normal curve. Histograms of the binomial distribution with $p = 0.3$, using $n = 8$ and $n = 50$ are shown in Figures 23(a) and (b), respectively.

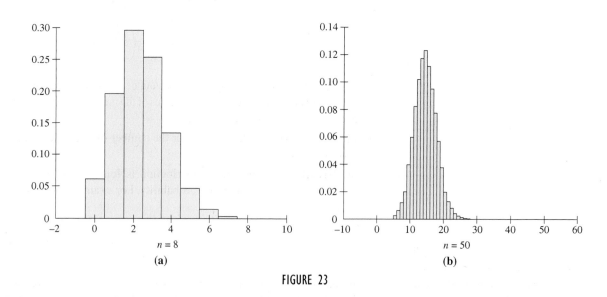

FIGURE 23

*Laplace's generalization, known as the Central Limit theorem, states that the distribution of the sample mean from *any* distribution approaches the normal distribution as the sample size increases. For more details, see any statistics book, such as *Elementary Statistics* (12th ed.) by Mario F. Triola, Pearson, 2014.

EXAMPLE 3 Normal Distribution Approximation to the Binomial

A coin is flipped 15 times. Use the normal distribution to approximate the probability of getting exactly 9 heads in 15 tosses.

SOLUTION

Method 1
Using a Table

From Example 2(b), the probability of getting exactly 9 heads in 15 tosses, or 0.15274, is the same as the area of the bar in blue in Figure 22. As the graph suggests, the area in blue is approximately equal to the area under the normal curve from $x = 8.5$ to $x = 9.5$. The normal curve is higher than the top of the bar in the left half but lower in the right half.

To find the area under the normal curve from $x = 8.5$ to $x = 9.5$, first find z-scores, as in the previous section. The mean and the standard deviation for the distribution, which we calculated in Example 2(a), are $\mu = 7.5$ and $\sigma = 1.94$.

$$\text{For } x_1 = 8.5, \qquad \text{For } x_2 = 9.5,$$

$$z_1 = \frac{8.5 - 7.5}{1.94} \qquad z_2 = \frac{9.5 - 7.5}{1.94}$$

$$= \frac{1.00}{1.94} \qquad = \frac{2.00}{1.94}$$

$$z_1 \approx 0.52. \qquad z_2 \approx 1.03.$$

From the normal curve table in the Appendix, $z_1 = 0.52$ gives an area of 0.6985, and $z_2 = 1.03$ gives 0.8485. The difference between these two numbers is the desired result.

$$P(z \leq 1.03) - P(z \leq 0.52) = 0.8485 - 0.6985 = 0.1500$$

This answer (0.1500) is not far from the more accurate answer of 0.15274 found in Example 2(b).

Method 2
Graphing Calculator

The TI-84 Plus C calculator can be used to find the normal approximation to the binomial. We use the `normalcdf` command, and enter 8.5 for the lower bound, 9.5 for the upper bound, 7.5 for the mean, and $\sqrt{3.75}$ for the standard deviation. The answer, 0.1519, is an even closer approximation to 0.15274 found in Example 2(b) than the answer using Method 1.

YOUR TURN 2 Use the normal distribution to approximate the probability of getting at most 10 heads in 15 tosses of a coin.

TRY YOUR TURN 2

CAUTION The normal curve approximation to a binomial distribution is quite accurate *provided that n is large and p is not close to 0 or 1.* As a rule of thumb, the normal curve approximation can be used as long as both np and $n(1 - p)$ are at least 5.

EXAMPLE 4 Speeding

Consider the random sample discussed in Example 1 of 100 drivers in Atlanta, where 40% of the drivers exceed the speed limit by at least 20 mph.

(a) Use the normal distribution to approximate the probability that at least 50 drivers exceed the speed limit.

APPLY IT

SOLUTION First find the mean and the standard deviation using $n = 100$ and $p = 0.40$.

$$\mu = 100(0.40) \qquad \sigma = \sqrt{100(0.40)(1 - 0.40)}$$

$$= 40 \qquad = \sqrt{100(0.40)(0.60)}$$

$$= \sqrt{24} \approx 4.899$$

As the graph in Figure 24 on the next page shows, we need to find the area to the right of $x = 49.5$ (since we want 50 or more speeders). The z-score corresponding to $x = 49.5$ is

$$z = \frac{49.5 - 40}{4.899} \approx 1.94.$$

From the table, $z = 1.94$ leads to an area of 0.9738, so

$$P(z > 1.94) = 1 - 0.9738 = 0.0262.$$

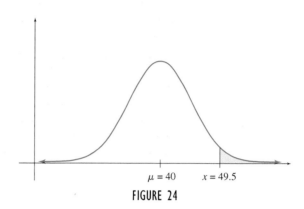

$\mu = 40 \qquad x = 49.5$

FIGURE 24

This value is close to the value of 0.0271 found earlier with the help of a graphing calculator. Either method tells us there is roughly a 3% chance of finding 50 or more speeders out of a random sample of 100. If the trooper found 50 or more speeders in his sample, he might suspect that either his sample is not truly random, or that the 40% figure for the percent of drivers who speed is too low.

(b) Find the probability of finding between 42 and 48 speeders in a random sample of 100.

SOLUTION As Figure 25 shows, we need to find the area between $x_1 = 41.5$ and $x_2 = 48.5$.

$$\text{If } x_1 = 41.5, \text{ then } z_1 = \frac{41.5 - 40}{4.899} \approx 0.31.$$

$$\text{If } x_2 = 48.5, \text{ then } z_2 = \frac{48.5 - 40}{4.899} \approx 1.74.$$

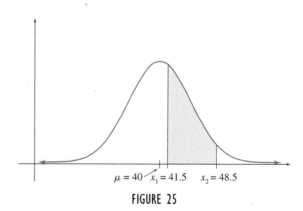

$\mu = 40 \quad x_1 = 41.5 \qquad x_2 = 48.5$

FIGURE 25

Use the table to find that $z_1 = 0.31$ gives an area of 0.6217, and $z_2 = 1.74$ yields 0.9591. The final answer is the difference of these numbers, or

$$P(0.31 \le z \le 1.74) = P(z \le 1.74) - P(z \le 0.31)$$
$$= 0.9591 - 0.6217 = 0.3374.$$

The probability of finding between 42 and 48 speeders is about 0.3374. Alternatively, the command `normalcdf` (41.5, 48.5, 40, 4.899) gives 0.3384. This is close to the value of 0.3352 found using the `binomcdf` command on a TI-84 Plus C.

YOUR TURN 3 Suppose that a test consists of 120 multiple choice questions, each with 5 answers from which to choose. Use the normal distribution to find the probability that if you guess at random, you get at least 32 correct.

TRY YOUR TURN 3

┌─ 9.4 WARM-UP EXERCISES ───
│
│ A standardized test has a normal distribution with a mean of 72.1
│ and a standard deviation of 8.3. Find the probability that a ran-
│ domly selected test score has the following property. *(Sec. 9.3)*
│
│ **W1.** Greater than 70   **W2.** Less than 90
│ **W3.** Between 60 and 80
└──

9.4 EXERCISES*

1. What must be known to find the mean and standard deviation of a binomial distribution?

2. What is the rule of thumb for using the normal distribution to approximate a binomial distribution?

Suppose 16 coins are tossed. Find the probability of getting the following results (a) using the binomial probability formula and (b) using the normal curve approximation.

3. Exactly 4 heads

4. Exactly 10 heads

5. More than 12 tails

6. Fewer than 5 tails

For the remaining exercises in this section, use the normal curve approximation to the binomial distribution.

Suppose 1000 coins are tossed. Find the probability of getting the following results.

7. Exactly 500 heads

8. Exactly 510 heads

9. 475 heads or more

10. Fewer than 490 tails

A die is tossed 120 times. Find the probability of getting the following results.

11. Exactly twenty 5's

12. Exactly twenty-four 6's

13. More than fifteen 3's

14. Fewer than twenty-eight 6's

15. A reader asked Mr. Statistics (a feature in *Fortune* magazine) about the game of 26 once played in the bars of Chicago. The player chooses a number between 1 and 6 and then rolls a cup full of 10 dice 13 times. Out of the 130 numbers rolled, if the number chosen appears at least 26 times, the player wins. Calculate the probability of winning. *Source: Fortune.*

16. (a) Try to use both the binomial probability formula and the normal approximation to the binomial to calculate the probability that exactly half of the coins come up heads if the following number of coins are flipped. You may run into problems using the binomial probability formula for part (iii).

    (i) 10   (ii) 100   (iii) 1000

    (b) If you ran into problems using the binomial probability formula for part (iii), tell what happened and explain why it happened.

(c) Someone might speculate that with more coins, the probability that exactly half are heads goes up with the number of coin flips. Based on the results from part (a), does this happen? Explain the error in the speculation.

APPLICATIONS

Business and Economics

17. Quality Control Two percent of the quartz heaters produced in a certain plant are defective. Suppose the plant produced 10,000 such heaters last month. Find the probabilities that among these heaters, the following numbers were defective.

    (a) Fewer than 170   (b) More than 222

18. Quality Control The probability that a certain machine turns out a defective item is 0.05. Find the probabilities that in a run of 75 items, the following results are obtained.

    (a) Exactly 5 defectives

    (b) No defectives

    (c) At least 1 defective

19. Survey Results A company is taking a survey to find out if people like its product. Their last survey indicated that 70% of the population like the product. Based on that, of a sample of 58 people, find the probabilities of the following.

    (a) All 58 like the product.

    (b) From 28 to 30 (inclusive) like the product.

20. Minimum Wage A recent study of minimum wage earners found that 50.6% of them are 16 to 24 years old. Suppose a random sample of 600 minimum wage earners is selected. What is the probability that more than 330 of them are 16 to 24 years old? *Source: Bureau of Labor Statistics.*

Life Sciences

21. Nest Predation For certain bird species, with appropriate assumptions, the number of nests escaping predation has a binomial distribution. Suppose the probability of success (that is, a nest escaping predation) is 0.3. Find the probability that at least half of 24 nests escape predation. *Source: The American Naturalist.*

*The normal distribution approximations of the binomial in the exercises were calculated with a graphing calculator and rounded to four decimal places. If the approximation value is found from the normal tables, the answer may be slightly different.

22. Food Consumption Under certain appropriate assumptions, the probability of a competing young animal eating x units of food is binomially distributed, with n equal to the maximum number of food units the animal can acquire and p equal to the probability per time unit that an animal eats a unit of food. Suppose $n = 120$ and $p = 0.6$. *Source: The American Naturalist.*

(a) Find the probability that an animal consumes exactly 80 units of food.

(b) Suppose the animal must consume at least 70 units of food to survive. What is the probability that this happens?

23. Coconuts A 4-year review of trauma admissions to the Provincial Hospital, Alotau, Milne Bay Providence, reveals that 2.5% of such admissions were due to being struck by falling coconuts. *Source: The Journal of Trauma.*

(a) Suppose 20 patients are admitted to the hospital during a certain time period. What is the probability that no more than 1 of these patients are there because they were struck by falling coconuts? Do not use the normal distribution here.

(b) Suppose 2000 patients are admitted to the hospital during a longer time period. What is the approximate probability that no more than 70 of these patients are there because they were struck by falling coconuts?

24. Drug Effectiveness A new drug cures 80% of the patients to whom it is administered. It is given to 25 patients. Find the probabilities that among these patients, the following results occur.

(a) Exactly 20 are cured.

(b) All are cured.

(c) No one is cured.

(d) Twelve or fewer are cured.

25. Flu Inoculations A flu vaccine has a probability of 80% of preventing a person who is inoculated from getting the flu. A county health office inoculates 134 people. Find the probabilities of the following.

(a) Exactly 10 of the people inoculated get the flu.

(b) No more than 10 of the people inoculated get the flu.

(c) None of the people inoculated get the flu.

26. Blood Types The blood types B− and AB− are the rarest of the eight human blood types, representing 1.5% and 0.6% of the population, respectively. *Source: The Handy Science Answer Book.*

(a) If the blood types of a random sample of 1000 blood donors are recorded, what is the probability that 10 or more of the samples are AB−?

(b) If the blood types of a random sample of 1000 blood donors are recorded, what is the probability that 20 to 40 inclusive of the samples are B−?

(c) If a particular city had a blood drive in which 500 people gave blood and 3% of the donations were B−, would we have reason to believe that this town has a higher than normal number of donors who are B−? (*Hint:* Calculate the probability of 15 or more donors being B− for a random sample of 500 and then discuss the probability obtained.)

27. Motorcycles According to a recent report, 24.1% of nonfatal injuries suffered by motorcycle riders occur between 3 P.M. and 6 P.M. If 200 injured motorcyclists are surveyed, what is the probability that at most 50 were injured between 3 P.M. and 6 P.M.? *Source: Insurance Information Institute.*

Social Sciences

28. Straw Votes In one state, 55% of the voters expect to vote for Nicole Foran. Suppose 1400 people are asked the name of the person for whom they expect to vote. Find the probability that at least 750 people will say that they expect to vote for Foran.

29. Smoking A recent study found that 46.3% of all ninth grade students in the United States have tried cigarette smoking, even if only one or two puffs. If 500 ninth grade students are surveyed, what is the probability that at most half have ever tried cigarettes? *Source: Centers for Disease Control and Prevention.*

30. Weapons and Youth A recent study found that 17.5% of all high school students in the United States have carried a weapon, including a gun, knife, or club. If 1200 high school students are surveyed, what is the probability that more than 200 students, but fewer than 250, have carried a weapon? *Source: Centers for Disease Control and Prevention.*

31. Election 2000 The Florida recount in the 2000 presidential election gave George W. Bush 2,912,790 votes and Al Gore 2,912,253 votes. What is the likelihood of the vote being so close, even if the electorate is evenly divided? Assume that the number of votes for Bush is binomially distributed with $n = 5,825,043$ (the sum of the votes for the two candidates) and $p = 0.5$. *Source: historycentral.com.*

(a) Using the binomial probability feature on a graphing calculator, try to calculate $P(2,912,253 \le X \le 2,912,790)$. What happens?

(b) Use the normal approximation to calculate the probability in part (a).

General Interest

32. Homework Only 1 out of 12 American parents requires that children do their homework before watching TV. If your neighborhood is typical, what is the probability that out of 120 parents, 5 or fewer require their children to do homework before watching TV? *Source: Harper's.*

33. True-False Test A professor gives a test with 100 true-false questions. If 60 or more correct is necessary to pass, what is the probability that a student will pass by random guessing?

34. Hole in One In the 1989 U.S. Open, four golfers each made a hole in one on the same par-3 hole on the same day. *Sports Illustrated* writer R. Reilly stated the probability of a hole in one for a given golf pro on a given par-3 hole to be 1/3709. *Source: Sports Illustrated.*

(a) For a specific par-3 hole, use the binomial distribution to find the probability that 4 or more of the 156 golf pros in the tournament field shoot a hole in one. *Source: School Science and Mathematics.*

(b) For a specific par-3 hole, use the normal approximation to the binomial distribution to find the probability that 4 or more of the 156 golf pros in the tournament field shoot a hole in one. Why must we be very cautious when using this approximation for this application?

(c). If the probability of a hole in one remains constant and is 1/3709 for any par-3 hole, find the probability that in 20,000 attempts by golf pros, there will be 4 or more hole in ones. Discuss whether this assumption is reasonable.

9 | CHAPTER REVIEW

SUMMARY

In this chapter we introduced the field of statistics. Measures of central tendency, such as mean, median, and mode, were defined and illustrated by examples. We determined how much the numbers in a sample vary from the mean of a distribution by calculating the variance and standard deviation. The normal distribution, perhaps the most important and widely used probability distribution, was defined and used to study a wide range of problems. The normal approximation to the binomial distribution was then developed, as were several important applications.

Mean	The mean of the n numbers $x_1, x_2, x_3, \ldots, x_n$ is $$\bar{x} = \frac{\Sigma x}{n}.$$
Mean of a Grouped Distribution	The mean of a distribution, where x represents the midpoints, f the frequencies, and $n = \Sigma f$, is $$\bar{x} = \frac{\Sigma xf}{n}.$$
Variance	The variance of a sample of n numbers $x_1, x_2, x_3, \ldots, x_n$, with mean $\bar{x}$, is $$s^2 = \frac{\Sigma x^2 - n\bar{x}^2}{n - 1}.$$
Standard Deviation	The standard deviation of a sample of n numbers $x_1, x_2, x_3, \ldots, x_n$, with mean $\bar{x}$, is $$s = \sqrt{\frac{\Sigma x^2 - n\bar{x}^2}{n - 1}}.$$
Standard Deviation for a Grouped Distribution	The standard deviation for a distribution with mean $\bar{x}$, where x is an interval midpoint with frequency f, and $n = \Sigma f$, is $$s = \sqrt{\frac{\Sigma fx^2 - n\bar{x}^2}{n - 1}}.$$
Normal Distribution	The area of the shaded region under a normal curve from a to b is the probability that an observed data value will be between a and b.
z-scores	If a normal distribution has mean μ and standard deviation σ, then the z-score for the number x is $$z = \frac{x - \mu}{\sigma}.$$
Area Under a Normal Curve	The area under a normal curve between $x = a$ and $x = b$ is the same as the area under the standard normal curve between the z-score for a and the z-score for b.
Mean and Standard Deviation for the Binomial Distribution	For the binomial distribution, the mean and standard deviation are given by $$\mu = np \quad \text{and} \quad \sigma = \sqrt{np(1 - p)},$$ where n is the number of trials and p is the probability of success on a single trial.

KEY TERMS

9.1
random sample
grouped frequency distribution
frequency polygon
(arithmetic) mean
sample mean
population mean
median

mode
statistic

9.2
range
deviations from the mean
variance
standard deviation

sample variance
sample standard deviation
population variance
population standard deviation
Chebyshev's theorem

9.3
continuous distribution

skewed distribution
normal distribution
normal curve
standard normal curve
z-score

9.4
binomial distribution

REVIEW EXERCISES

CONCEPT CHECK

Determine whether each of the following statements is true or false, and explain why.

1. The mean, median, and mode of a normal distribution are all equal.

2. If the mean, median, and mode of a distribution are all equal, then the distribution must be a normal distribution.

3. If the means of two distributions are equal, then the variances must also be equal.

4. The sample mean $\bar{x}$ is not the same as the population mean μ.

5. A large variance indicates that the data are grouped closely together.

6. The mode of a distribution is the middle element of the distribution.

7. For a random variable X that is normally distributed, we know that $P(X \geq 2) = P(X \leq -2)$.

8. For a random variable X that is normally distributed with $\mu = 5$, we know that $P(X > 10) = P(X < 0)$.

9. The normal curve approximation to the binomial distribution should not be used on an experiment where $n = 30$ and $p = 0.1$.

10. The expected value of a sample mean is the population mean.

11. The expected value of a sample standard deviation is the population standard deviation.

12. For a standard normal random variable Z, $P(-1.5 < Z < 0) = 0.50 - P(Z > 1.5)$.

PRACTICE AND EXPLORATIONS

13. Discuss some reasons for organizing data into a grouped frequency distribution.

14. What is the rule of thumb for an appropriate interval in a grouped frequency distribution?

In Exercises 15 and 16, (a) write a frequency distribution, (b) draw a histogram, and (c) draw a frequency polygon.

15. The following numbers give the sales (in dollars) for the lunch hour at a local hamburger stand for the last 20 Fridays. Use intervals 450–474, 475–499, and so on.

| 480 | 451 | 501 | 478 | 512 | 473 | 509 | 515 | 458 | 566 |
| 516 | 535 | 492 | 558 | 488 | 547 | 461 | 475 | 492 | 471 |

16. The number of credits carried in one semester by students in a business mathematics class was as follows. Use intervals 9–10, 11–12, 13–14, 15–16.

| 10 | 9 | 16 | 12 | 13 | 15 | 13 | 16 | 15 | 11 | 13 |
| 12 | 12 | 15 | 12 | 14 | 10 | 12 | 14 | 15 | 15 | 13 |

Find the mean for the following.

17. 30, 24, 34, 30, 29, 28, 30, 29

18. 105, 108, 110, 115, 106, 110, 104, 113, 117

19.

Interval	Frequency
10–19	6
20–29	12
30–39	14
40–49	10
50–59	8

20.

Interval	Frequency
40–44	3
45–49	6
50–54	7
55–59	14
60–64	3
65–69	2

21. What do the mean, median, and mode of a distribution have in common? How do they differ? Describe each in a sentence or two.

Find the median and the mode (or modes) for each list of numbers.

22. 12, 17, 21, 23, 27, 27, 34

23. 38, 36, 42, 44, 38, 36, 48, 35

Find the modal class for the indicated distributions.

24. Exercise 20   **25.** Exercise 19

26. What is meant by the range of a distribution?

27. How are the variance and the standard deviation of a distribution related? What is measured by the standard deviation?

Find the range and standard deviation for each distribution.

28. 22, 27, 31, 35, 41

29. 26, 43, 51, 29, 37, 56, 29, 82, 74, 93

Find the standard deviation for the following.

30. Exercise 20   **31.** Exercise 19

32. Describe the characteristics of a normal distribution.

33. What is meant by a skewed distribution?

Find the following areas under the standard normal curve.

34. Between $z = 0$ and $z = 2.17$

35. To the left of $z = 0.84$

36. Between $z = -2.13$ and $z = 1.11$

37. Between $z = 1.53$ and $z = 2.82$

38. Find a z-score such that 7% of the area under the curve is to the right of z.

39. Why is the normal distribution not a good approximation of a binomial distribution that has a value of p close to 0 or 1?

40. Suppose a card is drawn at random from an ordinary deck 1,000,000 times with replacement.

(a) What is the probability that between 249,500 and 251,000 hearts (inclusive) are drawn?

(b) Why must the normal approximation to the binomial distribution be used to solve part (a)?

41. Suppose four coins are flipped and the number of heads counted. This experiment is repeated 20 times. The data might look something like the following. (You may wish to try this yourself and use your own results rather than these.)

Number of Heads	Frequency
0	1
1	5
2	7
3	5
4	2

(a) Calculate the sample mean $\bar{x}$ and sample standard deviation s.

(b) Calculate the population mean μ and population standard deviation σ for this binomial population.

(c) Compare your answer to parts (a) and (b). What do you expect to happen?

42. Much of our work in Chapters 8 and 9 is interrelated. Note the similarities in the following parallel treatments of a frequency distribution and a probability distribution.

Frequency Distribution

Complete the table below for the following data. (Recall that x is the midpoint of the interval.)

14, 7, 1, 11, 2, 3, 11, 6, 10, 13, 11, 11, 16, 12, 9, 11, 9, 10, 7, 12, 9, 6, 4, 5, 9, 16, 12, 12, 11, 10, 14, 9, 13, 10, 15, 11, 11, 1, 12, 12, 6, 7, 8, 2, 9, 12, 10, 15, 9, 3

Interval	x	Tally	f	x·f
1–3	2	卌 I	6	12
4–6				
7–9				
10–12				
13–15				
16–18				

Probability Distribution

A binomial distribution has $n = 10$ and $p = 0.5$. Complete the following table.

x	P(x)	x · P(x)
0	0.001	
1	0.010	
2	0.044	
3	0.117	
4		
5		
6		
7		
8		
9		
10		

(a) Find the mean (or expected value) for each distribution.

(b) Find the standard deviation for each distribution.

(c) Use the normal approximation of the binomial probability distribution to find an interval centered on the mean that contains 95.44% of that distribution.

(d) Why can't we use the normal distribution to answer probability questions about the frequency distribution?

APPLICATIONS

Business and Economics

43. Stock Returns   The annual returns of two stocks for 3 years are given below.

Stock	2014	2015	2016
Stock I	11%	−1%	14%
Stock II	9%	5%	10%

(a) Find the mean and standard deviation for each stock over the 3-year period.

(b) If you are looking for security (hence, less variability) with an average 8% return, which of these stocks should you choose?

44. Quality Control   A machine that fills quart orange juice cartons is set to fill them with 32.1 oz. If the actual contents of the cartons vary normally, with a standard deviation of 0.1 oz, what percentage of the cartons contain less than a quart (32 oz)?

45. Quality Control   About 4% of the frankfurters produced by a certain machine are overstuffed and thus defective. For a sample of 500 frankfurters, find the following probabilities—first by using the binomial probability formula, and then by using the normal approximation.

(a) Twenty-five or fewer are overstuffed.

(b) Exactly 25 are overstuffed.

(c) At least 30 are overstuffed.

46. Bankruptcy   The probability that a small business will go bankrupt in its first year is 0.21. For 50 such small businesses, find the following probabilities—first by using the binomial probability formula, and then by using the normal approximation.

(a) Exactly 8 go bankrupt.

(b) No more than 2 go bankrupt.

Life Sciences

47. Rat Diets   The weight gains of 2 groups of 10 rats fed different experimental diets were as follows.

Diet	Weight Gains									
A	1	0	3	7	1	1	5	4	1	4
B	2	1	1	2	3	2	1	0	1	0

Compute the mean and standard deviation for each group.

(a) Which diet produced the greatest mean gain?

(b) Which diet produced the most consistent gain?

Chemical Effectiveness   White flies are devastating California crops. An area infested with white flies is to be sprayed with a chemical that is known to be 98% effective for each application. Assume a sample of 1000 flies is checked.

48. Use the normal distribution to find the approximate probability that exactly 980 of the flies are killed in one application.

49. Use the normal distribution to find the approximate probability that no more than 986 of the flies are killed in one application.

50. Use the normal distribution to find the approximate probability that at least 975 of the flies are killed in one application.

51. Use the normal distribution to find the approximate probability that between 973 and 993 (inclusive) of the flies are killed in one application.

Social Sciences

Commuting Times   The average resident of a certain East Coast suburb spends 42 minutes per day commuting, with a standard deviation of 12 minutes. Assume a normal distribution. Find the percent of all residents of this suburb who have the following commuting times.

52. At least 50 minutes per day

53. No more than 40 minutes per day

54. Between 32 and 40 minutes per day

55. Between 38 and 60 minutes per day

56. I.Q. Scores   On standard IQ tests, the mean is 100, with a standard deviation of 15. The results are very close to fitting a normal curve. Suppose an IQ test is given to a very large group of people. Find the percent of those people whose IQ scores are as follows.

(a) More than 130   (b) Less than 85

(c) Between 85 and 115

General Interest

57. Olympics   The number of countries participating in the Summer Olympics since 1960 is given in the following table. *Source: Sports Reference.*

Olympic City	Year	Number of Countries
Rome	1960	83
Tokyo	1964	93
Mexico City	1968	112
Munich	1972	121
Montreal	1976	92
Moscow	1980	80
Los Angeles	1984	140
Seoul	1988	159
Barcelona	1992	169
Atlanta	1996	197
Sydney	2000	200
Athens	2004	201
Beijing	2008	204
London	2012	205

(a) Find the mean, median, and mode of the data.

(b) Find the standard deviation of the data.

(c) What percent of the data is within 1 standard deviation of the mean?

(d) What percent of the data is within 2 standard deviations of the mean?

58. Broadway A survey was given to 313 performers appearing in 23 Broadway companies. The percentage of performers injured during practice or a performance was 55.5%. If a random sample of 500 Broadway performers is taken, use the normal approximation to the binomial distribution to find the approximate probability that more than 300 performers have been injured. *Source: American Journal of Public Health.*

59. Broadway In the survey described in Exercise 58, the demographics of the Broadway performers were recorded as shown in the next column. Assume that all of these demographics follow a normal distribution, an assumption that always must be verified prior to using it in real situations. *Source: American Journal of Public Health.*

(a) Find the probability that a female dancer is 35 years old or older.

(b) Find the probability that a male dancer is 35 years old or older.

(c) Compare your answers to parts (a) and (b).

	Mean	Standard Deviation
Dancer's Age (female)	28.0	5.5
Dancer's Age (male)	32.2	8.4
Height (in m) (female)	1.64	0.08
Duration as Professional in yr (female)	11.0	8.9
Total No. of Injuries as Performer (female)	3.0	2.2

(d) Find the probability that a female performer is 1.4 m tall or taller.

(e) Find the probability that a female performer has a career duration that is more than 1.5 standard deviations from the mean.

(f) Would a female who has more than 6 injuries during her career be considered a rare event? Explain.

EXTENDED APPLICATION

STATISTICS IN THE LAW—THE *CASTANEDA* DECISION

Statistical evidence is now routinely presented in both criminal and civil cases. In this application we'll look at a famous case that established use of the binomial distribution and measurement by standard deviation as an accepted procedure.*

Defendants who are convicted in criminal cases sometimes appeal their conviction on the grounds that the jury that indicted or convicted them was drawn from a pool of jurors that does not represent the population of the district in which they live. These appeals almost always cite the Supreme Court's decision in *Castaneda v. Partida* [430 U.S. 482], a case that dealt with the selection of grand juries in the state of Texas. The decision summarizes the facts this way:

After respondent, a Mexican-American, had been convicted of a crime in a Texas District Court and had exhausted his state remedies on his claim of discrimination in the selection of the grand jury that had indicted him, he filed a habeas corpus petition in the Federal District Court, alleging a denial of due process and equal protection under the Fourteenth Amendment, because of gross underrepresentation of Mexican-Americans on the county grand juries.

The case went to the Appeals Court, which noted that "the county population was 79% Mexican-American, but, over an 11-year period, only 39% of those summoned for grand jury service were Mexican-American," and concluded that together with other testimony about the selection process, "the proof offered by respondent was sufficient to demonstrate a prima facie case of intentional discrimination in grand jury selection. . . ."

The state appealed to the Supreme Court, and the Supreme Court needed to decide whether the underrepresentation of Mexican Americans on grand juries was indeed too extreme to be an effect of chance. To do so, they invoked the binomial distribution. Here is the argument:

Given that 79.1% of the population is Mexican-American, the expected number of Mexican-Americans among the 870 persons summoned to serve as grand jurors over the 11-year period is approximately 688. The observed number is 339. Of course, in any given drawing, some fluctuation from the expected number is predicted. The important point, however, is that the statistical model shows that the results of a random drawing are likely to fall in the vicinity of the expected value. . . .

*The *Castaneda* case and many other interesting applications of statistics in law are discussed in Finkelstein and Levin, *Statistics for Lawyers,* New York, Springer-Verlag, 1990. U.S. Supreme Court decisions are online at www.findlaw.com/casecode/supreme.html. In addition, most states now have important state court decisions online.

The measure of the predicted fluctuations from the expected value is the standard deviation, defined for the binomial distribution as the square root of the product of the total number in the sample (here 870) times the probability of selecting a Mexican-American (0.791) times the probability of selecting a non-Mexican-American (0.209) . . . . Thus, in this case the standard deviation is approximately 12. As a general rule for such large samples, if the difference between the expected value and the observed number is greater than two or three standard deviations, then the hypothesis that the jury drawing was random would be suspect to a social scientist. The 11-year data here reflect a difference between the expected and observed number of Mexican-Americans of approximately 29 standard deviations. A detailed calculation reveals that the likelihood that such a substantial departure from the expected value would occur by chance is less than 1 in 10^{140}.

The Court decided that the statistical evidence supported the conclusion that jurors were not randomly selected, and that it was up to the state to show that its selection process did not discriminate against Mexican-Americans. The Court concluded:

The proof offered by respondent was sufficient to demonstrate a prima facie case of discrimination in grand jury

selection. Since the State failed to rebut the presumption of purposeful discrimination by competent testimony, despite two opportunities to do so, we affirm the Court of Appeals' holding of a denial of equal protection of the law in the grand jury selection process in respondent's case.

EXERCISES

1. Check the Court's calculation of 29 standard deviations as the difference between the expected number of Mexican-Americans and the number actually chosen.

2. Where do you think the Court's figure of 1 in 10^{140} came from?

3. The *Castaneda* decision also presents data from a $2\frac{1}{2}$-year period during which the State District Judge supervised the selection process. During this period, 220 persons were called to serve as grand jurors, and only 100 of these were Mexican-American.

   (a) Considering the 220 jurors as a random selection from a large population, what is the expected number of Mexican-Americans, using the 79.1% population figure?

   (b) If we model the drawing of jurors as a sequence of 220 independent Bernoulli trials, what is the standard deviation of the number of Mexican-Americans?

   (c) About how many standard deviations is the actual number of Mexican-Americans drawn (100) from the expected number that you calculated in part (a)?

   (d) What does the normal distribution tell you about the probability of this result?

4. The following information is from an appeal brought by Hy-Vee stores before the Iowa Supreme Court, appealing a ruling by the Iowa Civil Rights Commission in favor of a female employee of one of their grocery stores.

   In 1985, there were 112 managerial positions in the ten Hy-Vee stores located in Cedar Rapids. Only 6 of these managers were women. During that same year there were 294 employees; 206 were men and 88 were women.

   (a) How far from the expected number of women in management was the actual number, assuming that gender had nothing to do with promotion? Measure the difference in standard deviations.

   (b) Does this look like evidence of purposeful discrimination?

5. Go to the website WolframAlpha.com and enter "normal probability." Use the results to calculate the probability of being 12.3 standard deviations below the mean, as calculated in Exercise 3(c). Compare this result with the result using a graphing calculator and using Excel.

DIRECTIONS FOR GROUP PROJECT

Suppose that you and three other students are serving as interns at a prestigious law firm. One of the partners is interested in the use of probability in court cases and would like the four of you to prepare a brief on the Castaneda *decision. She insists that you describe the* case and highlight the mathematics used in your brief. Be sure to use the results from the case along with the results of Exercises 1–3 in preparing your brief. Also, make recommendations of other types of cases in which probability may be used in law. Presentation software, such as Microsoft PowerPoint, should be used to present your brief to the partners of the firm.*